BITTER
HARVEST

BITTER HARVEST

The Intellectual Revolt behind the Iron Curtain

Edited by Edmund Stillman Introduction by François Bondy

FREDERICK A. PRAEGER, *Publishers*
New York

Books That Matter

First Published in the United States of America in 1959
By Frederick A. Praeger, Inc., Publishers
15 West 47th Street, New York 36, New York

Library of Congress Catalog Card Number: 59-7454
Printed in the United States of America
© 1959 by Frederick A. Praeger, Inc.

This Book Is Number 78 in the Series of
Praeger Publications in Russian History and World Communism.

TO MARY

EDITOR'S FOREWORD

The essays, poems, and short stories gathered together in this volume are all examples of that latter-day intellectual movement in the Soviet world which, for want of any better description, the philosophical heirs of Andrei Zhdanov and the Western Kremlinologists alike have termed "revisionism." The term, however, is one of art and, in the Soviet world, a pejorative: in a century driven to extremity by the pressing need to classify its intellectual diseases, this word may serve, but is hardly more satisfactory than any other. To call all these authors revisionists is to suggest (as perhaps the new priests and pharisees of the Soviet world have tried to do) that they are Marxist dissidents in the style of the now half-forgotten Eduard Bernstein; that they subscribe to a coherent or even a fixed body of neo-Marxist thought; or that, at the very least, whatever their theories, tastes, and predilections, their impulse to *revise* present doctrine betrays an intellectual homage to that doctrine or springs from a common emotional source.

This is not the case. Any of these propositions might be true of some of these men; not one is true of all. Their doctrines are dissimilar, and their methods diverse. The most that can be said of them is that, in some sense, they represent the political "left"; and they are unhappy men.

Neither will it do to imagine that they are all pleased with each other's company. The Polish poet Adam Wazyk is rather a hero to Hungarian intellectuals, but it is hardly to be supposed that Ilya Ehrenburg, that ambiguous intellect, approves a philosophical category that can be stretched to include him and Milovan Djilas as well. Some, like Djilas, have dared to take the plunge into the pit; once they were Stalinists, but now they have denounced the Party and that part of themselves that was the Party. Others (and the Russians are conspicuous among them) dare only to register a profound sense of emotional malaise.

There are Hungarians in these pages, some of them the men who made the last romantic revolution and died for it; there are Poles who live in the half-world, for whom ambiguity is daily bread; there are Russians, a Chinese, a Vietnamese, an East German, a Czech, a Balt; there is a Yugoslav for whom Stalin died in 1948, a man who thus came very early to his views.

The great thing about these men and what they have written is that they are there to see. It is not merely that they are anti-Communist or anti-Soviet; that would be easy. They have been in a dark place and come out on the other side. They have imposed themselves on reality, transmuting a political experience into the stuff of thought. They are against evil; and some of them, at least, have transmuted their daily vision of cruelty and meanness into the tragedy of man.

All of them, like the Hungarian poet Gyula Illyes, can say: *Doleo ergo sum*—I grieve, therefore I am.

There is always something arbitrary about the business of putting together an anthology. I do not claim that I have collected all the best such writing of the past few years. Some notable pieces—among them, Pasternak's *Doctor Zhivago,* Dudintsev's *Not By Bread Alone,* Dery's *Niki,* Manov's *Unauthentic Case*—were too long for the purposes of this collection or simply not available for use. I have merely put together the pieces which I have liked and which, quite apart from the political phenomenon they may represent, have an intrinsic merit of their own. This is true, I believe, even in the case of those stories, poems, and essays which, from the standpoint of technique, are painfully crude yet unbearably moving withal.

It is worth adding that I have held to one inflexible rule: all the pieces in this collection were written by men who, as citizens of Soviet society, have seen the things they describe, and none were written in circumstances of exile. It seems to me that it is from this sense of immediacy and constraint that they derive their peculiar emotional charge.

EDMUND STILLMAN

Rye, New York
October, 1958.

ACKNOWLEDGMENTS

I should like to thank the Yale and Columbia University Libraries, the New York Public Library, and the Council on Foreign Relations for access to materials not easy to come by; and I have a special debt to the Free Europe Committee whose journal *East Europe* is certainly the best public source of materials relating to the Soviet satellites. Similarly I should like to thank all the other publishers and publications (they are listed below) who so kindly gave their permission to reprint many of the selections included in this volume. I am especially grateful to Elizabeth K. Valkenier for her translation of Michal Bruk's *A Letter* and Stanislawa Sznaper-Zakrzewska's *The Young Woman Doctor on Prezydencka Street;* to Elizabeth Marbury for her translation of Iurii Nagibin's *A Light in the Window* and Nikolai Zhdanov's *Journey Home;* to Helen Hausmann for her translation of Guyla Hay's *Some Observations on Literary Censorship and Freedom;* and to Valentin Eyre for his translation of Dimitri Granin's *A Personal Opinion.* All of them are sensitive recreations of the originals.

—E. S.

The following selections are reprinted from and with the permission of the magazine *East Europe*, which is published by Free Europe Press, Free Europe Committee, Inc., New York:

WE TAKE OFF FOR HEAVEN, from the issue of October, 1957; THE SIXTEEN-YEAR-OLD, April, 1958; LONG JOURNEY, March, 1957; THE UNFINISHED SONG, August, 1958; QUARANTINE, April, 1958; NOTES FROM AMERDAGANDA, September, 1958; "A POINT, MISTER?" OR, EVERYTHING HAS CHANGED, September, 1957; A MEETING OF TWO YOUNG MEN, January, 1957; RESPONSIBILITY AND HISTORY, December, 1957; March, 1958; May, 1958; A POEM FOR ADULTS, January, 1955, (the magazine was then published under the title of *News From Behind the Iron Curtain*); TWO FRAGMENTS, April, 1958; MUD, June, 1956; LADDY, November, 1955 (then entitled *News From Behind the Iron Curtain*); FOR THE DIGNITY OF SCIENCE, April, 1957; and THE PRINCIPLES OF A SHREWD CANARY, March, 1957.

The publishers wish to acknowledge the following sources:

BEHIND THE BRICK WALL. Adapted from *One Sentence on Tyranny*, compiled by Gyorgy Paloczi-Horvath. Waverly Press (London), October 23, 1957. By permission of the publisher.

THE LEVERS. Reprinted from *Partisan Review* (New York), Summer, 1958, as translated by Miriam B. London. Copyright, 1958, by *Partisan Review*. By permission of the publisher.

WHAT IS SOCIALISM?   Reprinted from *The New Leader* (New York), February 18, 1957. By permission of the publisher.

A HEAP OF MACHINERY.   Adapted from *Background Information Notes*, March 12, 1958, published by Radio Free Europe, Munich. By permission of the publisher.

IS THIS THE TWILIGHT OF MARXISM?   Adapted from *Communists on Communism*. By permission of Intercontinental Press Service, West New York, New Jersey.

THE LESSONS OF STENDHAL.   From a condensed translation appearing in *The Current Digest of the Soviet Press* (New York: Joint Committee on Slavic Studies, Columbia University), September, 1957, Vol. IX, No. 33. By permission of the publisher.

TWO KINDS OF TRUTH.   Adapted from a translation from the French appearing in *Evidences* (Paris), No. 72.

AT THE SAME TIME.   Adapted from *One Sentence on Tyranny*, compiled by Gyorgy Paloczi-Horvath. Waverly Press (London), October 23, 1957. By permission of the publisher.

THE TESTAMENT OF A PARTY REBEL.   Reprinted from *The Observer* (London), March 17, 1957. By permission of the publisher.

CONTENTS

3. THE MORAL ISSUE: ENDS, MEANS, AND
    THE SENSE OF GUILT

4. PARTY, STATE, AND THE NEW CLASS

5. THE SILENT LAND

6. ART, SCIENCE, AND THE FREE INTELLECT

INTRODUCTION

This book is a collection of stories and poems, of literary and philosophical and political essays from Communist countries throughout the world. It is a collection which bears signal witness to the will of these countries' writers to break through ideological coercion and to achieve an independent and truthful expression of their own personal moods, experiences, and thoughts. It is also a collection which bears witness to the fact that writers and critics from Hanoi to Warsaw—via Peking, Moscow, Leningrad, Riga, and innumerable other places—are today seizing every opportunity which the lessening of terror and of official pressure provides to them for expressing themselves more freely. In such a collection of writings, a few basic questions usually arise: Do these selections testify only to the authors' longings and aspirations? Are these works justified merely as one or another "Description of a Struggle" (to quote the title of a story by Franz Kafka, that "decadent" author in whose writings some readers in Communist countries find more of their own real experience than they find in all the works of socialist realism)? Or are these outcries of protest, of despair, of anger, these searchings for truth, these strong affirmations of the humanistic creed—are these also works of poetry, of literature, of philosophy? Could they stand on their own merit as works we would value even if we ignored the circumstances under which they were created, if we ignored the courage and the fate of their authors?

There are three reasons why these questions are difficult to answer. First, the authors who are represented in such an anthology necessarily vary greatly in talent, and the importance of their statements is not always equaled either by their aesthetic value or by their philosophical validity. Secondly, one must bear in mind the fact that, in poetic writing especially, the translation more aptly reflects the idea or the thought content than it does the sound, the color, or the evocative power. (This is why everything we know about *Doctor Zhivago* through translations is inadequate.) Thirdly, the reader with an aesthetic sense cannot possibly exclude the human element. He can no more live in an "ivory tower" than can the writer, and so he can hardly disregard the circumstances under which such writings were created, no matter how much he might wish to judge the authors here collected apart from the circumstances of their lives.

Yet, one might also ask whether these nearly three dozen pieces, which, in spite of their occasional hidden meanings, speak so very clearly for themselves, need any introduction at all. In his remarkable preface to an anthology, entitled *The Broken Mirror,* which was similar in form although it was restricted to Polish writings only, the critic Lionel Trilling wrote: "One of the striking things about this volume is the frank directness of the writers as they deal with past events to which they had been committed, and the happiness with which they exercise their common sense and their plain human judgment; the air they breathe is the bright air of reason and intention, not the miasma of historical necessity." The same holds true for all the authors represented in this anthology. But it has to be said, too, that, paradoxically, we must exercise a certain restraint in professing our solidarity with these authors, for whom "free" expression entails great risks. We have to tone down our professions of solidarity with these colleagues of ours because our sympathy might be for them a handicap rather than an encouragement (though, for tragic reasons, this does not hold true for the executed Imre Nagy and for the imprisoned Milovan Djilas).

We cannot, however, renounce our right to become aware of these testimonies, to translate and to publish these authors, to read them. We know only too well that the governments under which these writers live might well use this publication as damning evidence against them; and we must be aware of the fact that we, who live in freedom and in comfort, have a great responsibility toward these writers, who live in highly uncomfortable circumstances. This is a responsibility which we cannot assume lightly, and yet we must bear in mind that the indifference and the silence displayed by the West toward the writers in the Soviet Union, in China, in Hungary, and in other countries have never helped anybody, and that in some cases the worldwide fame of authors and their works can have a certain protective value. What is important here is not to proclaim our sympathy noisily—a sympathy which we cannot necessarily feel for all the authors printed in this collection; a sympathy which some of them would reject as harmful and unwanted. The important thing is the need for documenting these works. We must discover them, and we must learn to understand the intellectual climate in which they were created and in which these authors, as well as others, write. This knowledge is essential.

Finally, it is important to be aware of the pressures which operate on these writers from that banality which is presently ensconced in the seat of power: it is important to be aware of the arrogant stupidity of commissars, of the know-it-all superciliousness of know-nothings—all of which is abundantly reflected in the "approved" literature—and to know that, despite these pressures, works such as these could be created. We also have to understand the wall of silence behind which many writers in Communist countries have retreated. In Moscow and in Budapest, this silence has recently been branded as a very special form of deviation. In short, it is necessary to describe the atmosphere in which these works have been created, and this may be the justification for writing this introduction.

Among the Hungarian writers whose speeches and writings demanded, even before the October revolution of 1956, complete freedom for literature, the old Communist playwright Gyula Hay should not be forgotten (*see* page 248). He, like Tibor Dery, has been in prison for long months. I do not know why his name is not mentioned as often as is that of Dery and of others. On November 2, 1956, the same day on which I saw Tibor Dery for the last time, I visited Gyula Hay in his apartment. I may be permitted to quote fragments of what he told me then, because it may help to reveal

the emotional and ideological transformation that took place in the
Communist intellectuals of Hungary and of Poland: I asked Hay
how it was that he and other "old Bolsheviks" were now openly
fighting the Party leadership. He replied: "There were many reasons
for the break. The first, I confess, was my instinctive disgust with
Stalinism's utter lack of taste and its insensibility in every field of
art and letters. As writers, we were all sharply aware of this fact.
Secondly, there was the experience of deep social injustice in our
society. A third motive was the glaring failure, even bankruptcy, of
our type of economic system. There was finally—and it may have
been the most important element—the pressure of our youth. . . .

"We writers," Hay explained to me, "have always thought of ourselves as the *avant-garde* in the struggle for freedom. This is a Hungarian tradition of which we are very proud. . . . I was supposed
to be a guide to our youth, but in reality, the youth had become a
guide to me. For years I had been lecturing them. I gave interminable ideological answers to every question. I could feel that my
young listeners found it all very shallow and boring. At first I
thought: how strange and incomprehensible it is that we, the older
generation, should work so selflessly to build the future of a happier
Hungary for our young people, and that these very young people
should not care at all! Why were they so blind, so unfeeling, so
cold? Gradually I began to wonder whether they were all, every last
boy and girl in Hungary, hopeless reactionaries. Or could it be that
we, the old men, were wrong, and that they were right? I began to
talk with more frankness. I looked at their problems with more
frankness. In my public meetings, which were attended by eager
thousands, I forced myself to answer every question directly. Some
weeks ago, they asked me at a meeting in Györ, 'What is happening in our uranium mines?' I knew the Russians were there, but I
could only answer: 'I just don't know. . . . But as a Hungarian
citizen, I ought to know! And you ought to know! Keep asking!'
And so they did."

He went on: "And as for me, I kept on asking, too. Had we in
this country been building a socialist society, marred only by some
ugly distortions, or was this a horrible régime for which I had no
name and which was all distortions and no socialism? Even now, I
long for the Party which once had our love and loyalty. But its
leadership has destroyed it. It is difficult to love a thing which does

not exist. I would still support a new and pure Marxist movement. But I would not want to become a Party member ever again. . . . Was I courageous in speaking for truth, even under Rakosi? The pressure of the young on us all was so great that I can only say, in the words of one of our poets, 'I was too much of a coward to remain dishonest!' "

There are many other testimonies which prove that the writers did not turn away from official propaganda because they, as individualists, wished to go their own way, but because they realized that they could not simultaneously serve as the advocates of officialdom and as the voice of the people—and because, when they had to choose between the rulers and the ruled, they chose solidarity with their people. On a different level, even the Russian writer Konstantin Simonov, a genius of adaptation and of propagandist eagerness, made this clear. He became chief editor of *Novy Mir* in order to control the "heretic" editorial staff. And yet it was he who permitted Dudintsev's novel to be published, as well as Dimitri Granin's short story entitled "A Personal Opinion," which is reprinted here; and when he thought he could dare to do so, he openly criticized the essays of literary criticism which he himself had written during the Stalin era. Apparently, he felt the need to regain his self-esteem. He wrote:

> One may ask: Why, if we said nothing about this at the right moment, should we speak of it now? This reproach weighs on the conscience of many of us, including the author of these words, but the Party teaches us that certain other mistakes—mistakes incomparably more serious and not the mistakes of mere literary criticism—had sometimes better be admitted late than not at all.[1]

From Hungary to the Soviet Union—we cannot and we should not draw a comparison between the genuine popular uprising, in which the Hungarian intellectuals took part, and the unrest which seized Russian intellectuals immediately after Stalin's death. Still, let us remember that, as soon as the shackles were loosened, Russian literature threw "socialist realism," with its idealizations and its other conventional formalities, overboard in favor of real, critical

---

[1] Konstantin Simonov, "In Memoriam: A. A. Fadyev, *Novy Mir* (Moscow), No. 6, June, 1956.

realism. And it will not be forgotten that the hatred of the lie, the abhorrence of the strait jacket of enthusiastic clichés, the revolt against despiritualization and dehumanization broke through in Soviet literature just as strongly as they did in the famous "A Poem for Adults" by Adam Wazyk, the great Polish poet. It may suffice to quote here fragments from a poem by the Russian S. Kirsanov:

WE NEED USEFUL HEARTS . . .

> . . . They come
> > as a large commission
> with some important mission.
> I recognize
> > the Double-Faced One—
> he will never say a superfluous word.
> The Indifferent One strides along
> so sedately and confidently,
> and next to him, moderately sedate,
> is his personal assistant.
> It is stupid to resist!
> They shove their fingers
> > into the artery.
> They come up and feel it
> like fabric for trousers.
> A short Statement is already drawn up.
> —Unsuitable.
> > Correct.
> > > It is a fact.
> For public consumption
> > such hearts are not needed.
> And, in general, novelties
> are not required
> > > on our market.
> We need useful hearts,
> like iron locks,
> uncomplicated,
> > convenient,
> capable of executing any order:
> To blacken? To blacken!
> To value? To value!
> To annihilate? To annihilate!
> To feed? To feed!

To roar? To roar!
To keep silent? To keep silent!
To destroy? To destroy!
To love? To love!
And no cardiograms whatever,
and in the future, for good order—
A penalty of two hundred grams
will be imposed for "seekings!"
The statement is signed
           and that's that!
The workers get the order—go home!
Because of this statement
          we are helpless.
What now? Go off to our respective streets?
And across the street
        my friend
is lying with his pulse not beating.
This is how—
        with a stab of a knife
they catch you from behind. . . .
But perhaps we shall revive him again?
But shall we have time, during one day?
. . . There is one more day in the week,
but the work
        is enormous!
Our shop is on the verge of tears.
This is what happened on Friday.
I leave, and on my heels
leave the women laboratory workers,
holding their hearts, as though in them
were gaping wounds.[2]

    The search for an inner security, by which the soul can live, may be symbolized by a search for roots, by a return to one's origins, to "the world of mothers"—all of which frequently take the form of a journey. The citified son in a higher position returns to the village where his parents live, the village he had forgotten and which he rediscovers now. Unavoidably he is confronted by the lives of the villagers—by their troubles in living and in speaking with the

---

[2] S. Kirsanov, "The Seven Days of the Week," *Novy Mir* (Moscow), September, 1956, as quoted in *Problems of Communism* (Washington, D.C.), January-February, 1958.

bureaucratic upper crust, in understanding its ideological jargon, its clichés, and its abstract (Moscow) concepts. This "return to the common people," which was such an important subject during the last century not only in Russian literature but also in Russian thought and ideas generally, now again appears to be the answer to an inner necessity, a fundamental longing. And again it is the discovery of the village by the city-dweller, the discovery of poverty by the privileged, the discovery of the social abyss by the thinking human being who is shocked by what he sees.

It is, as a result, not only because of its quality as literature that Nikolai Zhdanov's story "Journey Home," a story which has been much maligned in the Soviet Union since its appearance, has become one of the best examples of the new Soviet literature; for it is an equally valid example of the treatment of this great and many-faceted subject: i.e., the "return to the common people." The same theme is treated by the young and highly gifted poet Evgeny Evtushenko in his great poem "Stantsiya Zima." The twenty-year-old poet returns to his home, "a station on the Trans-Siberian Railroad west of Lake Baikal and Irkutsk":

> At twenty, I've looked over everything again— [3]
> What I said but shouldn't have said,
> What I didn't say but should have said.
> I saw that I often lived timidly,
> That I thought and felt and wanted little,
> That in my too smooth life
> Were more good intentions than deeds.

After recalling his forebears, settlers in Siberia (his great-grandfather had been exiled as a rebellious peasant), and dwelling on his largely carefree childhood, the poet resumes his contemporary theme—how "Complexity suddenly came of itself,/And really alarmed by it,/I came to Zima"—of recovering his balance in the simplicity of his childhood home.

> But his first impressions are grim:
> The obscene writing on a fence,

[3] The original poem appeared in the magazine *Oktybar* (Moscow), No. 10, 1956. This translation, together with the accompanying text, is reprinted from "Evgeny Evtushenko," by Michael Futtrell, in *Soviet Survey* (London), July-September, 1958, p. 77.

> And a drunk stretched out by the pub,
> And a quarreling queue by the district store. . . .
> A driver cursed the town soviet. . . .
> The beggar's stumps banged on the stones,
> An urchin chased after a cat with a stick. . . .

At last he comes to his own people. He is fed and toasted mightily, but when his sister mentions Stalin's death, they all at once become serious, and his uncle holds forth:

> So it turns out the doctors weren't guilty?
> Then why have the people been treated like that?
> It's a scandal before the whole of Europe . . .
> Beria, the villain. . . .

His uncle presses young Evtushenko, fresh from Moscow, to explain it all; but the uncle is put off by the youngster, who avoids answering by saying, "I'll explain later."

Evtushenko spends the time lazily enjoying the countryside. By the river he meets an old friend of the family; the gruff old-timer takes up one of Evtushenko's persistent themes:

> Young people were better before,
> The Komsomol is deadly dull nowadays. . . .
> I remember your ma when she was seventeeen. . . .
> I must say I'm worried,
> You don't have their spirit. . . .
> And I don't see any young thoughts in you. . . .
> There are young people, but there's no youthfulness.

As an example, the old grumbler cites his nephew, who, after election to the district committee, has acquired a metallic look and a smooth eloquence, and who has given up girls and football.

Typical of the official criticism of such writings are the following attacks:

> . . . When Evtushenko was roaming the countryside around Zima, it never occurred to him to take hold of the controls of a combine-harvester or the wheel of a lorry, or a rake or a scythe or a fork. . . . Evtushenko has not portrayed the heroism of labor. . . .

. . . Having lost the awareness of the real foe, Evtushenko has surrounded himself with imagined literary enemies, and here he is, enjoying laughing in their faces.[4]

The "return to the common people" does not have to be an actual journey; it can be a metaphysical transformation. This return to a real or a longed-for "primitiveness," to nature and human nature, is the discovery of something very old and something at the same time new. That is why Party-line criticism accuses all such attempts to revert to a world that is past and to values that are outmoded. That is why Pasternak is most of all condemned for his confessed adherence to the world of yesterday, to the values of the world of the past. And Pasternak, in contrast to the younger Soviet writers who do not differ from him in their choice of subject matter, really does have his roots in a different era with different literary standards. This point is made in the only Soviet essay which honestly analyzes his *Doctor Zhivago*—the reader's report which was drafted by the editors of *Novy Mir* and which explains their refusal to publish a novel. It was a report which was printed in *Literaturnaya Gazeta* only after the commotion caused by the Nobel Prize award. Official criticism doesn't ever consider the possibility that Soviet literature, whenever it deviates from the orthodox Party line, might conceivably not return to yesterday's values but might bring up something never before mentioned, might discover a new, heretofore unobserved reality. It is a thought neither permitted nor admitted in literary discussion, since it is "unthinkable" in the political-philosophical field that the "revisionists" might ever go beyond Marxism-Leninism and that they might even enrich it. In the orthodoxy of state and Party it is self-understood that any deviation from the official formula cannot be anything but a regression. This is a logical consequence of a dogmatism which has once and for all taken possession of everything "progressive" and which has declared "progress" its exclusive prerogative.

The journey to the village is only one of the forms dramatizing the clash between the world of the masters on top and the warm, motherly world beneath it. Another form is the clash between the

---

[4] V. Soloukhin, "Without Precise Positions," *Literaturnaya Gazeta* (Moscow), April 8, 1958, as quoted in *Soviet Survey* (London), July-September, 1958.

man endowed with imagination and creative initiative (in Dudintsev's novel, it is the inventor) and the unimaginative bureaucratic
saboteur who does not want his routine disturbed. In Dimitri
Granin's story, "A Personal Opinion," this conflict is treated in a
more sophisticated way than in Dudintsev's famous novel. Minayev,
the general manager, does not permit the suggestions of Olkhovsky,
one of his technical assistants, to be published. Although he himself
used to be animated by a drive for independence, he has for years
suppressed his own personality or, rather, he has saved it for a time
when he would be far enough advanced in the hierarchy to be able
to afford personality and independent judgment. He now realizes
that advancement does not bring this freedom and that it never will
bring it. If he sabotages Olkhovsky's suggestions for new methods,
he beats the "Olkhovsky within himself," he betrays his own buried,
but not forgotten, soul. This theme of conflict between creative and
bureaucratic man is especially condemned by the official critics because it shows up an "irreconcilable contradiction," and that is
something which, after all, cannot exist in the classless Soviet society.

This contrast between two ways of existence is carried even
further in Alexander Yashin's story, "The Levers." The leaders of
a *kolkhoz* voice their worries freely and truthfully, and their speech
is full of proverbs and popular wisdom. Suddenly the friends become
aware of the presence of the office cleaning woman, Marfa. "The
conversation of the friends broke off, as though they felt guilty of
something before one another." They feel caught like small boys,
and at the same time they are ashamed of their reaction; then they
hold a Party meeting, and suddenly they are different people:
"Everyone's face became concentrated, tense, and bored. . . .
Everything earthly, everything natural disappeared." Only after the
meeting is over, when they are on the street together, do they again
find their own personalities, and once more a discussion starts
"about life, about conditions, about work. . . ."

This solemn and intimidated behavior of man toward authority,
even if he himself represents this authority, is brought out ironically
in "Journey Home." After the village people have told him their
worries, the bureaucrat Pavel Alekseevich Varygin explains in his
Party jargon: "Everything depends on the level of the consciousness
of the masses." He himself feels uncomfortable when he uses such
clichés. But the *kolkhoz* peasant woman Derevleva "heard him with

an expression of satisfaction on her face . . . evidently satisfied that
the conversation was reaching essential depths." The representative
of the state is well aware that he has no ground under his feet, but
the phrases in which he himself does not believe impress those who
ought to know better. And why? Varygin represents the world of
their betters, the upper class, the city people, culture, power. The
return to nature, the return to the people is apparently just as difficult as is the rediscovery of one's own independent thoughts and
of one's own soul—perhaps even more difficult. Varygin leaves his
native village confused and thoughtful, but on the train he is already
suffused by a pleasant feeling "that tomorrow he would go to his
warm, well-furnished study, and sit at the table in a comfortable
armchair." And yet at the same time he remembers "the wooden
cross against the gray sky" and the question of the woman Derevleva: "Is it right, or not right, what they've done with us?"

In "A Personal Opinion," Minayev considers the virtue of silence
in all its ambiguousness. "Silence is the most convenient form of
lying. Silence eases the conscience, safeguards a man's right to a
personal opinion and his hope that conscience will one day find its
voice." This is one of the most important themes: silence as the last
secure corner and, simultaneously, as the last refuge of freedom—as
the only way left to preserve one's identity. It recurs again and again
in discussion and in the official criticism of literature, as well as in
literature itself, in novels, short stories, poems. This silence is interpreted by officialdom as insubordination, as revolt. It is well known
what the silence of the Hungarian writers, after the suppression of
their revolution, meant and how it was interpreted by those in
power. Yet it is not only in Kadar's Hungary but also in Khrushchev's Russia that silence is considered a weapon, a provocation.
This silence must be crushed as any opposition must be crushed.

The same Leonid Sobolev, who on December 7, 1958, laid down
the directives at the congress of the Soviet Writers' Union, had told
the writers of Moscow as early as 1957: "It is known that in music
a pause sometimes expresses more feeling and thought than the
melody. Your silence is dangerous. It causes disorientation among
the readers. What does it mean? What does it conceal? An arrogant
contempt for the opinion of others? A contemptuous belief in one's

own infallibility? An insulting 'How could you possibly understand us?' The pathos of readiness for sacrifice? What does this silence signify? Wo do not understand it. Neither do the people. . . . Do you know what became known to me yesterday and what shocked me . . . so that I felt compelled to mount the platform and to excite myself beyond the measure permitted by my physician? That in the Western press hypocritically friendly sentiments are being voiced concerning you, you who should speak today but do not. That a 'friendly' hand is being extended toward you? That they are ready to embrace you . . . that a rope is ready for you that would draw you even farther away from your own people? Do you know that you are being enjoined to commit 'the heroic act of being silent'? The heroics of silence! What strange and poisonous words! Be silent . . . and you will obtain recognition! You will have friends, your heroic act will be recognized by history!" [5]

At this meeting, A. Surkov also pleaded: "The 'feat of silence' is, in our circumstances, a screen concealing the meanness of a petit-bourgeois *fronde*. Having locked themselves into a small wooden box of silent retreat, one can easily find oneself aside from life. It is necessary to gather courage and to re-evaluate false positions."

Surkov wants to use persuasion on those writers who were guilty of silence. Nikita Khrushchev denounces them as if their silence were an act of intellectual terror. "They intimidate themselves and attempt to intimidate others." [6] Similarly, the silence of the Hungarian writers after November, 1956, was branded as terror. And it is true that such silence frightens the reigning powers.

Another form of silence, equally condemned, is escapism—i.e., the talking about something extraneous: "In various literary publications apolitical verses are sometimes published which have no content whatsoever and which are completely lacking in the preoccupations, the sentiments, and the hopes which are characteristic of the people of our country. Minor preoccupations, isolation from the life and the work of the people belonging to our era, snobbish imitation of decadent, old-time poetry—all these are pressing some poets to cultivate 'hermetism' and to employ a ridiculous style which is of artificial and non-grammatical construction, as is the case of the

---

[5] Speech in the closing session of May 17, 1957, of the Moscow Section of the Soviet Writers' Union, as quoted in *Soviet Survey* (London), September, 1957.

[6] Unsigned Editorial, *Novy Mir* (Moscow), No. 10, 1957.

poem entitled 'On the Sea-shore,' which was recently published in the periodical *Steaua*." [7]

We do not fully comprehend this silence if we recognize its existence only where it is talked about and attacked. Silence is a deep, mysterious undercurrent in every totalitarian state. The silence of the dead pervades the silence of the living. The silence of the living writers encompasses the eternal silence of an Ossip Mandelstam, an Isak Babel, a Boris Pilniak. Silence can have just as many qualities and sounds as speech. In Rakosi's Hungary it was a silence fostered by a fear, which was harbored by each writer for the other. In Kadar's Hungary it is a conspiratorial silence of consent, of mute trust of each in the other. Considering everything that has been spoken and written in Russia between 1953 and 1957, the silence there must also be of a different kind than has previously been the case.

In Iurii Nagibin's story, "A Light in the Window," power is represented by the "front parlor" of the convalescent home, with its desk and its television set—a parlor always empty, always reserved for an eventual important visitor who never arrives. For years there has been a silent, unspoken conflict between the director and the maid Nastia. One day Vasilii Petrovich finds the maid and a few children comfortably ensconced in the parlor. He chases them out with vile insults; the intruders retreat in dignified silence. And it is this silence which triumphs over the director's screams: "Vasilii Petrovich suddenly missed fire like a wet fuse. He fell silent, heeding an odd new feeling within him that spread to the tips of his fingers —a feeling of unbearable disgust for himself."

Everything that is said in this anthology about injustice and suffering of all kinds is shocking and poignant, but it is not unexpected. The arrogance of the Russian specialists as described in the story of the Vietnamese Minh Hoang, the despair of a mother who cannot properly care for her child, as told by a Polish writer, the deportation experienced by a Baltic author—all these are testimonies from "the other side of the moon." But the privileged one who suffers under the dehumanization, who feels the loss of the most important human dimensions, whose hatred of the atrophy of humanity must be self-hatred—this is a subject we can come to know especially well

---

[7] *Scienteia* (Bucharest), June 7, 1958.

through literature. The oft-described self-disgust of the bureaucrat is simultaneously a displacement of the self-hatred and of the guilt-feeling of these writers themselves, who have written so much which they did not really feel and believe. We find this guilt-feeling not only in the works of the young poet Evtushenko. We find it in the posthumous works of the Communist poet Bertolt Brecht, in a poem he wrote after the East German workers' revolt of June 17, 1953, using his own letters as a justification of the suppression of that revolt. It ends with these lines:

> Last night in my dream I saw fingers, pointing at me
> as at a leper. They were work-worn and
> they were broken.
> "Ignorant ones!" I cried,
> guilt-conscious.[8]

I am speaking about the special form of lie which is bred by the necessity to dissemble, to make oneself inconspicuous, to ensconce oneself, and live within oneself—the kind of lie which has infected . . . many, many of us writers. That lie is essentially a defensive mask which the imperfection of social relations . . . may force one to wear until it grows into one's face. . . .
—Marietta Shaginian.[9]

The enemies cunningly concealed themselves behind dictatorial orders and pompous phraseology. . . . We said: there must be something in all that; we raised our hands and voted for their calumny. We should have known. . . . But, oh bitter shame, I did not try to defend him. I thought: Perhaps I did not really understand him? Perhaps I failed to notice something.
—Margarita Aliger.[10]

Driven by Khrushchev's attacks to a humiliating confession of error, this same writer wrote the following lines:

I think that I will be able fully to explain the profound conclusions which I have drawn for my future only by working

---

[8] C.f. Wolfgang Paul, "Aus Bertolt Brechts spaeten Jahren," *Neue Deutsche Hefte,* November, 1958.

[9] As quoted in *The Times Literary Supplement* (London), August 16, 1957.

[10] Margarita Aliger, "The Real Truth," as quoted in *Problems of Communism* (Washington, D.C.), January-February, 1958.

wholeheartedly, by remembering always that the main task of a
Soviet writer is political work, and that it can only be performed
honorably by following unwaveringly the Party line and Party
discipline.

—Margarita Aliger.[11]

What these writers express is not just an indignation and an un-
masking. It is the inner conflict of men who in their political and
social reality have experienced that "alienation" which Marxists
consider a typical sign of the position of the intellect under capitalism. It is the frustration of an existence which is simultaneously
brutal and abstract, cruel and dry, and which can often be felt more
clearly in very small episodes than in major historical crises.

Much has been written about the great intellectual awakening in
Poland and Hungary. For the reader of this anthology, just as for
the author of these introductory notes, the decisive experience may
lie in an acquaintance with the Soviet writers. Even if a comparison
with the Russian writers from the time before the full development
of the Stalinist terror—a comparison which is made possible through
the book *Early Soviet Writers*[12] by Vyacheslav Zavalishin—is not
exactly complimentary to the newer Soviet writers, it should be said
that these Russian writers do not lag behind their colleagues of
Eastern Europe in their striving for truth and reality.

In our Western countries we occasionally hear it said—with a
mixture of seriousness and of irony—that Communist states at least
pay literature and ideas the compliment of taking them seriously
enough to consider them dangerous to the state; that Western tolerance toward literature and the contest of ideas is based on the fact
that in our countries ideas are no longer considered vital powers.
This is not the place to go into these problems of the so-called
"Western world." To utter such an opinion about the events in the
Soviet Union, in China, and in the satellite countries is wrong. It
forces into aesthetic terminology an explanation for a barbaric state
of affairs—a state of affairs in which true intellect is suppressed by
the craftiness and the cunning of those in power who have no use
for anything cultural if it is not "useful." If Soviet critics who

---

[11] Margarita Aliger, as quoted in *Literaturnaya Gazeta* (Moscow), October
8, 1957.

[12] Published by Frederick A. Praeger, Inc. (New York), 1958.

know better praise Khrushchev's brutal attacks on writers as pearls of wisdom, and if they do it in the same words they previously used to laud Stalin's philosophy and taste, they have shamefully insulted and sullied the honor of the rest of the world's writers just as much as they have sullied the honor of their colleagues in the Soviet Union.

Khrushchev's interest in literature can be seen in this statement: "For anyone who faithfully serves his people in a socialist society, the question of whether or not he is free in his creative work simply does not exist. . . ." [13]

There can be no other attitude but indignation toward the conditions of vulgarity and of falsehood under which the Soviet writers create—indignation and, at the same time, solidarity with all writers who succeed even under such circumstances in writing anything of literary value, anything human and honest. The constant attacks on all kinds of literary publications, not only in Moscow and Leningrad but also in the outermost provinces, prove that whole groups of such writers do exist. Just as the Western writers have no wish to be the voice of their authorities or of any kind of official propaganda, no good writers in the Communist world are inclined to such self-denial. Their works, like all great works of the literature of all mankind and, especially, of Russian literature, are not on the side of loud-mouthed power, but on the side of silent suffering. Their works can be said to have a partisan quality—the official jargon is fond of the term *partiinost*—but it is a partisanship to the human being, and it is exactly this quality which all the writings collected in this volume have in common.

François Bondy

Paris, 1959.

---

[13] N. S. Khrushchev, "For a Closer Tie Between Literature and Art and the Life of the People," *Kommunist* (Moscow), No. 12, August, 1957, as quoted in *The Current Digest of the Soviet Press* (New York), October 9, 1957.

1.

THE SENSE OF MALAISE

Marek Hlasko is the prodigious young talent who burst onto the Warsaw literary scene in 1956. His collection of short stories, *First Step to the Clouds,* became an overnight sensation. His dreary little novella, *The Eighth Day of the Week*—"the day that never comes" —followed soon after.

Hlasko's world is an empty one, but he writes: "It was not I who made up Warsaw, that Warsaw which was for so many years a city without a smile; it was not I who made up the Warsaw in which people trembled for fear; it was not I who made up the Warsaw in which the greatest treasure of the poor was a bottle of vodka; it was not I who made up the Warsaw in which a girl was cheaper than a bottle of vodka—it was that Warsaw that made me."

···

WE TAKE OFF FOR HEAVEN

Saturday is a jolly day. On Saturdays people in all parts of the country have a shorter workday; the suburban factories blow their whistles two hours earlier; turners, milling-machine operators, mechanics, and technicians wipe their greasy hands and utter the blessed words: "It's over." Offices, factories, building sites, shipyards, and ports become deserted. Tired and yawning, people return home on crowded streetcars, lazily jostle each other in buses which they perpetually resent, and doze on suburban trains, thinking about the pleasant prospect of Sunday grass. As everyone has noticed, people become better and more agreeable on Saturdays. Never do we see so many smiles as on Saturday afternoon: balding bookkeepers smile at the thought of Sunday when they can walk around the house in undershorts; sports fans anticipate the pleasures of the field; district Party activists delude themselves about having two extra hours of sleep; girls shut their eyes and imagine delightful Sunday walks through the forests; athletes, employees of the security police, routine-ridden clerks of the national councils, professors, old men, children, foremen, pilots, and dentists all smile readily on Saturday, a day when everyone has the greatest number of plans, ambitions, and hopes.

3

The nation lives for Sunday. Only the transportation depots do not share the general satisfaction. On the contrary, work in such places sometimes lasts even longer on Saturdays. In a burst of cleanliness, the drivers wait in long lines before the pumps to wash their trucks; then they sprinkle them with oil and rub them with soft rags, trying to make the battered vehicles, which have carried bricks, lime, and cement for the past week, shine like mirrors. On Saturday afternoons, the drivers bend over their motors and try to discover their imaginary and real defects: they clean the distributor points, burn the carbon from the spark plugs, remove the sediment in filter cups, adjust the ignition, change the diaphragms in fuel pumps, seal the gas lines, and adjust the valves. Simultaneously, they quarrel fiercely with the mechanics—those men who were not fit to become drivers —and display the utmost ingenuity in ascertaining the legitimacy of their assistants, the depot managers, foremen, and dispatchers—the actual masters of their lives and wages. Then, casting a longing look at the rows of shining trucks, now ready for use, they say: "A driver's life is a broken reed, indeed it is. I should have become a carpenter as my father wanted me to. . . ." And if it is not payday, they return to their homes. But even there they try to explain to their wives the difference between the clutch and the gearshift. Few occupations have so great an attraction for man and are so inseparably linked with his days and nights; and perhaps no other occupation is so much loved and hated. This, more or less, is how Saturday afternoon looks at a transportation depot. On payday, however, it is slightly different.

On one payday, a warm, fair Saturday afternoon in June, driver Tadeusz Jablonski returned to his base at about two o'clock and drove slowly through the yard, keeping his foot on the clutch, despite regulations. He looked closely at the row of parked trucks and asked the assistant:

"Where do we park?"

"Over there," replied his assistant, a red-haired youth with a good-natured face. He waved his hand: "Behind that Studebaker. There's an empty place."

"That's where Boratynski always parks. If I take his place, he'll start yelling as usual. I hate quarrels. Everyone is back so early today."

"It's payday," the assistant said tersely.

"That's true," Tadeusz said.

He rode a few yards farther, shifted into neutral, stopped the truck and jumped off. He was a tall, lithe young man, with fair, short hair and a rather expressionless though pleasant face.

"Park it next to the Ursus," he said. With his hand still on the steering wheel, he rested his foot on the running board; the motor was idling, and the wheel shivered like a frozen dog. "Just clean and grease the bearings and take off. If the nozzle doesn't go in, remove the bushing and push the wire through. Don't overload the motor. Take care of yourself."

He took his foot off the running board and turned to go.

"Mr. Tadeusz," the assistant said, "what about that thing?"

"What thing?"

"Shall we do it?"

"I have no time," Tadeusz said. "I have a date and can't come."

"Whatever you say," the assistant said. He looked disappointed and shook his head, repeating, "Whatever you say."

Then he shifted, grinding the gears, and, releasing the clutch awkwardly, drove off. For a while Tadeusz stood motionless, looking after the truck. It was a big military American GM "Banjo," the kind Warsaw drivers call "James." It is big, beautiful, and belligerent-looking, with an open cab, a powerful bumper, ten wheels, and three differentials; the motor is resonant and deep, like some powerful bells. Now only a few of them are in use, but from 1945 to 1950 every young driver dreamed of having a James.

Tadeusz stuck his hands in his pockets and walked over to the dispatcher's office. Handing his delivery receipt book to the dispatcher, he asked, "What about the money?"

"It's right here," said the dispatcher, a stout, gray-haired man with a flabby face. As a rule, dispatchers are former drivers who have ruined their health on the job but, unable to face being separated from it, fill in the itineraries of other drivers and tell long stories about the defects of their old trucks.

"How much do I get?"

"Just enough," the dispatcher said, passing a thick finger over the payroll. Then he winked knowingly. "I have the feeling you will float like a gondola today."

"Not at all," Tadeusz said. Being in a great hurry, he shifted impatiently from one foot to another. "I won't drink today. How much do I get?"

"Six hundred twenty-four *zloty* and thirty *groshe*," the dispatcher said, struggling with his pen, glasses, and a huge sheet of paper. "Here, sign."

Tadeusz counted the money and signed. He returned the payroll sheet, which bore the trace of grimy fingers, and said, "Good-by, Mr. Konopka. See you Monday. What time do you want me?"

"At six. Are you leaving already? Why are you so nervous?" The dispatcher put his glasses on his forehead. "All you young men are very nervous nowadays. In my day, we had nerves of steel. Nerves are the most important thing. I remember in 1928 I was driving from Piotrkow to Czestochowa . . ."

"Mr. Konopka," Tadeusz said furiously, "I have something important to do and I can't . . ."

At that moment all the loudspeakers in the yard sounded: "Attention, attention! Today at 1630 in the Union reading room a lecturer from the Association of Popular Science will deliver a lecture entitled 'How and When Will We Fly to the Moon?' The lecture will be illustrated with slides and followed by discussion. I repeat: Today at 1630 . . ."

"If only one could silence that parrot," the dispatcher said angrily. "He is shouting as if a Jew were about to be born. I am busy with my payroll, and he is talking about stars. If I make a mistake, who will compensate me? Am I right or not, Mr. Tadeusz?"

"It means," someone behind them said meditatively, "that there is a possibility . . ."

"What possibility?"

"Of flying to the stars."

"Nonsense," Tadeusz said lazily and without conviction. He turned to the speaker, and suddenly his eyes grew wary and angry. "What do you want here, Zawadzki?" he asked. He took his hands out of his pockets and blushed.

"Come on," Zawadzki said. He was a short, stout man, with a lean, nervous face; his eyes were small and very light. "I'm waiting for you," he said, looking at Tadeusz. "I returned with my truck two hours ago and have been waiting for you ever since."

"What do you want?" Tadeusz said hoarsely. His face grew even

darker, and there was a tickling coolness in his throat, as was usually
the case before a quarrel.

"Not here. Let's go outside. Good-by, Mr. Konopka."

"Good-by, Mr. Konopka," Tadeusz repeated mechanically. His
only thought was: be calm, you must be calm at any cost.

They passed through the gate arm in arm. Tadeusz felt like a taut
string. Zawadzki was calm and collected. Only a keen observer
would have noticed that the small blue veins on his lean face had
grown more visible.

"We'll go to the field," Zawadzki said after a while. Tadeusz
winced, interrupted in his thoughts. "To the field," Zawadzki repeated, "that'll be the best place for us to talk. Besides, my brother-
in-law is waiting there."

"Two against one?" Tadeusz asked, with a disagreeable laugh.

"Don't be silly, Tadeusz," Zawadzki said, looking at him with
contempt. "It's something else."

"What is it, then?" Tadeusz shouted. Again he took his hands out
of his pockets.

"I'll tell you all right," Zawadzki said. "Come on."

"Don't make it too long."

"You can be sure I won't dally with you."

They left the street and cut across the field. It wasn't really a field
but an empty lot adjoining the transportation depot. Broken bottles,
empty cans, cigarette wrappers, and all sorts of trash were scattered
on the ground. Near the fence, on ingeniously arranged bricks and
stones, people sat drinking heartily, for Saturday, and not Sunday,
is actually the workers' sacred day. They were yelling, embracing
one another, arguing and convincing themselves. Someone sang in
a hoarse baritone, "I shall not forget your burning eyes." Almost
every enterprise has such an ugly lot in its vicinity.

"Tadek," someone shouted over the fence. "Give us ten *zloty,* and
we'll have us a good tune. Mr. Zawadzki, come here for a minute."

"What a stupid ass," Zawadzki said. "After we . . ."

Tadeusz didn't hear the rest of the sentence. "Attention, attention!" the loudspeakers roared again. "Today at 1630 in the Union
reading room a lecturer from the Association of Popular Science will
deliver a lecture entitled 'How and When Will We Fly to the
Moon?' The lecture will be illustrated with slides and followed by
discussion. I repeat: Today at 1630 . . ."

"What do you want?" Tadeusz asked, after the loudspeaker stopped.

"I'm just about to tell you. Let's sit over there."

At the far end of the fence a man was lying on the grass. They went up to him and sat down on the bricks. The man jumped up. For a moment he stood drowsily, rubbing his eyes. Then he asked:

"Shall we take up a collection for a bottle?"

"Wait a while, Rusiek," Zawadzki said, and the man obediently lay down. He was small and dumpy. Zawadzki looked at Tadeusz. "I know everything," he said after a while.

Tadeusz said nothing. His heart was beating heavily and painfully. He moistened his lips and asked with difficulty:

"When did she tell you?"

"Today."

"Just like that?"

"How else? I didn't beat her."

"And now what?"

"You can both do what you want."

"We shall," Tadeusz said. He was recovering his spirits. Leaning against the fence, he stretched out his long legs. "You don't hold it against me, Zawadzki, do you?"

"No," the other answered quietly. He plucked a blade of grass and started to chew it. It was fragrant with sun and well-trodden earth. "Tadek," he said, looking ahead with empty eyes, "do both of you know what you want to do?"

"I'm not asking you for advice."

"Do you yourself know what you want to do?"

"I know that I love her. That's all I care about. I know you are a good man, and I'm damn sorry she's your wife. I can't look you straight in the face. But understand this: life is life. There is no life for me without her. I'd rather kill myself. And if you hold it against me, say so right away, for then there's no use in talking."

"Tadeusz," Zawadzki said, looking at the ground. "Life means nothing to me any more. I've had my share of it, and I don't wish it on anyone, not even my worst enemy. But listen to me. You'll take the woman and child from me—and then what?"

"We'll be together. Things will work out somehow."

"No," Zawadzki said. He pulled the grass out of his mouth and threw it away. His brother-in-law was dozing again. "No," he repeated, "it's damn rare that things work out. Nothing good will come of it. Do you have an apartment, Tadeusz?"

"That's not important. We'll live in a hostel."

"Yes," Zawadzki said, "in a hostel. In a hostel, where five people live in one room; in a hostel, where drunkards come home with whores every night, where a day doesn't pass without a brawl, where you won't be able to kiss one another without having ten witnesses present; in a hostel, where you'll long for each other like dogs, where you'll meet nights in a passageway, where others will constantly bother her. Will you live in a hostel, Tadeusz?"

"We love each other. One can take a lot. Why are you trying to frighten me? I'm not afraid of life," Tadeusz said.

He fell silent. From all along the fence came irritating screams; on the adjacent railroad siding there was the jarring sound of cars being shunted and the piercing blast of horns. Zawadzki was looking at the ground, and Tadeusz could not see his face. Zawadzki's brother-in-law woke up and said, "Shall we take up a collection for a bottle?"

Zawadzki drew closer to Tadeusz. His face was perspiring.

"Don't tell me how much a person can stand," he said quietly. "I stood much more than you think. I was in a concentration camp and saw things they will tell children a hundred years from now. I don't want your pity. I won't tell you that this woman and this child are all I have in the world. I shit on your pity. But you won't be able to stand it. You're young, you may have to live and enjoy yourself. And this will be the end of it. It's hard nowadays. She'll give you ten cigarettes a day and ten *zloty* each payday so that you can have a drink with your pals out in the free air. But you won't be able to treat your friends to vodka because you'll know that your wife is waiting for you at home, that you have another man's child whom you also have to support, and that your wife can't work because she is tied down. And you'll have plenty of regrets. One day you'll say to yourself: 'To hell with it all.' You'll rebel and go out with your friends and say: 'Where's my youth? Where's my pleasure?' And you will be right to say that. Nobody will blame you for it. But she will reproach you and beg and cry, and one day you'll look at her with hatred; you'll see that she's no longer young and pretty, and then, for no reason, for the first time, you will hit my wife."

He fell silent. Musing, he looked at his scratched, oil-bitten hands.

The jarring sound of trains could still be heard. Voices of various soloists drifted over the fence; one, stronger than the others, sang the tango, "Do you remember, my love?" The rattling of the last trucks returning to the depot acted as an accompaniment. The sun had already dropped behind the houses of the town, roofs shone red and gold, and shadows grew long and violet. The broken bottles and cans strewn over the lot gleamed like diamonds. The heated earth was redolent with damp; the wind light and dry, smelling of lime, pitch, and wet sand—nearby they were building a large development. Against the darkening sky, red walls dried in the sun. Zawadzki's brother-in-law got up and asked:

"How about a bottle?"

They had no time to answer. A powerful voice resounded in the early evening silence: "Attention, attention!" the loudspeakers roared. "Today at 1630 in the Union reading room a lecturer from the Association of Popular Science will deliver a lecture entitled 'How and When Will We Fly to the Moon?' The lecture will be illustrated with slides and followed by discussion. I repeat: Today at 1630 . . ."

"Let's each give ten *zloty*," the brother-in-law said, after the loudspeakers had stopped. "Now we have enough for a bottle." He took the money and left.

"I can't stand it," Tadeusz said in despair. "I've never had anyone—no mother, no friends. . . . I've always believed in love. How will I live without her? How? For what?" He looked at Zawadzki with bloodshot eyes. "I suppose you're going to tell me that I'm young and that I'll find hundreds of others, aren't you? Is that what you're going to say? Speak up!" He was shouting. "Come on, speak up! Why don't you say something?"

"For Christ's sake," Zawadzki said. He stretched out his arm, describing in an arc the scene before them. "How long will these lots last, these hostels, these five-*zloty* collections for vodka, these lists of malingerers, these crowds in streetcars, these lines for butter? How long will lovers have no place to live, how long will people have to part because of an apartment, washing, and trash like that? If I didn't know how things were before, I would think I was in hell now. I don't believe in hell, but if there is such a place, these bottles, these lines for meat, these girls at the hostels—they're worse than hell."

Tadeusz raised his head. He was crushing the grass with his heel. It was only now that he understood clearly that his love, his desires, and the most sacred words come to nothing—not because of unfaithfulness, separation, or death, but because of all the petty, annoying, wretched things this man had mentioned.

"Christ," he stammered hoarsely.

A red mist rose before his eyes. He straightened up and looked haggardly about him. Then he started to run. Stumbling on the empty cans, jumping over improvised tables, breaking bottles, crushing cucumbers, herrings, rolls, and sauerkraut, falling, getting up, he kept on. Hearing outraged shouts and realizing that he was being chased, he suddenly changed course; he ran toward the railway siding, where they were shifting cars. When he finally reached the deserted track, he saw an empty locomotive coming. "None of this is true," he thought, "none of it." The people behind were gaining on him, and he had the sensation of hot breath at the back of his neck. Uncoiling like a cat, he was about to throw himself under the wheels; at that moment a superhuman voice shouted: "Attention!" Tadeusz halted mechanically; the locomotive went by, and he saw the driver's face, covered with sweat. "Attention," the voice repeated. "Today at 1630 in the Union reading room a lecturer from the Association of Popular Science will deliver a lecture entitled 'How and When Will We Fly to the Moon.' The lecture will be . . ." He heard no more, for the people had caught up with him and knocked him down.

Pierwszy Krok w Chmurach (Warsaw), 1956.

Tibor Dery is a Central European revolutionary in the great tradition. Born in Budapest in 1896, he joined the Communist Party while still a young man and supported the revolutionary government of Béla Kun after World War I. With the fall of the short-lived Kun regime, Dery chose exile in Western Europe; his best work shows its affinity for contemporary European letters. Returning to Hungary after some years, he was jailed by the Horthy government for his translation of André Gide's *Retour de l'URSS*.

As an uncompromising critic of social injustice, Dery fared badly in Stalinist Hungary. "Nothing," he writes, "can replace freedom; nothing can possibly be superior to it." He joined in the revolution of October-November, 1956, and was subsequently imprisoned.

BEHIND THE BRICK WALL

Comrade Bodi left Karoly Brock Street, which led to the main gate of the factory, turned into the first side street, and a few minutes later came out onto the bank of the Danube. He still had half an hour until the relief of the night shift. He had time to take a stroll and enjoy the early spring sunshine. He had a headache.

Across the Danube, in Pest, he could see the long row of dust-colored warehouses and, farther off, the bridge, above which sea gulls slowly wheeled. The wind blew strongly from the west, ruffling the river and chasing the garbage along the water's edge. When the gusts became more violent, yellow clouds of dust suddenly rose into the air, darkening the sun. The river's edge, left derelict, was littered with rubbish. Some way off, beside the water, a stray dog, shaggy and emaciated, sniffed at some dried-up filth and watched uneasily as the man approached.

There the high, red brick wall which surrounded the factory broke the force of the wind a little. Garbage strewed the ground beneath the wall, but at least a man's eyes and mouth were not filled with grit and sand when the wind blew too hard. Comrade Bodi stopped a moment, his back to the wind. He leaned against the wall, turning to the sun his thin face with its day's growth of beard. Just as he was about to set off again, he noticed a brand-new piece of leather at his feet, partly covered with sand brought by the last gust of wind. It was twelve or fifteen inches long. Comrade Bodi picked it up, studied it carefully, then went on his way with the thick piece of leather in his hand.

He had hardly gone a few steps when another piece of strap fell in front of him, almost grazing his cap, and coming from the other side of the brick wall. A third and fourth followed, curving in a great arc over the wall. Comrade Bodi examined them for a few moments and then continued on his way. On the other side of the wall there was a low storeroom attached to the workshops.

Bodi made his way straight to the locker room. Every morning he slipped on a pair of oil-stained overalls to save his clothes.

"What's this?" asked a machinist, sitting on a bench nearby.

"What?"

The man had pulled off his shoe. His big toe, yellow and crooked, poked through a hole in his sock. Carefully, he removed the sock and held it up between two fingers.

"What's this?"

Comrade Bodi averted his head slightly. "Are you talking to me?" he asked.

"Yes, what's this?" the worker repeated, waving the sock in front of Bodi's face.

Bodi turned his head even more. "Take it away," he said quietly.

"Don't you know what it is?" asked the worker. "It's the 'sock of the New Man.' "

The night shift was already leaving. Some of the workers greeted Bodi. Others did not. Some had known Bodi for twenty years, ever since he had come to the factory, yet they passed without a word. Bodi went across the yard, where the wind lashed at his face once more. Here the air seemed denser, more solid, because of the litter suspended in it. In another part of the plant, employees arrived one by one at the main office. Comrade Bodi reached the office in his turn.

Behind the desk sat a corpulent man with a face marked by illness, flesh yellow and puffy beneath the eyes, jowls flabby and wrinkled. Bodi greeted him. The man nodded curtly, then asked, "What's wrong now?"

"They're stealing the leather now."

The fat man said nothing.

"I saw it with my own eyes."

"Where?"

"Shop Number Four," said Bodi. "They're throwing the belting over the wall. I was walking at the back of the factory."

The two men stared at each other without speaking.

"Makes leather to mend their shoes," said the fat man, the corners of his mouth twisted in a faintly sarcastic grimace.

An old man wearing eyeglasses, tall and stooping, came into the office. He gave a humble greeting and then, as if expecting a kick in the ass, fled precipitately into the next room. Two workers followed him; one, a slight girl with dimples, had a face as fresh as the peonies she had been picking that morning in her garden before leaving for the plant. Comrade Bodi waited until the door was shut, then rested his hand on the desk. The flesh of the hand was blue-white, the nails trimmed close.

"It can't go on like this," he said. "No, not like this. God! Not any more."

"I'll see about it," said the fat man. He spoke with a tired air, staring vacantly at the door through which the peony-girl had dis-appeared.

Outside again, Bodi had the wind behind him. An empty oil drum began to roll before the force of the wind; it clanged to a stop against the wall of the gasoline depot. The wind was fresh, a fine spring wind. The workshop windows set up such a rattling that he could hardly make out the din of the mechanical hammers.

In the workshop, someone was waiting for Bodi. He worked in a corner of the assembly shop, in a glassed-in cubicle through the door of which so much soot and dust blew that at night the shift had coal-black faces and hair gritty with metal dust. The place was full of people waiting or jostling. The foreman stood by the window, lost in some document, his glasses pushed up onto his forehead. The man waiting for Bodi stood with his head bent; he slouched against the wall and did not look up until Bodi took his place behind the desk.

"Hello, Ferenc," said Bodi.

The man took a step forward.

"What's up?"

"Do you know what's going on?"

Comrade Bodi looked at the production schedule the man held out to him.

"You know," the man went on. "You're responsible. What the hell does it mean?"

Comrade Bodi examined the sheet more closely. "Don't get excited, Ferenc," he said.

The paper continued to shake.

"Where do you get this crap?" the man went on, speaking in a low, desperate voice. "Ninety seconds per piece! What kind of a norm is that? You want me to live on love?"

"Don't get excited, Ferenc."

The man put the paper on the desk. "Where do you get a crazy norm like this?" he said, his voice still low. "Just tell me how. If you can show me how, all right. I'll go back to my bench. But show me."

"In the morning, from now on," Bodi said, "you won't have to wait until the materials arrive. You gain half an hour from that alone."

"You think so?" said the man, ironically. "What next?"

Bodi avoided his eyes. "You know it's necessary, Ferenc," he said. "Production costs are too high. We're eating into reserves. Expenses are so heavy that . . ."

"Is that so?"

Bodi looked at him out of the corner of his eye, to see if he was being sarcastic. "That is so," he replied. "Don't be funny."

"Funny?" said the man.

There was silence. Comrade Bodi turned to the door which had opened; no doubt it was a visitor for him. He folded the paper on the desk.

"How much do I take home?" the man said. "Don't give me that paper back. Work it out. See what I get deducted. See what I'll take home to the wife and kids. Work it out!"

"Put your back into it, Ferenc," said Bodi. "You'll make it up in a month." He got no reply; he raised his eyes. Ferenc was looking him in the eyes for the first time since the beginning of the interview. Comrade Bodi turned away his head. The man turned on his heels and left the cubicle without a word.

"There's a man who hasn't got any love for you," said the typist near Bodi.

A few minutes later Bodi walked through the workshop again—
the manager had just sent for him—and noticed that Ferenc's bench
was empty. The violent wind snatched the workshop door from his
grasp and sailed his cap toward a puddle of oily water that had lain
in a hollow of the clay-like soil since last week's rain. Two young apprentices sniggered when they saw the cap blowing along toward the
puddle. A third, coming toward Bodi, could have put out his foot to
stop it, but seeing Bodi running he looked the other way. The two
apprentices guffawed. The cap fell in the greasy water. Bodi shook
it out and went on slowly. He felt their eyes on his back.

On his way from the manager's office he skirted the administration building. Behind the metal shop, in a narrow alleyway between
the red brick wall and the workshop, he let himself slowly down to
the ground, his back against the wall. No one ever came here. His
head was splitting. The world seemed dark around him. His eyes
throbbed, misted over with tears of pain. His forehead ran with
sweat.

Usually these attacks came in the evening, between eight and ten
o'clock. Sometimes he suffered during the day, but the worst pains
did not come until evening, at supper or after. For two years now he
had not gone out after work nor after his evening meal, except on
the days when he had a Party meeting. On Sundays he stayed in
bed; on that day the pain never left him. He tried all kinds of
analgesics: aspirin, pills, sedatives—the whole range of cures. What
helped most was to lie down with his head hanging off the bed.

Here, beyond the workshop where no one came, he told himself he
could rest for just a quarter of an hour. He stretched himself at full
length. He was at the foot of the wall, sheltered from the wind which
crept into the alley, sometimes raising dense clouds of dust. He rested
his neck on a brick and tilted his head backward. Above him long,
boat-shaped clouds sped so quickly across the blue sky that they
made him dizzy. "I'll shut my eyes," he said to himself. As he shut
his eyes, the wind whistled in his ears. Go back again to the doctor?
What for? For two years he had trailed from one hospital to another. At first the doctors had suspected a tumor on the brain: they
examined the back of his eyes, X-rayed his skull and brain. Then
they had sent him to a nerve specialist. Then to the general section.
Six months before, they had done a cisternal puncture. "Undress

and don't worry. I am going to insert a needle in the nape of your neck. It won't hurt. Don't move, or the prick could cause a fatal lesion. It will only hurt for a moment. Don't be afraid. Be calm." He had not felt much pain, but when the thick needle had plunged into his neck he had felt something he would never forget. It was worse than anything until then.

Back in the cubicle the foreman asked: "What did the old man want?" He pushed his glasses back on his forehead.

Bodi shrugged.

"Production costs?"

"He talked about that."

"What else?"

"The thefts."

"Our fault, I suppose?"

"Well," said Bodi, "I'm a member of the council for discipline."

"That's a big leg up."

"He's right," Bodi said. "I'm not active enough. I lack vigilance, enthusiasm. He's right."

"You think so?"

"Yes," said Bodi. "I think he's right"

"What are you shutting your eyes for?" asked the foreman. "Are you sick? What's the matter?"

"Nothing's wrong. Nothing at all."

The foreman stepped toward Bodi. "You look like a corpse."

Comrade Bodi began to laugh. "No, I'm fine. By the way, yesterday was Karcsi Olajos' trial."

"The fool! What did he get?"

"Six months."

The foreman looked at Bodi without a word. His round Magyar face, with its little stiff mustache, had gone white with rage.

"That's a hell of a story to take around," he said. "Six months! What an article for the wall newspaper. Christ! Six months for a few yards of copper wire. How many yards?"

"Four or five," said Comrade Bodi.

"Goddam fool!" said the foreman. "He gets himself six months for five yards of copper wire. No appeal?"

"No appeal."

The foreman looked out of the window. Outside, men were pushing along a wheelbarrow full of scrap. "Nothing will stop them," he
muttered. "What a fool. What did he want the copper wire for?"

"To hang out his washing," Bodi said. "Copper doesn't leave rust
marks on the washing."

The next day they arrested two of the men who had stolen the
leather—a lathe operator of about forty and his accomplice, an old
man who worked in the factory stockroom. They had been cutting
the straps and hiding them under their coats. The Party organization called a meeting in the main workshop. The manager and Party
secretary were there. Three or four hundred men gathered around
a big drawing table in the middle of the workshop.

The two culprits stood on the table. The lathe operator, motionless, his face chalk-white, arms dangling, looked down at the sheet
of rusty tin plate that covered the table. Beside him the old man
stood gawking at the silent crowd. Now and again he smiled: he did
not understand what had happened to him. He wore a canary-
colored beret which he kept pushing back and forth on his bald
head. He seemed tired from working all night. He shifted his weight
to each foot in turn, moving his old lined face to right and left, as
if begging for help. Above his head the factory loudspeaker bellowed
happy marching tunes.

Comrade Bodi's speech only took a few minutes. The sullen-faced
workers listened without moving. When Bodi paused between his
slowly spoken sentences, they could hear the scraping of the old
man's iron heels on the metal table top. Other workmen arrived
from nearby shops, and the crowd around the table grew. Above
the table the arm of a crane had stopped in mid-transit. Five or six
men stood in the idle bucket, just above the two thieves. The lathe
operator stood motionless; sweat ran down his face. The old man
continued to rock from one foot to the other, smiling emptily.

Just before the end of the meeting the canary-yellow beret slipped
from the old man's head and fell to the floor. An old workman bent
down to pick it up and put it on the table. In his confusion the old
man rolled it up and stuffed it in his pocket. He left his hand there,
and as the meeting ended one might have thought he was listening

to Comrade Bodi's speech, smiling jauntily, not caring at all. The men standing near the table saw that he had wet his pants.

Before the morning shift ended, the word went around that the lathe operator had committed suicide. He had hanged himself in the washroom. He had made a noose of brass wire, climbed on a toilet seat. Then, with his head in the noose, he had stepped off into space. When they found him, his body was already cold.

"Well, what did you say at the meeting?" Mrs. Bodi asked when he got home that night.

Comrade Bodi was stretched out on the couch, his head hanging over the edge. He had his usual migraine but seemed calm. The large room was lit only by a little lamp with a pink shade on the bedside table.

"What could I say?"

The pale little woman paced up and down the room, wringing her hands. "My God, my god! The Lord will punish us," she wailed. "They'll all say it's your fault. What did you say?"

"I made a speech," said Bodi.

"Saying what?"

"What I had to say."

The little pale woman went on wringing her hands and wept.

"Don't get upset," said Bodi.

"What?"

"Don't get upset. Sit down. You make me dizzy."

She sat down near him and put a cold, bony hand on his forehead.

"What did you say?"

"I said what I had to say."

"The Lord will punish us. Why did it have to be you?"

"The manager picked me."

"But why did it have to be you?"

Bodi did not answer.

"God will punish us. Why did it have to be you?"

The man tilted his head still farther back, just above the floor which glowed under the red light of the lamp. "I'm a member of the council for discipline," he said, looking at the pallid face of his wife. "It was up to me to speak. I couldn't get out of it."

"What did you say?"

"Stop moving around like that," said Bodi. "You make me dizzy. Sit down on the couch."

The woman sat down again on the couch, at her husband's feet. "The good Lord will punish us," she said. "It was no job for you. You're too good. You'll make yourself ill. How did you speak?"

"With great care," said Bodi, looking up at his wife's face. "I said what I could in his favor."

"What?"

"That he was a first-class skilled worker."

"God will punish us," the woman repeated. "What else did you say?"

"I said that he had worked in the factory for fourteen years. I said that he never missed a single day, that he was a good timekeeper, dependable in his work."

"God will punish us anyway," she said. "What else did you say?"

The man held his head between his hands. "I said that he had been a Party member since 1945, that he had fulfilled all the tasks that the Party set him, but that for some time he had done his political work grudgingly. I said that Communists must set an example . . . that they must always be first . . ."

"Yes," said the woman. "You would say that."

". . . that they must set an example in production and also in discipline."

"Naturally," said the woman. "You said that."

Comrade Bodi looked at his wife's face. It was red in the lamplight. "That's what I said. And I said that when a Communist harms the State and does not respect Socialist property, he is twice a criminal and has no place alongside honest workers."

"God will punish us," said the woman. "He stole because he wasn't earning enough."

Slowly the man lifted his head onto the couch. "That's what they all say."

"Poor man! Look at your own shoes," said his wife. "When will you have the money to buy yourself another pair?"

Comrade Bodi did not look at his shoes. He stared at his wife's face which had aged so much in recent years. Their godchild, who was married and lived in Miskolc, had hardly recognized her when she visited Budapest last winter.

"Go to bed," he said. "I'll sleep on the couch. Turn out the light."

"Did anyone else speak?"

"Yes."

"How many?"

"Two."

"What did they say?"

"They didn't say anything," muttered Bodi. "Go to bed. Put out the light. It was all decided in advance. None of the workers spoke."

"Because they all steal," said the woman. "Poor men. We are poor people, too. When will the poor have a little peace?"

Three days after the suicide, at lunchtime, Comrade Bodi walked down the narrow alley between the metal shop and the red brick wall. He stretched himself out at the base of the wall, his head resting on a brick. He had a headache. A strong wind blew. From time to time a cloud of dust and litter rose and, when the lull in the wind came, fell back to the ground like a veil. The sun went in and out behind the swift clouds. Comrade Bodi stretched out for a moment, then got up, dusted his trousers and went toward the shop. At the end of the alley he saw a man with his back turned toward him, carrying a bulky package under his arm. When the man saw Bodi, he began to run. Bodi continued slowly on his way.

The man turned back. "All right, Bodi!" he said. "You bastard, tell them."

Bodi walked on.

"You saw me, you bastard," the man shouted. "Tell them. Do you think it matters? I'm not afraid to die."

"I won't denounce you," said Bodi.

"You're lying, you louse. I know your kind. I won't run away from you. Come on. Go to the police. Here's the proof for the bastards."

"Get the hell out of here," said Bodi.

The next day Comrade Bodi did not go to the factory. He spent the whole day at home. He fixed the leaky kitchen faucet; he fixed the washer and packed it with caulking; then he went to see about some plumbing fixtures. He knew the owner of a neighborhood workshop. He worked until late in the afternoon. Then he fixed the kitchen table and polished the stove. The next day he bought two cans of white paint and painted all the kitchen furniture. He put two coats on the garbage can because the first was rough. He stayed home a week, until the end of the month.

Arriving early, he left Karoly Brock Street, which led to the main gate of the factory, turned into the first side street, and a few minutes later came out onto the bank of the Danube. He still had half an hour before him until the night shift.

The spring sunshine was warm and clear. The light was like crystal over the wide river. On the far bank—Pest—the long row of dust-colored warehouses was framed by sky, shimmering in the crystal air. Behind them smokestacks rose black, as far as the horizon, in a sky empty of birds. The Danube flowed silently. No ripple disturbed its surface. If it had not been for the sharp stench of ammonia from the factories and the piles of garbage scattered on the sand, he would have stretched out on the ground at the water's edge.

The red brick wall glowed in the sun. In an angle of the wall, well beyond the stockroom, Bodi saw a piece of leather. He walked on his way. A pleasant breeze blew in from the river. Every now and then it drove away the stink from across the brick wall.

"Hello," said the foreman. "Are you better?"

"All right."

"Flu?"

"That's it."

The foreman rummaged around in his desk. "Me too—every year around this time."

The foreman stood up, pushed his steel-rimmed glasses down onto his nose, and went toward the door. He gave Bodi a pat on the back.

"Don't worry, Bodi," he said. "All right?"

"Of course," said Bodi.

"And the wife?"

"Not too bad."

"That's good," said the foreman. He left the cubicle.

A young girl came into the dimly lit place with a little dance step, laughing. She had a face as fresh as the peonies she had been picking that very morning in her garden at Budafok before setting off for the factory.

Comrade Bodi stared vacantly at her for a moment, then, without knowing, sighed and sat down again behind his desk.

In the evening his wife set the table in front of the open window. The window looked out onto the island where the shipyards lay.

"Do you like it?" she asked.

Comrade Bodi liked noodles and cabbage. "Good."

The woman poured out a glass of water for him and cut a piece of bread.

"A headache?"

"No."

"No pain during the day either?"

Bodi thought for a moment. "No. None."

"It makes me laugh," said the woman a little later. "You always have to have a piece of bread with your noodles and cabbage. For eighteen years. You eat bread with everything—soup, vegetables, noodles, even cake."

The man looked at his wife's face, waiting to see what she would say next.

"You told me eighteen years ago, when I gave you your first meal. 'Listen,' you said, 'I'm an eater of bread. I even eat it with noodles. Bread always on the table, always a piece beside my plate.' "

Comrade Bodi continued to look at his wife.

"For eighteen years now I've been cutting bread for you."

Bodi nodded his head. "That's true."

"Of course, it's true," said the woman, laughing. "Eighteen years now. But you don't eat what I cut."

Comrade Bodi looked at the piece of bread lying untouched beside his plate. At his side his wife was laughing so much that her thin, faded face was suddenly filled with a youth that effaced its lines.

"For years now. You sit down to the table, you look to see if there's bread by your plate, then you go after the noodles with a spoon. The bread, that stays where it is."

"It's true."

The woman laughed again. "You're getting old, Bodi."

"I must be," admitted the man.

"You're no longer an eater of bread."

The woman looked out of the window at the Danube, which shone with a dark brilliance.

"You didn't have a headache yesterday, either. Did you? You didn't lie on the couch, and you didn't ask me for medicine."

"Didn't I?"

"No. It must be at least four or five days since you asked for medicine. Unless you bought some yourself."

Staring in front of him, he shook his head. "No, I didn't buy any," he said. "Four or five days?"

"Thank God!" said the woman with a sigh. "Thank God. May the Lord be praised! Perhaps you won't need any tomorrow either."

"Maybe," said Bodi.

He grew suddenly gloomy, stood up and went to the window.

"Maybe," he repeated, morosely, as if to himself.

Irodalmi Ujsag (Budapest), August 25, 1956.

The revisionist movement in Poland and Hungary was well advanced by early 1955; but in the Soviet Union the tide of socialist realism and the "positive view" receded more slowly. In December, 1956, the second volume of *Literaturnaya Moskva*—and with it, Yashin's story—appeared, quickly becoming something of a *cause célèbre*. The work of the "lonely individuals without a sense of common cause" (as one angry Soviet critic put it) whose stories and poems made up the volume might have seemed embarrassing even in the days that followed the Twentieth Party Congress and Nikita Khrushchev's lurid account of Stalin's crimes; a few short weeks after the Hungarian revolt, they were tantamount to treason.

Yashin's story, like Dery's, is yet another exploration of that inner tension between *partiinost*—the sense of Party—and the human impulse.

THE LEVERS

In the evening in the *kolkhoz* office, as always, a kerosene lamp was burning and a battery radio crackling. A program of marches was on, though hardly audible. At a rectangular pine table four persons sat talking. The tobacco smoke was so thick that the flame in the lamp barely flickered, as during a large meeting. It seemed that even the radio was crackling because of all the smoke in the hut. On the table there stood an earthenware pot for cigarette butts. It was already full. From time to time, fire flared up from a cigarette tossed into the pot. Then the bearded livestock breeder Tsipyshev would cover the pot with a fragment of broken plate glass from the table top. Every time this was done someone cracked the same joke: "Burn your beard, and the cows will stop being afraid of you."

To which Tsipyshev invariably replied, "If they stop being afraid, then maybe they'll increase the milk yield."

And everyone laughed.

They shook cigarette ashes on the floor and on the windowsills, but threw only butts into the pot.

They had been sitting long, talking unhurriedly—a little about everything—and trustingly, without circumspection, like old and good friends.

Through the semi-darkness there peered from the timbered walls some chance placards and slogans, a list of the members of the *kolkhoz* with a monthly record of the number of workdays put in, a fragment of an old wall newspaper, and an empty all-black slate divided into two equal parts by a white line. On one half was written in chalk "black"; on the other half, "red."

"You know they brought sugar again to the *kolkhoz* shop a couple of days ago," said the storehouse keeper, Sergei Shchukin, the youngest of those present, in whose dress a citified appearance was already to be noted. He wore a shirt with a tie. From the breast pocket of his jacket a fountain pen and a comb protruded.

"Someone let you in on it, eh?" slyly asked a third person of those seated at the table, a stout, somewhat bloated man missing his left arm, with a bedraggled tarpaulin raincoat—apparently of wartime vintage—thrown about him.

"No one let me in on it. Mikola himself sent a woman around to my house with about two kilograms, saying we'd settle later."

"And you took it?"

"I did. If you don't, you can sit all your life without sugar. You, too, would have taken it."

"Well, he won't send *you* any, Piotr Kuz'mich!" Tsipyshev said, laughing in his beard and screwing up his eyes in a sideward glance at the one-armed man. "He's mad at you. But Sergei is in good with him," he said turning to Shchukin, "Sergei didn't remove him from his storehouse post, even though he took his place."

Sergei Shchukin had just recently been an ordinary *kolkhoznik*. On entering the Party a month before, he began to talk about the fact that all commanding positions in the *kolkhoz* should be filled by Communists, and that it was simply embarrassing now for him not to advance to a better job. He met with agreement. It was remembered that the *kolkhoz* storehouse keeper had already been spoken to several times for stealing, and Shchukin was put into the storehouse. At the scheduled general meeting no one saw any reason to object to this decision. Shchukin bought himself a fountain pen and began to wear a tie. And his predecessor went to work in the *kolkhoz* shop. It was about him that there was now talk.

"As far as taking the sugar goes, I took it," said Shchukin after some thought, "but where is the justice of it, after all? Where does the sugar go, where's the soap, where is everything?" After these words, he reached for his comb and began to smooth back his thick, young, unruly hair.

Then the fourth person present put in his word, "Why do you need justice? You're now the storehouse keeper."

The fourth person was a man of middle age, but already graying, pale and apparently not very well. He smoked incessantly, more than everyone else, and coughed a good deal. When he stretched his hand toward the pot to discard the stub of a cigarette that had already singed his fingers, his big, thick nails could be seen, and under the nails earth—not dirt, but earth. This was the brigadier of the farming brigade, Ivan Konoplev. He had the reputation of being a fair man but irascible. He spoke rarely but caustically. Usually no one was offended by his sharp words; apparently people did not sense in them any dislike toward themselves. Shchukin likewise was not offended.

But the one-armed man, whom all called by both his first and middle names, Piotr Kuz'mich, objected, "Well, justice—you know that's necessary. That's what keeps us going. Only I, for one, fellows, don't understand something again. I can't understand what is going on in our district. You know, they said, plan from the bottom, let the *kolkhoz* decide what is best for it to sow and what isn't. But they don't confirm the plan. For the third time they've returned it for corrections. It seems they collected all the *kolkhoz* plans, weighed them, and it turned out they don't agree with the district plan. But the district plan is given from above. You can't make much out of this either. Well, so an obstacle has been struck. The sparks fly, but nothing comes of it. Again there's nothing left of our plan. That's justice for you. They don't believe in us."

"Justice in our district is given a seat only in honorary presidiums, so that it shouldn't be offended and should keep quiet," said the pale Konoplev, and he tossed a butt into the pot.

Shchukin also put in his word, "Justice is needed only for meetings, on solemn occasions, just like criticism and self-criticism. It can't apply in real practice—isn't this what it comes down to?"

A guarded and somehow uneasy look suddenly crossed Tsipyshev's face. It seemed this confidential conversation had ceased to please him.

"Okay, hammer away, but mind where the chips fly," he remarked roughly to Shchukin; and immediately changed his tone, as though he regretted his bluntness. "Justice, brother, is justice. . . . But, now, give *you* a seat in an honorary presidium, and you'll even stop seeing the ground below you," he said and laughed, shaking his mustache and beard.

Tsipyshev's beard grew not only on his chin but on his cheeks and behind his ears, merged with his thick reddish brows, and hung over his eyes; when Tsipyshev laughed, his whole face laughed, his whole beard, and his eyes shone from somewhere out of the depths of hair.

"I was the other day to the district committee to see the big man himself," continued Piotr Kuz'mich, referring thus to the first secretary of the district committee. " 'What are you doing with us?' I say. 'The *kolkhozniks* won't agree to change the plan for the third time, they'll take offense. We need flax. It's flax that we should seed our best land with. We've already had experiments with both rabbits and crop rotation. How many people were used up for nothing! As a result, there was no grain—which just did the state harm. Let me have,' I say, 'just ten, well, let's say, twenty hectares for the first time, but not a hundred, not a thousand. When we get used to it, we'll add on to it ourselves, we ourselves will ask for more. Don't give everything at once.' 'No!' he says, 'at once. You've got to,' he says, 'overfulfill the plan, you've got to actively implant the new.' 'Actively, all right,' I say, 'let it be active, but you know this is the north, and there are not many people, and the land wants its own way. You have to persuade people. Lenin pointed out—you must actively persuade.' And he says, 'Well, it's up to you to persuade them! We persuaded you before, when we organized the *kolkhozes,* now you persuade the others, carry out the Party line. You,' he says, 'are now our levers out in the country.' So he says, but he himself just shrugs. It seems that not everything is so sweet for him either. But there's no give in him, he doesn't understand what the Party wants, he's afraid to understand."

"It's a rough situation!" said Shchukin as though interpreting these words, and again reached for his comb.

"And it won't be sweet. He won't sit here long anyway," said Tsipyshev. "He's taken the wrong approach to people, he's too strict. He doesn't listen to people, he decides everything himself. People for him are only levers. But I look at it this way, boys, this is exactly what bureaucracy is. Let's say, we come to him for a meeting. Well, talk like a human being, simply and openly. No, he can't without being strict, he's absolutely got to be boss. The way he takes a look around at everyone down his nose and snarls, 'Let's begin, comrades! All assembled?' Well, the heart goes out of you, and so you sit, waiting to be cussed out. If he'd only come out with it straight when something is not right! People would move mountains for one straightforward word. No, he can't.

"He thinks that the Party will lose authority if he talks with the people like a human being, in a plain way. Why, he knows that we earn in the *kolkhoz* a hundred grams for a workday, but he repeats the same thing over and over: 'With every year, the earning power of the workday is growing and prosperity becoming greater.' There are no cows left in our *kolkhoz,* but he goes on: 'With every year, cattle raising in the *kolkhoz* is increasing and on a more solid basis.' Why doesn't he say: 'You aren't living so hot because of this and this . . . but we will live better.' Say it—the people will take to their work more willingly."

"It's a rough situation!" said Shchukin, again concluding Piotr Kuz'mich's heated words.

Ivan Konoplev was finishing off another cigarette. He appeared on edge and constantly trying to say something—apparently something harsh and caustic—but a severe asthmatic cough suddenly seized him and forced him from the table. At the doorway Konoplev lifted the broom and spat long into the corner. The livestock breeder Tsipyshev said to him sympathetically, "Changed your tobacco, again, probably, did you? I told you long ago—smoke only *makhorka,* the stalk variety, it'll be easier on you."

Having coughed up a bit, but still without straightening up, Konoplev raised his head and said hoarsely: "Our district heads have lost the habit of how to talk with the people, they're ashamed. They understand everything themselves but are afraid to take the leap. What's persuasion have to do with this? They're relying on levers. They see the boarded-up homes in the village, but don't want to talk of this out loud. All there's concern about is that there will be all round numbers in the reports. But what about people, what are they left with?" And Konoplev again was racked with coughing.

"All right, all right, keep quiet, or your whole soul will jump out of you!" Tsipyshev got up from the table and went to the doorway to Konoplev. "You wait a bit, Ivan, we'll wangle a pass to a rest home for you from the district committee. You'll go to the ocean for the air, at the same time you'll have a look at how people live there, you'll learn a few things and tell us about it. You'll give us all a bracing up."

Konoplev met him with an impatient motion of his hand as though to say, "Sit, why are you coming over here, go away!" but because of his coughing could not say a word. Tsipyshev returned to the table.

"His wife will give him such a pass, he won't recognize his own family afterward," said Shchukin. "She's a sharp one. Cough as much as you like, smoke, drink, only don't take a step away from her."

"Our air here is not worse than sea air," noted Piotr Kuz'mich musingly. "Air we have! It used to be once, to cure a cough, you went to a tar works or tapped resin. A man would live three—four weeks in a pine woods, would gather some of this resin from boxes into barrels, and without noticing it, all of a sudden, he's making money and at the same time his breathing's easier. Do they buy this resin anywhere nowadays? Somehow I haven't heard about it. They made some kind of turpentine out of it and rosin for violinists. Now, I bet, they play without rosin."

"They've substituted plastic for it. Take a look!" Shchukin showed his comb. "It's also made out of plastic."

No one looked at Shchukin's comb.

"Our lamp is dying out altogether, boys," Tsipyshev raised his beard in the air.

From the doorway, Konoplev responded, "You'll die out without air. Even a lamp needs air."

For the last time Konoplev rattled the dry broom and returned to the table. His face was pale, his breathing difficult.

"I understand our situation this way," he said. "Until there's trust in the most ordinary peasant in the *kolkhoz,* things won't work right, we'll have no little grief ahead to swallow. They write in our papers —a new man has appeared. True—he's appeared! The *kolkhoz* has made over the peasant. True—it made him over. The peasant is no longer what he was. Good! Then you have to trust this peasant. He's also got a mind."

"A wolf didn't eat it up," slyly confirmed Tsipyshev.

"There you are! It's not enough just to teach us—you have to listen to us. But the way things are, everything comes from above, always from above. The plans are handed down from above, chairmen from above, the harvest yield estimate from above. There's no time to persuade people, and it isn't even necessary, it's easier not to. Just hand down directives, in other words, and recommend. They stopped cultural work—it was too much trouble. Clubs and reading rooms function only in reports. There's no one to give lectures and talks. What's left are campaigns for getting things ready and getting things in; five-day, ten-day, monthly deadlines . . ."

Konoplev stopped for breath, and Piotr Kuz'mich took advantage of this to put in a word: "It happens this way, too: the wedge won't go in, so the tree's at fault; as they say, the tree has a rotten spot. Just try and disagree in the district committee. They give you advice, recommendations, and it's not advice but an order. If you don't carry it out, that means you've slackened the reins. If the *kolkhozniks* don't agree, that means it's a political failure."

"But why a failure?" Konoplev almost shouted. "Aren't we concerned at heart with the same cause, do we have different interests?"

"Well, you know, brother, they don't pat the district committee on the head either, if anything goes wrong. They have to deliver, too, and how!"

"And how, and how!" Konoplev fumed. "Next to us, in the Gruzdikhino District, things are done differently. Shurin came here a few days ago, and he says that there the chairmen don't quake in their shoes when the chief calls them up to the district committee. There isn't this fear. The secretary comes to the *kolkhoz* informally and talks with people, not as though he were carrying out a written directive."

On the shelf in the front corner the radio started up more audibly. It still crackled and hissed like an expiring foam fire extinguisher, but now through the crackling and hissing, instead of music, someone's stammering speech was coming through. Letters from the virgin lands were being transmitted. Some young fellow or other was talking about the success of his work in the Altai region. The men at the table listened.

"They call us Muscovites here, although we're from different towns. We stick together, we don't take anything lying down. The harvest last year was out of this world. You walk into the wheat just like into reeds. Even the oldsters don't remember such crops. There weren't enough places to pour the grain, it was rough . . ."

The young fellow addressing his dear mamma, but in such a way, as if he had never pronounced this name before. He was obviously intimidated by the microphone.

"Take a look," said Piotr Kuz'mich, "they have their troubles there, too: no place to pour the grain." He poked his arm in the direction of the radio, and the tarpaulin raincoat slipped off his armless left shoulder.

"Not everyone, after all, can go to the Altai region," muttered Konoplev, and, again taken by coughing, he got up from the table, took the pot of cigarette butts in both hands, and went to the doorway. There he pushed aside the broom with his foot and threw the butts into the corner.

And then it was revealed that in the hut, during all the time this talk was going on, one other person had been present. From behind the wide Russian stove there resounded an imperious old lady's voice.

"Where are you throwing things, you old croak? You're not the one who has to sweep. I just washed the floor, and you mess it all up again."

From the unexpectedness of it, the men started and exchanged looks.

"You still here, Marfa? What do you want?"

"What I want! I'm keeping watch on you. You set fire to the office, and they'll have me in court for it. The broom's dry, and what if suddenly there's a spark, God forbid. . . ."

"You better go home."

"When I have to—I'll go."

The conversation of the friends broke off, as though they felt guilty of something before one another.

For an instant the street became audible, the sound of the wind, girls singing in the distance.

Sergei Shchukin turned off the radio, the voices of the virgin land dwellers broke off.

Again they began to tear off pieces of newspaper, pulling it out little by little from under the cracked glass on the table top and rolling up cigarettes, both plain and twisted into L shapes. They were silent for a long while, smoking. And when they began again to exchange short remarks, these were already idle remarks, not about anything, not meant for anyone. About the weather—the weather was rotten, in such weather your bones ached. About newspapers—there are different kinds; if you roll a cigarette from some, all you get is a bitter taste and there's no tobacco smell. Then there was something said about yesterday—someone had to go somewhere, but didn't go. Then about tomorrow—ought to get up earlier; the old lady has finally got around to making pancakes. Idle words, but they were already uttered in muffled voices, quietly, with a glance around now and then and at the stove, as though behind it were concealed not Marfa, the office cleaning woman, but some sort of outsider, some obscure person with whom one must be on guard. Tsipyshev grew serious, no longer talked, did not smile, only asked about three times, by the way, without addressing anyone in particular, "What's keeping this teacher? We ought to get the Party meeting started."

Only Shchukin suddenly acted a bit strangely. He could not sit still, the stool under him scraped. His eyes—young, impudent, and sharp—shone upon everyone defiantly. It was as though Shchukin suddenly saw something that no one else had yet seen and therefore felt his superiority over the others. Finally, he could not hold back and laughed loudly.

"Boy, that darned dame gave us a scare!" said Shchukin, laughing.

Piotr Kuz'mich and Konoplev exchanged glances and also laughed.

"It's true—the old she-devil. Bellowing all of a sudden from behind the stove. Well, I thought . . ." Ivan Konoplev finished the sentence with difficulty, "Well, I thought the big man himself had come—caught us in the act. . . ."

"We got scared like little boys in someone else's cabbage patch."

Laughter discharged the tension and returned them to their normal state.

"And what are we afraid of, fellows?" Piotr Kuz'mich suddenly said, musingly and a bit sadly. "Why, we're already afraid of ourselves!"

But Tsipyshev did not smile this time either. It was as though he

did not notice that Konoplev and Piotr Kuz'mich also had burst
into laughter but only looked at Sergei Shchukin—sternly, like an
elder.

"You're young still to laugh about this. If you'd lived as long as
we have . . ."

But Shchukin was beyond quieting down. Besides, both Konoplev
and Piotr Kuz'mich were obviously on his side. They winked jauntily at him and kept on laughing.

"That's the way it is. That's how we're afraid," said Konoplev.

Behind the stove Marfa was silent.

Two young fellows of Komsomol age tore into the office.

"Why are you here?" Tsipyshev turned bodily to them.

"We want to listen to the radio."

"You can't. We're about to have a Party meeting."

"Where should we go then? There are a lot of us outside."

"Wherever you want."

Having said this, Tsipyshev looked around at his friends, as
though he wanted to find out whether they approved his action.

Piotr Kuz'mich did not approve.

"I'll tell you what, my fine fellows," he said, addressing the boys.
"We'll whiz through our Party meeting here, we'll have a talk, and
then you can take over command."

Finally, the teacher herself came—Akulina Semenovna, young,
short, looking almost like a little girl. She wearily untied and removed her gray wool kerchief from her head and stuck herself away
in the corner under the wooden shelf with the radio. With her
arrival, Tsipyshev also became more lively. But this liveliness took
the form of starting to talk to the teacher with exaggerated sternness,
like a superior.

"How come, Akulina Semenovna, that you make everyone wait?"

Akulina Semenovna looked guiltily at Tsipyshev, at Piotr Kuz'-
mich, then at the pot filled with cigarette butts, at the lamp, and
lowered her eyes.

"Well, we were held up . . . in school. Piotr Kuz'mich," she
turned to the one-armed man, "I should like to settle a matter before
the meeting. There is no firewood in the school . . ."

"About business afterward," Tsipyshev interrupted her, "now we
have to get through the meeting. The district committee has been
requesting a long time now that there be two meetings a month, and

we can't even get together to get one on the record. How are we going to account for this?"

Ivan Konoplev sighed audibly at this point, and Tsipyshev again for a moment seemed to feel embarrassment, lacking confidence in himself, and timidly looked around, as though asking to be excused for his words. But all kept silent. Then Tsipyshev's voice finally acquired firmness and authority. What had happened? His beard straightened out, lengthened, his eyes grew hard, in them vanished the live spark that had flickered during the simple friendly conversation. To the cleaning woman, Marfa, Tsipyshev now addressed himself in the tones of command: "You, Marfa, leave! We're going to have a Party meeting here. We're going to talk."

And Marfa—as though she sensed the change that had taken place—did not disobey, did not grumble. She said, "Go ahead and talk. Don't I understand? I'm leaving."

When the door quietly closed after the subdued Marfa, Tsipyshev arose and uttered the very same words that, in such instances, were uttered by the secretary of the Party district committee, and even in the same dry, stern, and seemingly conspiratorial voice in which the secretary of the district committee spoke before the start of a meeting. "Shall we begin, comrades! Are all assembled?"

He said this, and it was as if he flicked the switch of some sort of miracle-working mechanism. Everything in the hut began to be transformed beyond recognition—the people, the things, and even, it seemed, the air.

Shchukin and Konoplev noiselessly moved back from the table. Piotr Kuz'mich remained seated where he was, only he gathered up the tarpaulin raincoat that had half fallen from his shoulders and placed it aside on the bench. The teacher, Akulina Semenovna, drew back even more in the corner under the radio. Everyone's face became concentrated, tense, and bored, as though these people had set themselves for something long, long familiar but, all the same, solemn and important. Everything earthly, everything natural disappeared. The action was transferred into another world, into a complex setup, to which these simple, warm people were still not accustomed and which they still did not quite understand.

"Are all assembled?" repeated Tsipyshev, surveying those present as though there were at least several times ten.

But there were now, as we already know, only five in all. The livestock breeder, Stepan Tsipyshev, turned out to be the secretary of the Party organization. He had been elected secretary recently on the recommendation of the district committee. Flattered by this, Tsipyshev tried his best to fulfill his role, and being a novice, he unwittingly began in everything to imitate the "district boss." True, he sometimes dealt ironically with himself, but he nevertheless carried out every directive from above with such zeal and literalness—all from fearfulness of committing some error—that at times it would have been better had he not dotted every last "i." The zonal political instructor of the district committee, who had been present at the election of Tsipyshev, joked that Comrade Tsipyshev had not a few virtues, but he also had shortcomings and that his chief shortcoming was his beard. Tsipyshev took this joke seriously, as a directive, and resolved privately to remove the beard and all other hair from his face, but there had not as yet been an opportune occasion to do so.

Piotr Kuz'mich Kudriavtsev, the one-armed man, turned out to be the chairman of the *kolkhoz*. Ivan Konoplev, as was already noted, was the brigadier farmer. Sergei Shchukin was the storehouse keeper. From the time that Shchukin was made storehouse keeper and his predecessor struck from the record, as a result of being transferred to work in the *kolkhoz* shop, there were no rank-and-file *kolkhozniks* in the party organization. Akulina Semenovna —well, she was of the intelligentsia altogether, even though she was a fellow villager and depended in everything on the *kolkhoz* administration.

"The first to take the floor will be the chairman of our *kolkhoz*, Comrade Piotr Kuz'mich!"

Piotr Kuz'mich Kudriavtsev got up.

Tsipyshev sat down.

The Party meeting began.

And there began that same thing, about which the members of the Party organization—including the secretary himself—had just spoken among themselves with such frankness and insight, inveighing against the soulless officialism, bureaucratism, slavish literalness in actions and words.

"Comrades!" said the chairman of the *kolkhoz*, "the district committee and district executive committee have not confirmed our production plan. I believe that we have not provided for some things and allowed them to take their own course. This is not to our credit.

We did not carry on any explanatory activity among the masses and did not persuade them. But people must be persuaded, comrades. You and I are the levers of the party in the *kolkhoz* village—this was pointed out to us in the district committee and the district executive committee. . . ."

The teacher, with cautious, stealthy movements of her hands, in order to disturb no one, again tied the kerchief around her head. Her face became hidden from view, and what she was thinking of now, no one could say.

But Shchukin again began to smile. He took from his pocket his lifetime pen, rotated it in his hands, then took out his comb, looked through it at the lamp, softly blew on the teeth, and put the comb back, not combing himself after all. His face expanded more and more, and in his eyes there appeared a sly, mocking light. It seemed that in just another moment Shchukin would again burst into laughter. But he did not laugh and only nudged Konoplev in the side and whispered to him: "You see what's going on? Do you recognize him now?"

Konoplev also smiled, but crookedly, without humor.

"All right, now, let him have his say. This is how it has to be. Piotr Kuz'mich is now on his job. The way it is in the district committee, that's the way it is with us. Like master, like man."

"But what about truth?"

"Truth—it will have its way. It will soon reach us, too, brother, and it will come like a thunderclap."

"But we'll have reached the end of the rope."

"We won't."

And Konoplev drew up to the table, moved the pot closer, and smoked without end. He did not venture to cough, he restrained himself, although everything gurgled and wheezed in his chest.

Kudriavtsev—Piotr Kuz'mich—did not speak long. The essence of his report was that the fighting ability of the Party organization would be placed in doubt by the district committee if the *kolkhoz* plan of crop rotation for the next year were not immediately corrected and in unconditional accordance with the directives of the district committee and the district executive committee. All those who took part in the discussion agreed with this. It was not possible otherwise.

Akulina Semenovna and Shchukin and Konoplev took part in

the discussions. No differences of opinion were revealed, just as
there had been none during that friendly conversation before the
start of the Party meeting. True, the agreement and unanimity now
were manifested in a somewhat different, one may say reverse, sense.

Tsipyshev was pleased with the single-mindedness of the Communists and spoke himself on the second question. Somehow, the
zonal secretary of the district committee of the party had directed
attention to the fact that political-educational work was not set in
progress in the *kolkhoz* and had reported about the pertinent facts
in a memorandum to the first secretary of the district committee.

"The best people, comrades, are not encouraged by us," said
Tsipyshev in this connection, "the laggards are not punished, there's
no competition. You've only to take a look at our red-black board
—the picture is clear. We have to lead the masses, comrades! I think
we ought to do as follows: Specify several *kolkhoz* units to receive a
bonus, pick one or two persons for this purpose in each unit—and
penalize some others, so it should be right on both sides. They'll approve of our action in the regional committee."

The meeting unanimously resolved to single out five persons for a
bonus, three for a penalty. Conversation arose only on this question:
in which *kolkhoz* units people should be found for encouragement,
in which for punishment.

They had no time to write even one resolution—Marfa returned,
in order to clean up and lock the office. Piotr Kuz'mich proposed
that the drawing up of the resolution be entrusted to the Party secretary.

"You write you-know-what," he whispered, pleased that the
meeting had come to an end. "In conditions of heightened enthusiasm and will to work there is proceeding full steam ahead
throughout the *kolkhoz* . . ."

"Throughout the country . . ." prompted Shchukin.

They got ready quietly to go home, and it was as though everyone in his heart had a sense of fulfilled obligation and at the same
time of embarrassment, dissatisfaction with self. But on the
threshold boots were already clomping, the young people appeared
in the doorway.

"Did we come on time?" asked one of the two young fellows who
had already come into the office.

"On time!" answered Piotr Kuz'mich. "Just the right time. Come in, all of you."

Into the hut burst the cool air from the street. The flame in the lamp revived, stools were moved around, windows opened.

"You sure have smoke in here!" the girls clamored.

With the appearance of the young people, Akulina Semenovna straightened up, pulled the kerchief from her head. These were people of her own age, she felt freer with them. Sergei Shchukin also began to hop around, pulled his necktie tighter, and was already inseparable from the girls.

The radio, which had been turned on, suddenly spoke out loud and clear. Reports on the preparation for the Twentieth Party Congress were being broadcast. Everyone listened to this message.

Piotr Kuz'mich, as though grown softer, before leaving said to Akulina Semenovna, "There'll be firewood, don't worry. I'll see to it." But Tsipyshev went over to Sergei Shchukin and squeezed his arm above the elbow. "You're staying here?"

"Yes."

"Well, see to it that there shouldn't be anything, you know . . ."

When the chairman of the *kolkhoz*, Kudriavtsev, and the farmer, Ivan Konoplev, walked from the office down the dark, dirty street, there started up again the conversation about life, about conditions, about work—the very same that went on before the meeting.

"Let's see now what the Congress will say!" they repeated from time to time. And again these were plain, warm, straightforward people—people, and not levers.

Literaturnaya Moskva (Moscow), Vol. II, 1956.

Bohdan Drozdowski is a young Polish poet whose verse is sometimes very close in feeling to the stories of Marek Hlasko. Although he describes himself as a candidate for membership in the Party, he has often, it seems, been attacked as "anti-Party." Drozdowski replies: "People tell me—that poem of yours about the drunken activist is anti-Party. . . . But I want to write the truth. The truth about what is good and what is bad. . . ."

His first book of verse, *Moja Polska* ("My Poland"), was published in 1957.

....

THE SIXTEEN-YEAR-OLD

Last night
at the corner of Piotrkowska and Tuwim streets
a sixteen-year-old girl
made up like a violet
caught me by the sleeve
let's go
her eyes like forget-me-nots
her mouth still fresh
as a blooming dahlia
and already this
let's go
I went
we went
she earns four hundred *zloty*
at the post office
pair of nylons two hundred
her father's old-age pension hundred twenty
how can one live
she said
thus: let's go
she cried because I did nothing
I said I had a wife
and son

they love me
and twice a month
my wife expects money
she doesn't wear nylons
I said
we are building heavy industry
ships for export
jets are very expensive you know
one costs a billion pairs of nylons
a billion lipsticks
purple violet *et cetera*
that's why we earn little
She nodded
and went back
to the corner of Piotrkowska
and Tuwim streets
to wait until we build heavy industry
and fully equip our army
that sixteen-year-old
made-up girl like a violet.

Nowa Kultura (Warsaw), January 6, 1957.

Dygat's sad little story speaks for itself: "One more step, perhaps two, and old age will get me by the neck."

Stanislaw Dygat was born in 1914, the descendant, he says, of a French grenadier who turned back from Napoleon's invasion of Russia. His connections with France and French culture have always been close. Interned in a German concentration camp during World War II, he returned to Poland to publish a record of his experiences which became something of a best seller. More recently, he has been identified with the reformist, or liberal, wing of the Polish Party. His latest novel, *The Journey*, was published in 1958.

■■

LONG JOURNEY

Marion was standing at the window. A pink fog hovered above the roofs. The black lines of antennas and wires cut sharply into the bluish sky. Far away, a chimney smoked. Farther away, an engine blew a violent whistle. Below, in his neighbor's room, the radio played "Domino, Domino."

Marion sighed.

Terrible things were happening behind his back. His children fought furiously and hurled vulgar words at each other. His wife was peeling the potatoes, shouting at the children, and in her angry words Marion could easily detect rather disagreeable allusions to himself.

He thought: "One more step, perhaps two, and old age will get me by the neck."

Girls dressed in brightly colored skirts walked by in the street.

He thought: "These are the last moments in which to get something out of life. These are the last moments in which to collect wonderful memories, and not despair, for my old age. I should disregard everything and do something."

His children, tired of fighting among themselves, came close to him and began asking questions which he was unable to answer. He sat down and began reading the paper. His wife put a pot full of potatoes on the stove. She began asking him commonplace questions and became angry when he answered her in monosyllables. He had time for everything, except her.

The children continued to fight. One of them threw a wooden block at the vase, and it broke. Water poured slowly down. Marion put aside his paper and thought:

"I still have the night. I still own my dreams. Nobody has the right to invade my dreams."

At night his wife nagged at him. She wept, and because he said nothing, lying in the dark with his arms under his head and only sighing now and then, she bit him on the nose.

On his way from the office, Marion met Alfred.

"I am leaving for Brussels tonight. A conference," he said.

"You do make something out of life," Marion said.

"Huh!" Alfred said.

"You do," Marion said. "You go abroad, see the world. You share great adventures with others. You will have something to remember in your old age."

"You can have all that here," Alfred said.

"Can you?" Marion said. Suddenly, he thought of something. Something that made him hot all over.

"Listen," he said. "I would like you to do something for me, really. . . . One more step, perhaps two, and I will be old. Seeing that you are going away, I thought that perhaps you could do me a favor. . . . Leave your keys with me—you know, to your apartment."

"You old son-of-a-gun," Alfred winked at him. "I would never have suspected."

"Come on, try to understand." Marion was on the verge of crying.

"Sure, sure," Alfred agreed. "As one man to another. Here you are. . . ."

Marion clutched the keys in his hand. He felt strange, and he shivered ever so slightly.

"I have a meeting tonight," he said to his wife in a voice which sounded foreign and unpleasant to him. "I will be late, maybe very late." She did not say much, though usually her answers were full of insinuations. Perhaps she was sorry she had bitten his nose.

As he opened the door of Alfred's apartment, his hands trembled and his throat was dry. Quickly, he took off his coat; ran, smiling, into the room; flung out his arms and took a deep whiff of air. The room was quiet. A scent of lavender and English cigarettes still lingered in it. It was full of postcards from foreign places and of articles, everyday articles, which are unknown in Poland. Gaily, he began to dance until, completely exhausted, he had to sit down in an armchair. He reached for the phone and spoke into the humming emptiness:

"Service? Director Jack Brown of Alabama speaking. Reserve two seats on the plane to Rome tomorrow. If Gina Lollobrigida asks for me, show her upstairs. I am not at home to anyone else. . . ."

He put down the phone and picked it up again:

"Director John Brown of Alabama speaking. Send up supper for two. Whisky, champagne, lobsters, caviar . . ."

He fell silent and began to stare at the wall opposite. He put aside the phone, shook his head, and took out a paper. He held it for some time in front of his eyes, got up and walked toward the window.

Pink twilight hovered above the roofs. Black lines of antennas and wires cut sharply into the gray sky. Girls dressed in brightly colored skirts walked by in the street.

He hid his face in his hands, propped his elbows against the glass, and began to cry.

Przeglad Kulturalny (Warsaw), September 9, 1956.

2.

THE GOALS OF SOCIALISM

Leszek Kolakowski is another one of the formidable young Poles who burst the bonds of dogma in the years following Stalin's death. Relatively unknown until 1956, he served a lengthy apprenticeship in the Party, rising to the position of professor of modern philosophy at the University of Warsaw and editor of Poland's leading philosophical journal. His mentor for some years was Adam Schaff, a man who emerged in 1955 as a spokesman for Marxist conservatism in the course of a running debate with Josef Chalisinsky—a debate which itself became a landmark of the Polish "thaw." Later, Schaff brought Kolakowski himself under fire: "When people who call themselves Marxists begin to build an annex to Marxism out of their Kantian-existentialist positions—this is ideological bankruptcy."

"What Is Socialism?" was written for publication in the Polish student journal, *Po Prostu,* banned in 1957. The article never appeared in print, but it was circulated in manuscript at the University of Warsaw. A copy eventually found its way to the West.

WHAT IS SOCIALISM?

We will tell you what socialism is. But first we must tell you what socialism is not. It is a matter about which we once had a quite different opinion than we have today.

Well, then, socialism is not:

A society in which a person who has committed no crime sits at home waiting for the police.

A society in which it is a crime to be the brother, sister, son, or wife of a criminal.

A society in which one person is unhappy because he says what he thinks, and another happy because he does not say what is in his mind.

A society in which a person lives better because he does not think at all.

A society in which a person is unhappy because he is a Jew, and another feels better for not being a Jew.

A state whose soldiers move into the territory of another country first.

A state where anyone who praises the national leaders is better off.

A state in which one can be condemned without trial.

A society whose leaders appoint themselves to their posts.

A society in which ten people live in one room.

A society which has illiterates and smallpox epidemics.

A state which does not permit travel abroad.

A state which has more spies than nurses, and more people in prison than in hospitals.

A state in which the number of officials increases faster than that of workers.

A state in which one is forced to resort to lies.

A state in which one is compelled to be a thief.

A state in which one is forced to resort to crime.

A state which possesses colonies.

A state whose neighbors curse geography.

A state which produces excellent jet planes and bad shoes.

A state in which cowards live better than the valiant.

A state in which lawyers in most cases agree with the state prosecutor.

Empire, tyranny, oligarchy, bureaucracy.

A state in which the majority of people seek God in order to find solace in their misery.

A state which awards prizes to pseudo-authors and knows more about painting than the painters.

A nation which oppresses other nations.

A nation which is oppressed by another nation.

A state which wants all its citizens to have the same opinions in philosophy, foreign policy, economics, literature, and ethics.

A state whose government defines its citizens' rights, but whose citizens do not define the government's rights.

A state in which one is responsible for one's ancestors.

A state in which one part of the population receives salaries forty times higher than those of the remainder.

Any system of government toward which most of the governed are hostile.

A single, isolated state.

A group of backward countries.

A state which utilizes nationalistic slogans.

A state whose government believes that nothing is more important than its power.

A state which makes a pact with crime, and then adapts its ideology to this pact.

A state which would like to see its foreign ministry determine the political opinion of all mankind.

A state which finds it difficult to distinguish between enslavement and liberation.

A state in which racist agitators enjoy full freedom.

A state in which there is private ownership of the means of production.

A state which considers itself solidly socialist because it has liquidated private ownership of the means of production.

A state which has difficulty differentiating between social revolution and armed assault.

A state which does not believe that people must be happier under socialism than elsewhere.

A society which is very melancholy.

A caste system.

A state which always knows the will of the people before it asks them.

A state which can mistreat the people with impunity.

A state in which a view of history is important.

A state in which the philosophers and writers always say the same as the generals and ministers, but always after them.

A state in which street maps of cities are state secrets.

A state in which the returns of parliamentary elections are always predictable.

A state in which there is slave labor.

A state in which feudal fetters exist.

A state which has a world monopoly on scientific progress.

A state in which an entire people, through no desire of its own, is moved to a new location.

A state in which the workers have no influence on the government.

A state which believes that it alone can redeem humanity.

A state which considers itself to be always in the right.

A state in which history is a servant of policy.

A state whose citizens may not read the greatest works of contemporary literature, not see the greatest works of contemporary painting, and not hear the greatest works of modern music.

A state which is always well pleased with itself.

A state which asserts that the world is very complicated, but actually believes it to be extremely simple.

A state in which one must suffer long before one can get a doctor.

A society that has beggars.

A state which believes everyone to be enamored of it, whereas in truth it is the opposite.

A state which is convinced that nobody in the world can conceive anything better.

A state which does not mind being hated as long as it is feared.

A state which determines who may criticize it and how.

A state in which one must each day refute what one affirmed the day before and always believe it to be the same.

A state which does not like to see its citizens read back numbers of newspapers.

A state in which many ignoramuses rank as scholars.

That was the first part. But now listen attentively, we will tell you what socialism is: Well, then, socialism is a good thing.

                                                            Warsaw, 1956.

Minh Hoang is one of the Vietnamese dissidents who clustered around the Hanoi journal *Van* and flourished for a brief time in the era following Mao Tse-tung's injunction, "Let a hundred flowers bloom, a hundred schools contend."

"A Heap of Machinery" appeared at the close of 1957 and quickly came under attack. As one hostile critic put it: "A cursory reading of this story might lead us to think that it is an attack on excessive bureaucracy. Actually, the issue of bureaucracy is nothing more than an outline around which the author sketches a bitter picture of relations between the leaders and the led, between the higher and the lower echelons in our society today. . . ."

Minh Hoang's technique is crude: he is still the undereducated colonial intellectual. Not the least significant feature of the story is his venomous sketch of the Soviet technical advisors.

The story has been somewhat shortened in translation.

A HEAP OF MACHINERY

Each day the sun beat down on the wooden crates stacked at the entrance to the half-finished factory. Each day Thang, the boss of the construction site, went there at noon. Each day he kicked the wooden slats to see if they were sound, peeped through the cracks, and, nostrils quivering, poked his nose into a knothole to sniff the state of things.

The sun was like fire; the heat burned through to his bones.

"If this goes on," he thought, "the wood will warp and the cracks will widen. The sunlight will get inside and rust the steel. The whole pile of machinery will be lost." The heat was fierce; no one knew when the sky would pour rain. And after the rains, the damp would get in, coating the beautifully complex and glittering steel of the machines, violating their virgin perfection. "There is nothing anyone can do about the weather."

The devil himself could not explain how this vast mountain of delicate machinery had suddenly been delivered to the construction site. They had piled the crates in the open air, naked to the scorching rays of the sun. Thang was a responsible construction boss. He could not refuse the new responsibility of guarding the heap of machinery. A troublesome duty indeed! But in his usual way Thang bent his back to the new load. He would do the best he could.

He went to his superiors and asked that they buy tarpaulins to shield the crates from the weather. Always they refused. He insisted. Always they said: "Only a few days more, and we will install the machinery inside. No need to buy canvas." He asked: "Who will install these machines?" But always they answered vaguely: "We will think about that later."

And each time Thang left these unsatisfactory audiences with a long face.

The construction gang would ask how the audience had gone, what had happened. Thang would answer curtly: "They refused." Then he would hang his head and say nothing. He would walk over to the heap of machinery and bang his fists against the warped slats and suddenly begin to shout—to no one in particular: "The bastards! After a telephone call, a visit. After a visit, a telephone call. And still they pretend not to understand. 'Overcome difficulties, Thang,' they say. God! After the rain, the sun. After the sun, the rain again. And when the whole damned heap of machinery is a mountain of rust, they'll come running with wild eyes and see if they can overcome the difficulties."

Then he would mutter to himself: "All these things belong to the people, but they don't give a damn. 'Overcome difficulties, Thang. Be patient, Thang. Take the global view.' "

He was tired of hearing the same old tune. They loaded him with responsibility; when he asked for a little money to meet expenses, they haggled with him, *piaster* by *piaster,* as if he meant the money for himself. "All the mulberry leaves fall on the backs of the silkworms."

Who can imagine that a cadre's job is a good one?

Thang worried and sweated. From the first day that construction work had begun—and the work gangs lived like dogs—the authorities had never given them any thought. But the work gangs never saw the authorities; they only saw Thang, the boss of the construction site. They held him responsible for their wretched fate. Once a worker had lost his head, banging his fist on the table and shouting at Thang: "Is a hunk of iron more valuable than men?

Even buffaloes have their sheds and feeding troughs. What have we got? Half of us sleep in the open and use the fields for a latrine. So this is your policy toward us, is it?"

From the construction site to the head office, it was about ten miles, and every day Thang walked the distance, coming and going. But when he reached the office, the answer was always the same: "Comrade, please explain to the workers that we are a poor country. We lack everything. We must overcome difficulties, do you understand? Overcome difficulties."

But when he returned to the site, the workers would shout: "Which difficulties do you mean?" One young worker whispered to his friend: "We'll teach them a lesson. If we don't, they'll always pretend not to hear."

This was not all. After a while the director grew tired of Thang and his visits. "Listen, Thang," he would say, "you're a weak and ignorant man. Don't badger higher authorities for help. Overcome difficulties." Thang would go home with a long face.

Thang realized that he had been too humble in his dealings with the director. The director's name was Mr. Bao, and he had a round face with sagging jowls and a mustache like a walrus. His jowls quivered when he talked. Mr. Bao was really the one in charge of building the factory; but he never told Thang what to do.

One day Thang was inspecting the crates, kicking the slats to see if they were still sound, when he saw a jeep speeding along the road to the construction site, raising a great cloud of dust in the air. Thang knew at once that it was the director. The car braked to a stop, and the director, full of dignity and self-importance, climbed out. He pumped Thang's hand with a great show of cordiality. Finally, he said: "Well, where are the machines, Comrade?"

Thang was about to reply, but the director did not wait. "Oh," he said, "there they are. Dear, dear, Thang. They're bound to rust there."

Thang said: "Dear Comrade, you know how many times I've asked for money to buy tarpaulins, and always you said there was no money at all. We were always going to install the machines—tomorrow or the next week certainly. But you see, the floor of the factory is still wet."

"Well," said the director, "you'll simply have to find a way to save them. What about the other buildings where the floors are dry?

Why not the men's sleeping quarters, for instance? Surely the men can find room for a few small crates. Dear, dear, Thang. We'll have to do better than this. The machinery will rust. Call the men together, and we'll discuss the matter."

Thang replied: "Yes, Comrade. As you say."

He called the work gangs together. Thang saw at once that the men were sullen. They hated him, and the discussion went badly. They began to complain. One worker with bright, staring eyes and dark, beetling eyebrows spoke up. His voice came to Thang like the intermittent burst of a machine gun. His words fell on Thang's face like invisible blows.

The denunciation shocked Thang. Was he afraid? Yes, but he did not really understand why. Of what was he afraid? The worst thing of all what that these harsh voices had reached the ears of a man Thang recognized as his boss.

But the meeting had hardly begun when there came the distant hum of a second car approaching on the road. The sound grew; there was the blare of a horn. A splendid limousine sped through the gate and drew to a stop. The director made hurried excuses to the assembled men. He would go now, he said, to greet the comrade advisors. They would have an opinion. He lit a cigarette, adjusted his spectacles, gathered up a half-dozen new papers to stuff in his already thick briefcase, and bustled off to greet the friendly specialists.

Three of our advisors stood before the heap of machinery, chatting and laughing. When Mr. Bao and Thang reached them, they all shook hands. One of them jovially slapped Mr. Bao on the back and tried to speak to him in pidgin Vietnamese supplemented by copious sign language.

Thang understood what the advisor was trying to say, because the same words kept coming over and over. "Machines . . . you move, okay? Move. You move . . . machines." But for Thang the real question was how it could be done. Thirty or forty men would probably be too few to move a single crate. And what would happen if one end of a crate were lighter than the other? If the crate tipped and fell, a dozen or more workers would be killed. But Mr. Bao said nothing; he nodded his head.

Then the friendly advisors had a good idea. The machines would be moved by trucks. But that would imply a road from the heap of machinery to the factory entrance. That would take ten days. Meanwhile the crates would still be exposed to the weather, and the rains would come soon. And since it would be impossible to lift such large and heavy crates by hand, they would need tripods to serve as cranes, to avoid accidents to the workers. But that would take eight days.

Mr. Bao went on nodding his head.

Thang's head swam; the blood pounded. He wanted to run to the chief advisor, wanted to make him understand. He would ask for a little money to buy tarpaulins; but an invisible wall held him back. The car doors slammed, and the motors started. The limousine led the way out the gate, followed by Mr. Bao's jeep. A choking cloud of dust hung over the construction site. Thang coughed and put a handkerchief to his nose.

A black rain cloud formed on the horizon to the east; the wind blew up. The banana leaves shook to and fro like an idiot's hands grasping in empty space. Lightning flashed; thunder growled far away. It seemed to Thang that the construction site was under artillery barrage. The rain lashed at the huts, at the wooden crates. In the driving sheets of rain, the warped slats of wood looked like the lips of a dying man, like the lips of a man suffering the ultimate agony.

The raindrops drove at Thang's face. The words—"My machines, my machines"—were a groan. *Dear Comrade, move the machines. Dear Comrade, move the machines. Move them. Move them.* But who would move them? Where could they be put?

Thang ran to his home and snatched up his old raincoat. He ran through the rain to the heap of machinery. He spread it over one of the crates.

And the pitiless rain poured down.

Van (Hanoi), 1957.

"Swamps and gullies and bluish hills. . . . In the white swamp a few scant pines . . ." The Siberian wastes were for more than a century the fate of political offenders—and after World War II, of whole nations.

Harijs Heislers, a Latvian poet, tells of one man caught up in the Baltic deportations.

THE UNFINISHED SONG

1.

Certain memories a man can
Save for many and many years.
Once, as a winter day ended,
We began to gather this song.

It was in school, on New Year's Eve,
Our joy was mingling with the waltz.
Her cheeks were burning as we danced,
Answering the touch of my hand. . . .

When a couple is just eighteen
There is so much that is not said.
I could not find the words just then
To tell you what was in my heart.

But we are certain
    they will not come back,
Night does not return
    after the morning dawn.
How much we longed
    for spring to come,
Bringing peace
    and May and graduation!
Our shouts for joy:
    Hey, I can do anything!

And a shy whisper
        from pretty lips says: Come.
There are paths going forward—
        we thought so then,
We had just one goal
      to which our steps were going.
But sometimes—
        daylight is shrouded by fog,
And without warning
       a shadow falls on the window.

2.

There are paths going forward—
        we thought so then,
We had just one goal,
        and we would reach it.
Going to school,
        with a briefcase full of books,
One also carries along
        one's first inspiration.
In the west still
        the wind stirs the ashes,
And at the Oder
        mines lacerate the earth.

3.

The sky is a basket of blue spring flowers,
Filled with golden hearts of stars.
Eyelids grow heavy,
        but at the hall door
There are voices, a strange commotion.
Disturbed from sleep, one gets up
        grumbling
To see what the late callers have to say.
"Pack your things, you have to come
       with us!"
The soldiers say, avoiding your eyes.
"Go with you?"
        one asks, looking for a coat.

An arm fumbling for a sleeve,
Overcome by a sudden weakness—
In a moment like this one gets as
  weary as from a lifetime.

An abyss has opened up underfoot,
The ceiling seems to be collapsing.
Suddenly there is not quite enough air
  in the room—
One breathes
  with an effort.

All that has been planned, one sees
  collapsing,
Everything cherished, one feels
  disappearing.
In the street there is still darkness,
Best friend of pain and suffering.

The bright blue basket of flowers is gone,
Drowned in the dark hues of thunder
  and rain clouds.
Gone is the closed door,
  around the corner,
As the car speeds away.

4.

I understand, this is a mistake,
But my heart cannot yet understand.
Like a perch caught on a strong line,
My heart cannot find rest tonight.

When at least the tracks begin to hum,
It feels as though my cheeks were damp.
Somewhere pines rustle in the wind,
And time stands still for one short tick.

This is a mistake and must be righted—
Innocent,
   one cannot be deported!
But the train, rattling through the
  darkness,
Moans like an angry bull.

At last the train stops at a station,
My bones are stiff from hours of travel,
In the western sky, flaming like a poppy,
I see the sun fall in a smoky haze.

I see far off, at the horizon,
The craggy Ural mountain ridges.
Here a man could walk for hours
  and days,
Losing his track in the wind-blown snow.

The blizzards drive the snows so hard
That even in daylight men get lost.
So here you are, my future home—
Swamps and gullies and bluish hills.

In the white swamp a few scant pines
Are wrapped in the pale haze of frost.
Now,
   defying the cold, you must
    blossom here,
Blossom,
   days of my youth! . . .

7.

Rolling white clouds play in the sky.
The sun sinks down the horizon.
At last I petition the Minister,
I can remain silent no longer.
—Lavrenti Pavlovich Beria—
  how shall I say it,

That my guiltless youth is fading away?
Avoiding sharp words or phrases,
I put it all down on paper.

An early frost arrests the Indian summer.
A golden scarf falls on the reddish moss.
Only a few scant leaves still cling
To twisted shrubs and branch of birches.

Driven by winds, winter again approaches,
Driven by longing, my thoughts roam far.
Who will visit you this evening?
Who will kiss the snowflakes from
        your lashes? . . .

8.

No answer comes to my petition,
Of course, the Minister has many
        things to do.
However, still I hope and trust—
        that it will come,
If not tomorrow, then surely the day
        after.

Anxious for news, I cover many miles,
Trudging through snow which clings
        to my felt boots.
At last
            I read, over the signature of
                Beria:
Refused.

I stare at the word as at a stupid joke,
I cannot believe it, yet I must.
The paper burns in my trembling hand,
Scorching a tender wound.

I cannot believe it!
            Again I hold the paper

To let my fingers feel it.
I must believe it!
           In vain I plunge outside,
Running away from my doubts.

                    9.

Heavy winds howl by day and night,
Railway tracks are buried by the snow.
My cheeks burn, my brow crawls
     with sweat,
The crowbar's metal sears my hands.

The frozen clay will not yield to force,
It has been frozen hard so long.
Could this really be a simple error,
Or maybe even
           deliberate evil?

I have not yet said these words aloud,
But now my bitterness flows over.
Doubts grow heavy, feeding like leeches,
Each moment they grow more oppressive.

But perhaps I do not realize my guilt?
Perhaps I deserve this punishment?
I have no peace, reaching for answer,
I have no peace, but must find the
     reason!

My memory probes far to the past
And tries to weigh every step I took.
I am not guilty!
           But Stalin in the Kremlin,
Why does he not rectify this error?

Faith becomes confused with wondering,
Each new day rises pale and gray,
I replace my crowbar with a hoe,
But what can replace my clinging
     doubts?

10.

Shall I write again?
What good would it do?
Am I the only wanderer on these paths?
Many of us vainly flee from pain,
Many in whose hearts there is no peace.

Some of us lost Klaipeda or Riga,
Others mourn a village on the Volga.
Is it not uniquely of our time:
Some are guilty, others must suffer?

It is because our land was occupied,
Not everyone could go to battle,
And we must pay with never-healing
          sores
And gaze upon an alien river bank?

This is not what Lenin made us fight for!
Loud despair bursts from my lips.
Like woodpeckers in my head,
          the questions,
Never stopping, hammer away.

              Zvaigzne (Riga), December, 1956.

Occasionally, life imitates art: the inarticulate find words. In this letter, published early in 1956, a Polish boy tells of his agony.

■■■

A LETTER

How many shocks can a normal man stand? How many times in his life can he change his thinking? How long can he go on doubting everything. Please . . . answer me, you journalists, writers, specialists in the human soul. You know that young people these days are reviled and that our cynicism, our inadequate ideological commitment are the subject of a hundred sermons. Listen to me.

I am eighteen years old. When I was ten, they told me that the cause my dear brother died for was a false cause. In my childish mind he had always stood for courage, heroism, and honor. I can barely remember him now; I was only six years old in 1944, when he died. But I kept his diary, letters, photographs. Best of all, the last snapshot—Lech standing there with wind-tousled hair. That was my favorite picture of him, and even now, when I think of heroes, I imagine them like that. I was proud of my brother. I boasted to other boys in school about my Lech; he fell at the age of seventeen fighting for his cause.

But when I was ten years old they taught me in the history class that I had no reason to be proud. He fell fighting for a rotten cause, they said, for the cheap emigré government in London, not for the real Poland. Until then I had thought there was only one Poland . . . but it seems there were several.

There was the Poland of my parents and of my brother Lech; there was the Poland they talked about in school; and there was still another Poland, my aunts' Poland—my aunts who were always full of righteous indignation. So at ten I gave up believing in the "Fatherland." Until then, it had seemed a holy word; but I didn't know any more which was *my* Fatherland. I thought about it, but I couldn't understand. I cried, and, after a while, I decided the word meant nothing.

I had no Fatherland, no hero-brother to set an example. I had only a poor, misguided brother who had gone astray. And I did not want to be poor and misguided.

Still, I had God.

When I was fifteen years old I gave up God. God, it seemed, was on the side of the men who had murdered Lech. He was the one who looked on with cold eyes at all the misery about me, at all the things that tore my heart to shreds. He was the one who had created the misery. For many long hours I knelt in the dark, deserted church. My soul cried out; I threatened, implored. I hated God, and at the same time I loved him very much. My poor, stupid Lech had loved him too.

So it seemed that God did not exist at all. Of course, you know how terrible it is when you feel your faith melting away inside, and still you yearn. Surely you know those sleepless nights, the terrible battle in the naïve soul of a child. This is what happened to me when I lost my faith. But finally there came a day when the cross was only a hunk of wood, Christ only a mannequin, and the sacrifice of the holy mass an empty ritual. Then I got help, from a school-mate five years older than I, a Communist. He brought me to that ideology which, until then, had only been the dry stuff of lectures or, worse, something people grumbled at or derided.

Well, the ideology gave back my lost faith in the world, a faith in the sense and direction of life. Those were my happiest years. I fought and fought and fought for the cause—at home, in the streets, at school.

I ran from one meeting to another. I argued, persuaded, made myself responsible for everything. I believed in the Idea, and in those who were engineering the Idea.

Three years passed—three years of conscious life. Now I am eighteen. And it seems that my aunts were right all the time—about the third-degree methods, the UB, Stalin's dictatorship. History really was falsified. The very people who had snooped and made entries in my personal dossier—when I asked them for an explanation, they could only mutter vaguely about Beria and the "Stalin era." They recommend jazz now—the same jazz they denounced two years ago as a symptom of the decadent West. Now they preside over serious discussions of youth organizations in Yugoslavia, the same Yugoslavia which two years ago they lampooned in stupid songs.

And I?

I do not know how I can change my soul for a fourth time without turning it into a rag. I could not stand up straight even if I wanted to. I am ashamed of my mentors, ashamed of the Party, ashamed of those who always temporized and sniveled. I am ashamed of the thieves, and I am ashamed of the dupes. I am ashamed of those who perpetrated this evil. I am ashamed of you—you petit-bourgeois ministers of state, journalists, poets, and novelists. You never understood my torment.

I am ashamed of all of you, and I am ashamed for all of you—and most of all, I am ashamed of myself. I am ashamed of my stillness and credulity. I don't know how to keep my head up, and I don't know if I will ever be able to hold it up again.

For I have no convictions left to me; there is nothing left to believe. If one cannot trust man, ideas turn to dust. What will become of me? I don't know. Will a genuine Communism be possible now? After a courageous confession of evil, will a new, clean time come? Perhaps, but I doubt that I shall be with you because I have no reason to trust you. I wish you well, wish you all success; but, if you please, do not wonder at the apathy of the young people!

Our times were certainly not easy. If we were too late to carry rifles, the path before us was hardly strewn with rose petals. Our cynicism is not born of corruption and luxury; it is no sense of selfishness, no mere seeking after comfort that induces us to reject the dogmatics and the preachers. We—the young ones, between eighteen and twenty years of age—we have grown up in the new time you promised; but we are not happy. We are in despair because we see before us new things that are really very, very old. We are in despair because we have lost the things in which we believed.

I am ending this letter now, and I commend my generation to the respectful attention of the Writers' Union.

MICHAL BRUK
Second-Year Student at the Warsaw Polytechnic Institute.
Nowa Kultura (Warsaw), April 22, 1956.

The image of the political prisoner's return is a *leitmotif* of contemporary revisionist fiction. In Tibor Dery's little novel *Niki*, the engineer's wife asks:

"Were you told why you were arrested?"

"No," Ancsa replied. "I was told nothing."

"And you don't know, either, why you were released?"

"No," the engineer replied. "I wasn't told."

In "Quarantine," Pawel Hertz extends the image to an entire society in the days after Stalin's death—and for him the world is still a "small black sack of blood."

Pawel Hertz served under Soviet command during World War II. Returning to Poland, he became something of a literary man about Warsaw, directing the Russian Classics Department of the State Publishing Institute and translating Proust and Ehrenburg into Polish. He resigned from the Party in 1957, when the journal *Europa* was suppressed.

QUARANTINE

This, then, I write at dark winter dawn
under the light so cruel that it burns
and bares my ribs down to my bedrock.
Outside is the world, the small black sack of blood,
and each one of my experienced nights—
beating a slow and unwilling rhythm.
The criminal has left; but still in corners
and blind windows, hardly noticed, lie
in wait fear, shame, plague, and weeping.
The smell of lime lingers in the gutter.

Oh, how infected is this snow-dressed city,
where yellow gas lamps sizzle and the deadly
wagons roll. It is all delusion,
as life itself. My heart, long prisoned,
fingers on my thin ribs at last the message

that plague is here no more. Night forwards it.
So—quarantine. All former pale patients,
new from prison and death resurrected,
unshot, but surely marked by death already—
see their hair, their eyes and faces—
feed their reason with most recent hate.

Others read Tacitus quickly to console
their thought with the thought that in his time
the air was even darker with the plague;
and mixing Roman madness with imperial
tyranny and the cruelty of monks,
say, slowly nodding their heavy heads:
all that was already, we know all.

And others are still burying their dead,
moving pale lips in silent prayer
and asking that their dead be dead in rest,
as if this death did not make peace for all.
And others clench their fists in anger,
while trembling wives and mothers beg them
to learn forgiveness as we do forgive
the sinners their sins, their crimes.

This, then, I write at dark winter dawn
in this huge city which is now a ruin
between the palace of Byzantium and
the ditch where lime is kept; I write
from a small fragment of still living asphalt
and sizzling, dying, yellow gas lamp light.

This, then, I write at dark winter dawn,
not knowing where to turn or what to say.
When I am told forgive them—I say nothing;
when hate commands me hate—I say nothing;
as if, by silence, I were making prayer
and moving to shut the coffin's lid
in tacit horror; within that coffin
lies a festered corpse, which stares

and bares in angry hunger jackal teeth.
This, then, I write at dark winter dawn
from within my land, where in the north
runs the cool sea. Mountains sleep south,
and on either side two lazy rivers flow.

Nowa Kultura (Warsaw), April 14, 1957.

A student radical, guerrilla leader in World War II, Vice President of the Federated People's Republic of Yugoslavia, and Marshal Tito's heir apparent, Milovan Djilas was expelled from the Party in 1954 and later jailed for his heterodox views. His book *The New Class,* an analysis of contemporary Communism, was something of an international sensation; he has emerged as a leading spokesman for those Marxists who postulate a new contradiction—between the interests of the working class and the new bureaucracies in the Soviet world which have succeeded to the power and privileges of the old.

For Djilas, Stalin died in 1948 when Yugoslavia was propelled into ideological and political warfare with the Soviet Union. He thus came to his "revisionism" early in the game. "Class Struggle" is an early essay, one of a series that appeared in 1953.

....

CLASS STRUGGLE

The concept of the class struggle opened a new era in the history of social science. The unwritten story of mankind came into focus, and the written story became transparent to analysis. Mysticism, which had earlier obscured events and personalities, man and man's fate, began to fade.

It is understandable, of course, that Marx's discovery was foreshadowed in the work of a multitude of historians and philosophers —and in the revolutions and wars themselves—from the time of the French Revolution onward. In that great convulsion the separate social classes discovered themselves and threw themselves into conflict; so began a process culminating in the first self-conscious struggle of the modern proletariat, the Revolution of 1848.

It is clear enough that Marx did not invent the class struggle. He discovered it in the historical pattern of the past and in the social reality of his own era. It was an incontestable fact—a law that applied whether men were aware of it or not, regardless of what they thought or expressed concretely in moral codes or forms of social organization.

The unique importance of any scientific discovery is the way it enables men to manipulate hitherto blind forces of nature and society for their own ends. The unique importance of Marx's discovery was that it clarified the goals and orientation of the combatants. But it did not give these combatants a universal key, applicable to every situation. Social reality is in a constant state of flux; reality creates new conditions and enlists new forces. Thus, in every new situation, it is necessary to struggle again and again, to create new forms of the struggle, and to mobilize new forces.

After Marx, it was clear to all socialists and all progressives—many of them quite independent of Marx—that the history of modern society was fundamentally the struggle between labor and capital. The differences dividing the socialists arose from the problem of *how*—with what means—the struggle was to be carried to victory. No one since Marx has denied the mere existence of the class struggle and of class differences. The divisions of theory and practice are only pertinent to the ways in which class differences are to be eliminated. As for which of the factions is right, theory alone, as usual, cannot tell us. In some degree this is an empirical problem. But in Russia—and in Yugoslavia—factual evidence has destroyed all those theories which teach that the struggle of contemporary society can be solved only through the use of force and revolution. The conditions and forms of the struggle have changed and still go on changing; and in that connection the theoretical aspects and political programs have changed, too.

From this standpoint, it is easy to see why it was that before the war the Yugoslav Communist Party sought to sharpen the class struggle. The revolution was already in sight, and it broke like a storm, shaking the consciousness of the people to their depths. Though we spoke often of intensifying the class struggle, the truth is that we were unable to sharpen it beyond its true conditions (i.e., the consciousness of the people, the possibilities of organization, and the available means of struggle). But we were able to manipulate these existing conditions, to raise the awareness of inevitable battle, and to nurture ourselves as the future leaders of the revolution. So it was, in one way or another, that the theory and practice of a sharpening class struggle were true and justified, so long as the fight for power was necessary. Theory and practice corresponded to the actual course of development and to the possibilities before us. Presumably, all this was justified after the war as well, so long as it was necessary to strike at the sources of bourgeois economic strength and to augment the power of the working people.

But what of the class struggle now, when conditions are quite changed? And most particularly, what is the state of the theory and practice of an ever-intensifying class struggle? Perhaps the existence of the class struggle does not depend on the theory, but the form and success of the struggle do.

The truth is that while the structure of classes in our society has changed, theory has remained more or less static. The bourgeoisie are only a remnant of their former selves. And in the big cities the petit-bourgeoisie no longer exist at all. The struggle against the bourgeoisie ("reactionaries")—based as it is on abstract theory and Party line, and not on the letter of the law—must inevitably descend into bureaucratism, into conflict with simple men because of this or that opinion which they hold, perhaps even because of some justified grievance against artificial or arbitrary forms of work. (Not too long ago, the newspapers reported the trial of a worker who listened to the BBC and shirked from joining the work brigades. The courts acquitted him; but they gave an inane reason—namely, that more political indoctrination of the accused would be necessary. Is it the business of the courts to weigh a man's conscience? How long will we continue to hand down *ideological* and not *legal* opinions. How much longer will sentences be set on the basis of dialectical and historical materialism and not the law? What of those State organs, in the very heart of Belgrade, who dragged this man before the courts?)

The enemy of socialism and democracy is not only the bourgeoisie but that proliferating bureaucratism which endlessly violates the law and seeks to impose its ideological and political power on the people. This bureaucratism uses its powers and sometimes even seeks out the "enemy" for the sole purpose of justifying its existence and expressing its incorruptible fidelity—to itself and its own ideology.

These tales of a sharpening class struggle violate legality and democracy. There is no need either to intensify or palliate actual conditions according to some planned ideological pattern. We need only adjust ourselves to reality, adopt the proper laws, and then obey them. We must fight where the enemy actually exists, and then with means sanctioned by law.

The duty of the State organs—the courts, the political police, the ordinary police—is not to sharpen the class struggle, but to preserve and execute the laws. In my opinion, these organs must—especially in those districts where this kind of thing happens too often—rid themselves of the meddlesome interference of the Party in their work; otherwise, they cannot possibly avoid, however good their intentions, a failure of democracy. They will continue to pattern their work after political and ideological blueprints, and even local schemes. They must become the organs of the State and the law—which means "of the people"—and not of political interests and opinions within the Party.

These are the absolute preconditions of freedom and democracy, of a step forward. If these organizations continue to sharpen the class struggle, ignoring the content of the laws, then they must inevitably mete out privileged treatment to those who agree with them, or to those whom they consider in their wisdom more trustworthy or sympathetic. And so they will go on weighing the virtues of the citizenry, dividing them into lower (non-Communist) or higher (Communist) classes. They will say the division is one between socialism and capitalism, but it will not be so. The real division will be into bureaucratism and oppression of the people.

Only democracy—permanently developing democracy—can clarify the class struggle and diminish class differences.

Borba (Belgrade), December 31, 1953.

Political satire is an art much cultivated in the Soviet world, but in recent years it has proved to be a two-edged weapon. "My windows face the street, and I can see the shop. There is a gold-lettered sign hanging above it which proclaims COFFIN RENTALS, but the gold has peeled, and an old sign underneath, STORAGE AND SALE OF COFFINS, attracts the eye more than the new." Apparently, as the landlady puts it, "the Paradise of Amerdaganda is a true paradise."

"Notes from Amerdaganda" was published in the Warsaw monthly, *Nowa Kultura,* a journal which became a rallying point for the dissidents who joined in Poland's "bloodless revolution" and later saw their power drain away.

■■■

NOTES FROM AMERDAGANDA

There's a flower shop on the corner.
Flowers were delivered from the flower shop on the corner.
That's fine. I'll put on my pants right away.
While shaving, I utter the chosen recitations of the tourist, since I dislike sign language. I am staying at a boarding house called Amer Paradise. The boat trip took longer, but it was cheaper, and I arrived in this great port city on the *Amerdagandan Nightingdale.* There I transferred to the *Arrow,* also *Amerdagandan,* because in Amerdaganda everything is Amerdagandan. I debarked in the morning. A policeman was waiting on the dock. He dispersed the bystanders efficiently, adjusted his cap adorned with the emblem of a hippopotamus (that's the national emblem: a hippopotamus head wreathed with roses), and called a taxi. What a surprise. Four barefooted men supporting a boat on two long poles.

"Please get in. Fare according to the meter. The man on the right has a meter on his left leg."

"But . . ." I was at a loss for words, and pointed my finger.

"Oh, I understand." The policeman tossed his stock in the air and caught it between his teeth. The dunce probably wanted to show off. "The shape of the conveyance is dictated by tradition. When the city was built, the main thoroughfare was constructed right smack over the river bed in order not to upset the symmetry of the construction plans. There were difficulties, but they had been overcome. The river has flowed on for more than ten years."

"But . . ."

The policeman smiled. "You're interested in bridges?"

The bystanders disappeared suddenly.

"No," I answered forcefully. "I only want to know why people have been substituted for wheels?"

"Momentary rubber difficulties, but we are struggling victoriously."

The policeman whistled. The barefooted ones set off at a gallop. They imitated a car horn expertly and were very good at passing. In no time at all, we were in front of the boarding house.

There's a flower shop on the corner. . . .

My windows face the street, and I can see the shop. There is a gold-lettered sign hanging above it which proclaims COFFIN RENTALS, but the gold has peeled, and an old sign underneath, STORAGE AND SALE OF COFFINS, attracts the eye more than the new. Despite the early hour, more than ten persons are waiting in line. At first I thought that Amer Province was having lumber difficulties. But it turned out that for the last twenty years someone has been bumbling in the production of gold paint, and that's why the old STORAGE AND SALE keeps haunting the customers with its funereal blackness, although the peeling gold letters are faithfully repainted four times a year. Information from the chambermaid. She peeks in here all the time and asks if I have everything to keep me happy. I use a familiar form of address because she bears the rank of junior sergeant on her blouse. The woman who owns the boarding house is a major. The bell is out of order. There's a pitcher of Amerdagandan cherry brandy in the W.C. Someone carved a heart on the toilet seat.

"Flowers have come from the flower shop on the corner."

"That's fine, I'll put my pants on right away," I said, my face covered with lather. I said the wrong thing, because it was the chambermaid who spoke, using the Chosen Speech.

"Psst!" She put a finger to her lips and crossed her eyes. A delivery man with a huge package stood in the doorway.

"Flowers? For me?"

"Flowers for you." The mention of pants gave the chambermaid an attack of giggles. She was still shaking.

"Why flowers?"

"Because it's your birthday."

"From whom?"

"You're among friends. Where should I put them? Here? There?"

Indecisively, I pointed my shaving brush. "How about there?" There was a table behind the couch, but the junior sergeant had eyes only for the latter.

"Yes, could be. But first things first. Put the flowers on the window sill so that they can be seen from the street."

The messenger, an old man with a beard down to his waist, lifted the package to the window sill. He began unwrapping it. The horse blanket went first. Then gray paper. This was followed by a layer of newspapers, a piece of cardboard and plywood scaffolding. Finally, he took off his cap and stretched out his hand. The chambermaid gave him a smack across his fingers with her keys. He left very angrily, murmuring boastfully that he would be back.

"Ah, the smell of lilacs." The junior sergeant sighed very deeply, and a button popped. Things changed beneath the blouse, but not too much so. "Ah, my rank is sewn on. I could rip it off. It's not allowed with the rank on. There's a strict penalty."

Flowers! Flowers! And a lathered face.

The lilacs were in the middle. Half a yard high, with yellowed stems, they sprouted from a huge flower pot. The pot, however, remained inconspicuous, because everything was covered with matting adorned with a multitude of ribbons, also matting, but a different shade. Under the lilacs there were three primroses, and behind the primroses an Amerdagandan violet with five buds. Each flower in a massive pot. The pots on a two-inch wooden board. Metal tape handles attached to steel rods embedded in the board held the pots in a viselike grip. In addition, just in case, there was a length of extra-wide tape girding the pots. The tape was held together with nuts and bolts. The whole contraption was topped with a copper rod supporting the lilac stalk. Soft horizontal metal brackets embraced the blooms and a spiral wire gripped the yellowish cluster in a properly inclined position. Moreover, a tiny container with faucets was attached to the wire. When opened, five faucets poured small

streams of cow dung mixed with water into the flower pots. The
metal shone with grease. Red lead glittered on the bolts. Thanks to
the construction, a flower basket was unnecessary. The profuse folds
of matting, however, gave the impression of a basket. The odor
emanating from everything was unusual. The dominating smells
were cow dung and metal grease. I could detect no odor of lilacs,
although the chambermaid insisted it was expressly that which
stopped her breath and covered her with perspiration. And the soap
had dried and was peeling on the couch. Suddenly a knock on the
door. You could call it a "yoo-hoo."

"That's fine. I'll put on my pants right away."

The junior sergeant left, supporting her rank with dignity. The
white-haired messenger came in, holding a French—or, rather, an
Amerdagandan—key.

"I'll unscrew the screws in the lilacs." He poked, puttered, turned,
oiled, and regulated. Then he suddenly asked what country I came
from. My answer delighted the old man. Now he boldly inquired
whether I had known anyone named Sztruks? Ryps? Tuks? Pyk?
Fik? Or was it just plain Szryk? I made a mental note that madmen
in Amerdaganda deliver flowers instead of being kept in strait
jackets. I explained as gently as I could that I knew no one by that
name, but that I would send a cable right away and bring the
answer to him in the flower shop. The old man protested vehe-
mently: "No, not for the world! I'll remember the name. A cable?
No, would not, should not, cannot!"

He left. Even out in the street he still kept banging his head with
his fist, but somehow he couldn't remember. He had at least reminded me that I hadn't shaved. Lathering my face again, I decided I would write about my trip some other time. I'm still faced
with the return trip, only in reverse order. And descriptions are so
tiring.

When the chambermaid returned, I had shaved. From the doorway she began boasting about her invention: rank insignia on snap
fasteners! Then she cried out, "Fah," and pushed three carnations
right under my nose. "Another bouquet!"

Wanting to take a sniff, I inclined my head and cursed with pain.
The carnations were also wired, although there were no nuts and
bolts. Anyway, what's wrong with that? Nothing that would give

rise to harmful conclusions. The couch springs are another matter though. On the suggestion of Miszpucha, the chambermaid, I asked the owner whether the springs could be repaired. That pleasant lady smiled compassionately. "Typical foreigner! He sits on the couch! All right, fine, I'll think about it. The Paradise of Amerdaganda is a true paradise. Eggs for breakfast? Very good, I'll lay them myself."

Nowa Kultura (Warsaw), April, 1957.

The temptation to compare Hlasko to the "Angry Young Men" in England or to the "Beat Generation" in America is irresistible; but Hlasko knows why he is angry.

Hlasko's work is uneven, but here the deft ambiguity of the meeting between the barber and the journalist reaches a high pitch of art. Hemingway is an obvious influence.

In 1957, Hlasko began a year's tour of Western Europe. At home, he wrote, his library was confiscated; the Polish government refused to extend his passport. In October, 1958, he announced his intention of going into exile, "aware," he said, "that my remaining in the West can serve as a pretext for the most distorted commentaries in a country where man is still measured by infantile schematic abstractions and childishly simple political formulae. . . ." But a few months later, homesick and distraught, he was not so certain. He would return to Poland, he was quoted as saying, "sometime—in the near or more distant future."

For Hlasko, in the last analysis, ideology is secondary. "Whatever doesn't come from Poland or isn't connected with it doesn't interest me at all," he has said.

. . . .

"A POINT, MISTER?"
OR, EVERYTHING HAS CHANGED

The train stopped at a small station. A journalist got off. Carrying a leather suitcase, he walked past the funny old wagons. It was a cloudy fall day, and thick drops of fog were settling on the leafless trees. The man stared up at the sky and shuddered in disgust—it looked like a dirty rag. The stationmaster walked along the platform with a small red flag. He was like an old mustached walrus. The man who had gotten off the train barred his way.

"How far is it to town?"

The stationmaster stopped.

"You want to go to town?" he asked, beating his palm with the flag handle.

"That's why I'm asking you," the journalist said. "My next train isn't due for a few hours. I'm going farther on." He passed his hand over his face. "I need a shave. I haven't slept for two nights, and I probably look like a bandit." They moved on over the damp gravel. The train had already left, and the smoke was disappearing lazily in the dim air. The rails shone wetly.

"How far are you going?" the stationmaster asked.

"Far enough."

"Perhaps you work for the Supply Department?"

"Where did you get that idea? I work for a newspaper."

"My son works for the Supply Department. He lives in Warsaw. Are you from Warsaw?"

"Yes."

"Kazimierz Majewski. Do you know him?"

"No."

"They travel all the time."

"They shouldn't. They should stay home."

"Why?"

"You can fall out of a train. Or catch cold."

"Once I met a woman on a train," the stationmaster said.

"And what happened?"

"Nothing. She went on her way."

"Very noble of her," the journalist said, and yawned. Then he asked: "Well, how far is it to town?"

"Not far," the old man said. His mustache was wet. Then he winked and asked: "Are you sure it's a barber you want?"

"What difference does it make to you?"

"I was thinking that maybe you'd like some vodka. I have some at home."

"Nothing has changed in these lousy small towns," the journalist said angrily. "I was born in a hole exactly like this. Is there also a brothel next to the church?"

"No. A drugstore."

"I have heard that there have been a lot of changes here," the journalist said. "That they have built this and that. Is that so?"

"It's true," the stationmaster said. "You'll see for yourself when you get there. The town isn't far. A fifteen-minute walk. Will you stop at my place?"

"No," the journalist said. "Good-by."

Fifteen minutes later, he was actually in town. A few carts were idling in the marketplace; the horses stood dozing, their heads drooping over the fodder bags; straw was scattered all over the street. Evidently, this was market day. It was raining, and the pedestrians shivered with cold.

"Where's the barber?" the journalist asked a man of nondescript face, profession, and age.

"What?"

"The barber."

"What barber?"

"Is there a barber?"

"Where?"

"Here."

"Here?"

"Yes. Here."

"What about him?"

"Oh, shit! Do you understand that?"

"No," said the nondescript man, and his face reflected the effort of thought. "I come from this place, Mister. As for the barber, he's right over there. Beyond the nook."

"Not beyond the nook. Around the corner."

"Well, I don't know about that."

"But I do. Good-by."

He found the barber immediately. A brass plate hung over his door, and in the shop window a mannequin in a fancy wig looked out with thoughtless eyes on the gray emptiness of the street.

The journalist went in.

"Good morning," he said.

"Good morning, Mister," the barber replied. "Sit down."

The journalist sat down and stretched his legs. He was dead tired; he had been traveling for the last three nights and had seen a lot of new faces and learned many things. Many people had tried to cheat him. He longed to return to Warsaw and stretch out on his own bed. He had a small, dark girl with a Mickey Mouse face, and all the time he was thinking that maybe someone else was sleeping in his bed with his girl.

The barber put a towel around his neck and said: "Did you take the pump with you?"

"What pump?"

"Didn't you come by bicycle?"

"No," the journalist replied. "Why? Do they steal?"

"Steal? I couldn't say that. But the Director of Mutual Aid lost his pump, and his tire valve is leaking, so it's better to take the pump with you. That's life, you know."

"I do," the journalist said, and looked up at the barber. The barber was an old man. He had a bald head covered with funny, jagged down, withered ears, and a sharp look in his beady black eyes.

"Shampoo?"

"No."

"No shampoo?"

"No."

"No shampoo," he repeated. Then he thrust his fingers into the journalist's hair and said, "Hold your head a bit lower, please. So? What then? A shave and a haircut?"

"A shave and a haircut."

"No shampoo?"

"No."

"Ah," the barber said, and his face took on a look of extreme concentration. For a moment he stared silently at the journalist with the eyes of a surgeon. The he said: "Will you have a point cut?"

"Heaven forbid. I want a regular cut."

"Naturally," the barber said. "Naturally, you want a regular cut. Nowadays nobody wants a point. Before, people used to like it. Mostly the tough guys. One of them used to live just a few buildings away. A certain Loniek Maciejewski. On Saturdays he always came here and said, 'Hey, Mr. Sobsiak. Give me a regular, legal point. But be sure my hair stays in place properly, or else . . . You know me, and know how I am.' That's the way he used to speak. What a hoodlum. The worst in town. Believe me, you wouldn't like to get socked in the nose by him. Do you believe me?"

"Absolutely," the journalist said, and made himself more comfortable.

"He had friends. Of course they were just like him. Every Saturday they met in front of the church and played a game called 'sucker on the line.' They drew a line on the pavement, and anyone who happened to cross it got hit on the head."

"What for?"

"For nothing. Just for fun. They don't go there any more. Things have changed."

"Have they?"

"Oh yes," the barber said with animation. "They haven't changed by themselves though. People have changed them. It's true, everything has changed. Did you know they were building a factory here? For musical instruments. Boys have already been sent to learn the trade. Before the war there was only one specialist here in musical instruments. Used to repair organs. A little on the alcoholic side. People called him 'master.' He used to say, 'You scum. Call me master. I am in charge of delicate work. If I drop dead, the churches will close, and all of you will die in a state of sin. A church without music has no standing with God, not even if each of you puts ten *zloty* in the collection plate.' So the people called him 'master.' He drank. Drank as nobody before him ever drank, and as nobody ever will. Sometimes it lasted for three days, and sometimes for five. He walked around the town shouting, 'I shake the dust off my feet and curse you.' He knew the gospel and spent most of his time in church. He also spoke Latin. He had his hair cut here. Liked a nice point. What kind of cut do you want? A point?"

"A regular cut," the journalist said, and sighed. The mirror in front of him was dotted with flies. The journalist looked at the black spots for some time. Then he asked: "What happened to him?"

"Him?" the barber repeated. "Nothing. Right before he died, he cried: 'There is no God, you scum. If you want to listen to music, get electricity and buy radios instead of going to church.' Vodka had ruined him. People don't drink so much now. Everything has changed. There's no time for that sort of thing. Great things will be happening here, Mister. People have changed: they work, they have trades, they think in a completely different way. I myself have become a different man. Sometimes I even think I ought to say to hell with this barbering business. Cream?"

"Yes," the journalist said. He looked up at the barber. "You're an old man. What would be the use of changing trades now? It would be too hard."

"Yes," the barber said. "I'm old. You don't even know how old I am. I'm almost eighty. My daughter lives in Venezuela. I also have a grandson. Would you like to see his picture?"

"What for?" the journalist said. "What the hell do I care about your grandson?"

"That's the trouble," the barber said, frowning. "Why should you care? But sometimes I would like to talk about him. The trouble is, there's nobody to talk to. Before, people used to sit in front of their houses talking and gossiping. But no more. They haven't time: either they're working or going to the movies or listening to the radio. And the young people like sports. I'm the type who likes company best. A word is a word. Before, people used to talk to each other much more. They knew how to say things. In the old days we had a mayor. He used to come to me and say: 'Well, Mr. Sobsiak, tell me something.' He always got his hair cut here."

"In a nice point?" the journalist asked.

The barber thought for a minute.

"No," he said, "he was as bald as the moon. But his wife had a lover who had beautiful hair. Had it cut *a la pointe*. I tell you, Mister, we had great fun with that lover. Everyone knew about him except the mayor."

"For heaven's sake, shut up," the journalist said. He thought of his Mickey Mouse, and his brain grew numb with terror; once, when he was still an insignificant beginner, he had been deceived for a long time; after he had succeeded, with great difficulty, in climbing half an inch up the ladder, he was convinced that no girl would ever love him for nothing, just for himself.

"You think I'm lying?" the barber asked.

"I'm not interested," the journalist answered. "Where I live now most of the women think that socialism begins with the behind and not with the head. I'm sick of it."

"You're still young," the barber said, "so listen to what an old man tells you. In the past the women in this town did have lovers. Sometimes a husband caught his wife red-handed, and then the whole town rushed to watch him beat her up. There was a certain Barcikowski, a harness maker, who once caught his wife with a lover; he threw the lover down the stairs and beat his wife for a week, asking, 'Is the last one mine or not?' You see, they had five children, and the youngest, who had been born about six months before, had red hair. Barcikowski's hair was dark and straight as wire, so he couldn't believe that the last child was his. He beat her and kept asking, 'Tell me, is it mine or not?' After a week of this,

she died. Her last words to him were: 'The fifth one is yours, but
the other four—they aren't yours.' Then she passed away. Barcikowski drank a bottle of vodka. Then he took an ax—and that was
the end of the five of them. Well, Mister, lots of things like that
happened in this town. But now it's different. Everything has
changed. People build, they work, and they have no time for fool-
ing around. Now everyone has something more important to think
of."

He stopped talking, took a step backward, and looked at the
journalist with the eyes of a man who had just completed a great
work of art. Then he said:

"Finished. No shampoo?"

"No shampoo," the journalist said. "Don't you plan to come to
Warsaw one day?"

"I'm too old," the barber answered, clinking his instruments.
"That kind of trip is not for me."

"You would see many people."

"People are everywhere."

"True," the journalist said. "Well, I'm glad I came to you, chief.
I was returning to Warsaw in a bad mood. People in the provinces
aren't truthful, they're afraid. Now I feel better about going back."

"It's always pleasant to go home," the barber said. "Home is
always home."

"That's not the point. But it's good to see that in a small, lousy
town like this, where it's always raining and muddy, where there's
no electricity and night life stops if one whore gets a toothache, man
has changed so completely. It's very good to see."

"It's true," the barber said. "But it's no wonder. This is a mo-
mentous time, and so people are changing. I, also, have become a
completely new man."

"Do come to Warsaw sometime."

"I think I shall die soon."

"As you say."

The journalist left and again tramped through the mud in the
marketplace. The horses were dozing, their heads drooping the same
way as before. Drunken peasants slept on their carts. It was raining,
and the town absorbed the damp like a repulsive mushroom. The
journalist walked on, whistling.

When he reached the station, the stationmaster said to him:

"Well? Have you had a haircut?"

"I have," the journalist said, raising his hat a bit.

"Will you visit me for a while?"

"Now I can come with you," the journalist said, and followed the stationmaster into his cabin.

The stationmaster filled two glasses.

"All the best," the journalist said.

"All the best," said the stationmaster. "That barber who cut your hair is a decent guy. I also had my hair cut by him—when I still had some."

"I even know how."

"How?"

"In a nice point."

"How did you know that?"

"The press knows everything," the journalist said. "He's a good chap. Has an open mind and sees many things." The journalist tapped the stationmaster on the knee and asked: "Everything's changed, hasn't it?"

"That's right," the stationmaster said.

"How about some more vodka? We'll drink to these changes. I also come from a small town, and when a man is born in such a town, he spends half his life thinking that the world never changes. I shit on small towns. It's nice that everything has changed, that people have changed, that women have changed. Cheers!"

He raised his glass and in that moment saw his eyes in the mirror. Mechanically, he drew nearer and saw that his hair was in a hideous point cut. Leaving his vodka, he darted to the platform and left for Warsaw. Many months have passed since then, but he is still asking himself: "Did that idiot make a fool of me or not?"

Pierwszy Krok w Chmurach (Warsaw), 1956.

3.

THE MORAL ISSUE:
ENDS, MEANS, AND
THE SENSE OF GUILT

Fyodor Dostoyevsky died in 1881, but his oracular vision of the twentieth century and its pitiless ideologies haunts the Soviet world still. "A Meeting of Two Young Men" conjures up the specter of two self-accused murderers—the university student, Raskolnikov, and Ivan Karamazov—and, rejecting the claims of objective morality, renews the concept of evil in our time.

Gyorgy Paloczi-Horvath joined the Communist Party in 1947 and edited the Budapest journal *Tovabb* (Forward). In 1949 he was arrested as a deviationist—his views on psychoanalysis and Marxism were suspect. The next six years were spent in Hungarian prisons. He joined the Hungarian revolution, and when the revolt was suppressed, he went into exile in the West.

■■

A MEETING OF TWO YOUNG MEN

The silhouettes of two young men emerged from the twilight in this meeting, two shadows, two who never existed, two who for that very reason were more real than reality, and will continue to live as long as there are human beings on this earth.

The questioning took place somewhere in that twilight zone between dreams and awakening, when one is still half-asleep, too deeply relaxed to say anything but the truth, when one's feelings have not yet been guided by well-thought-out consideration—or by the barriers or stop signs of reality.

We were sitting in an enormous amphitheater, all of us, and this theater with its faint blood-red glimmer looked like the inside of a human skull. We were standing downstairs, in front of the blackboard on the podium, and before us on the benches, rising in a half-circle high up, sat the eyewitnesses—and those were also us. We were the ones who spoke, lived, exclaimed in the crossfire of the witnesses' eyes, who knew all and remembered all. . . .

Deep down in the hall, from the small door on the side where the lecturer usually enters, out of the uncertain light two young men emerged. One of them took a step forward. Deep-set eyes, signs of

89

suffering, defiance, and some terrible weariness in those eyes. "Do you recognize me?" he asked in a hardly audible voice.

"Of course," I whispered. "It's you, Rodya! Rodion Romanich Raskolnikov, university student."

"*Former* university student," he corrected me. "That's right. They used to call me that name too."

"I don't know any of your other names," I answered, somewhat awed.

"It doesn't make any difference. We'll get to that, to those other names, too. We'll find out. . . . Well, do you still remember what I taught you?"

"Yes, Rodya, I do. Don't be angry if I can't quote your words exactly, but I never forgot the essence of it. You taught me that not even the exceptional man has a right in good conscience to commit crimes, not even if it were the only means to realize an ideal, to save all mankind."

Raskolnikov made a nervous little gesture. "I told you exactly the opposite of that. Don't you remember? This is what I said: 'Let's presume that it would have been impossible, as a result of a number of coinciding factors, for Kepler or Newton to inform mankind of their discoveries unless they sacrificed one or ten or a hundred, or I don't know how many, human beings. In that case, in my opinion, Newton would have been justified in killing those human beings.' Isn't that what I said?"

"Yes. True. That's what you said. But your own life, that taught a different lesson. Just the opposite, the part of you that was your essence when you had your first real cry upon the breast of Sonia."

"Right. If you were able to learn this, then our meeting was not all in vain." Rodya stepped back toward the other shadow, but in the twilight it now seemed as if he had changed somewhat. He became a "fresh, playboy-like, dashing fellow." And there, next to him, stood an eighteen-year-old with an "expectant look," the one who answered the most important question of the time.

The two young men stepped more to the front. A crowd seemed to have gathered around me, the rows of the audience also seemed to have multiplied, and the number of witnesses who remembered all seemed to have increased.

"I wonder if you've recognized me," the older one inquired.

Several voices answered: "The Karamazovs, Ivan and Alyosha Karamazov."

Ivan Karamazov, who only a minute before had been Rodya Raskolnikov, bowed gracefully when his name was mentioned. Alyosha smiled vaguely.

Ivan sat upon the edge of the demonstration table with his feet lightly crossed. Alyosha stood next to his brother and leaned against the table. Ivan looked through the multitude. "And do you recall our teachings?"

I wanted to say that I had always remained faithful to them; I wanted to talk about that summer night when there, on the shores of Lake Balaton, breathing so quietly, I had the feeling that we would have to live ever after by the answer Alyosha had given. Somehow, however, no sound came out of my throat. No one gave an answer. Instead, it was Ivan who answered for us all.

"You can only answer that in unison. Well, where's the chorus? No answer?" There was deadly silence, and he turned to Alyosha. "I ask you once again, just as on that occasion in the restaurant, when we had finished the fish chowder . . ."

"Go ahead, ask," Alyosha muttered and looked down, for he was ashamed for us all.

Ivan kept his look fixed on Alyosha and put the question, slowly, carefully pronouncing every single word, the question, the very question of the time: "I beg you to answer frankly. Try to imagine that you yourself are actually building the structure of mankind's fate, with the purpose of giving human beings happiness at last, to secure peace and balance of mind for them. But in order to achieve that, it would be unavoidable that some torture be inflicted, even though on just one little creature, because its tears shed, unavenged, were essential for the completion of the structure. Would you, would you, be willing to go ahead with the work at that price? Answer, and don't lie!"

"No. I would not do it," Alyosha answered, barely audible.

Mercilessly, Ivan went on. "Then, could you possibly conceive of the idea that human beings, for whom this building is actually being done, would accept the happiness resulting if this involved the bloodshed of one small creature tortured unjustly, and further, that if they accepted it, they would be able to be happy forever after?"

"No, I would not think that possible, brother," Alyosha answered, with sparkling eyes.

Ivan was silent a moment. His gaze seemed as indifferent as the stars coldly watching on long winter nights. "And you, the others, all of you, would you think that possible?"

"No, we do not," the chorus responded, murmuring, now audible for the first time. But from the long rows of the audience there were eyes fixed on us, eyes that remembered all and kept staring at us: the chorus.

"You have answered too quickly, my friends," Ivan declared, and once again he turned to Alyosha, and now spoke only to him. "You know what happened to them, don't you? Well, let me tell you. They, too, were trying to build the structure of mankind's fate, the happiness of future generations. They wanted to make the world clean, livable, magnificent. They fell in love so deeply with the generation of tomorrow, with the mankind to come, that there was hardly any love left for those who happened to live in today's world. They were brought up in a manner which only filled their hearts with cold and abstract feelings, and they thought that the generation of the day after tomorrow could be happy even if it was conceived in suspicion and fear. Their egos, which we will call their souls for your sake, Alyosha, were split into a unit of today and one for the day after tomorrow. Their today-ego, the individual as such, remained faithful to the teachings of Ivan-Rodya. They remained faithful in their private lives, as much as mortals can, to that which simple people usually term true and right. But their other ego—the one building the day after tomorrow—felt that everything was permissible against the people of today, provided it would benefit the man of the day after tomorrow."

Alyosha raised his hand and looked at us askance, sadly, and there was pleading in his voice as he declared: "But now you already know and see that you cannot go on living like this. By now, you know that this is not the path toward happiness. By now, these builders, the ones who are building the happiness of the many, know that on their way toward victory they must prove their righteousness through all their lives, that their cause must be clean, and it is a right cause, isn't it, Ivan? A right cause must be fought for with right means!"

"You are too soft-headed, Alyosha," Ivan declared, and his eyes glared at us, at all of us. He looked at us, and then he looked at the eyewitnesses. They sat as if frozen into stone, with their arms folded, their looks remembering all. They did not move, their eyes did not blink; the eyewitnesses just sat there, all of them, the living and the dead, and by now it was impossible to ascertain where the accusation was actually coming from. Was it from Alyosha, or was it from them?

"It is not enough to repent," Ivan declared, and his words fell on us like guillotines. "No, it's not enough to be sorry for all. You must *understand, too.* Do you understand it, you miserable creatures? Do you understand what has happened to you? I explained to you that you were brought up in a way which split you into two, the one of today and the one for the day after tomorrow. Do you know what our doctors call this? Schizophrenia, split personality. Yours was an organized and directed schizophrenia. You did the splitting up yourself, into a conscious and unconscious personality, into an honest private person and a ruthless, immoral happiness-builder. And what was the result with some individuals? The worst part of the split ego swallowed the other part. But it is not to those that I want to talk now. You should look at those who accuse, the living and the dead. Look at them and remember. *You must understand* that you cannot build a clear, magnificent future with a split personality, with a double standard of morality."

The chorus now glared at the witnesses, the ones who saw everything, and sat there with folded arms, their breathing loud and deep, their sparkling eyes seeking the dead, cold looks of those who were the accusers. The final cry and promise was about to break through their sealed lips with elemental force: "We promise, we promise, that nothing, nothing was in vain. We promise you that never, never again. We promise . . . we promise. . . ."

But the oath could not be heard in the blood-red twilight of the skull-amphitheater. The lips were frozen. The oath, like all great oaths, was not uttered aloud. It keeps alive in each human being individually.

Irodalmi Ujsag (Budapest), July 7, 1956.

The early Kolakowski, it seems, was chiefly remarkable as a precocious doctrinaire: one of his youthful *Essays on Catholic Philosophy* denounces "those lying formulae that 'man is the end of society,' 'society is for man . . .'" Yet the crux of his new philosophical position—a syncretist amalgam of Marxist, Kantian, and existentialist elements—is certainly this: "A Communist movement which sacrifices its ideology to current tactical needs is necessarily condemned to degeneration and defeat, for then it can continue to exist only by invoking the support of the state and by employing such means as permit it to impose its will by force. The moral and intellectual values of Communism ought not to be a mere embellishment of its activities but the very condition of its existence . . ." And elsewhere he writes: "Surely the concept of Communism ought to embrace the concept of man under Communism as well. . . . Communism as an end cannot be reduced, by some sterile use of abstractions, to a system of property relations alone."

"Responsibility and History" is Kolakowski's most ambitious work so far.

* * *

RESPONSIBILITY AND HISTORY

I. The Conspiracy of Aesthetes

"You state," says the Intellectual to his opponent, the Revolutionary, "that at a certain historical moment the specific interest of the working class becomes completely identified with the interests of all mankind, and not only preserves all-human values but is the only force capable of saving them. But what proofs do you have for this assertion, apart from a vague historico-philosophic speculation? What right do I have, in the name of that speculative dialectic of the future, to renounce at present the highest values of human existence? And experience so far does not confirm your optimism—on the contrary, it shows that this specific interest, as you understand it, is often realized contrary to all human values. And here are examples. . . . The first, the second, the thousandth. . . .

"If you represent a certain historical reality, on what basis do you ask me to affirm it morally? Just because it is a reality? I will not support any form of historical existence solely because somebody persuades me that it is unavoidable—even if I believe in its unavoidability, for which at present there is no evidence. If crime is the law of history, is the realization of this law reason for me to become a criminal? Why should that be so? You do not let me measure your moves with a measuring rod of absolute values because, in your opinion, such values either do not exist at all or are purely imagined. But on the other hand, you yourselves talk about all-human values which must be absolute; thus, silently, you introduce into your doctrine axiomatic absolutism in a vague and equivocal way in order to destroy it immediately with equally equivocal 'historical relativism.' With this package, you come to me demanding that I should immediately renounce all the highest creations of human culture because your doctrine promises to return them to me intact after an indefinite period of time.

"Therefore, you demand for your own historical philosophy and your own history unlimited moral credit, although at every step they both unmask their insolvency. You, who rashly agree to give up everything to the Moloch of current reality in the unjustified hope of having it returned—you do not voice a philosophy of responsibility; he who really wants to be responsible for the treasures which human history has discovered and produced will defend them at all costs—that is, also at the cost of separating himself from the chaos of current struggle if they can be preserved only outside the battlefield."

"But it is noteworthy," the Revolutionary remarks at this point, "that you know how to save these eternal values only together with your own person. It is also strange that, doubting my historical ground, you do not notice at all the direction at which the other side of history is aiming, of whose existence there is no doubt. Pyres of books are on fire there. What did you do to save them? Do you think it will be enough if you yourself learn them by heart? There, intestines are torn from bellies, and faces are trampled by heavy boots. What did you do to prevent this? Perhaps you think that you will achieve something with your sermons about universal love, preached to fully armed soldiers? That you will extinguish fire by repeating the Ten Commandments?"

The Intellectual answers:

"Pyres are burning on both sides of Mount Sinai. Do you want me to count them to compute your moral superiority? It would be a miserable victory. You constantly tell me that the threat to human freedom is so huge that, in order to overcome it, it is worthwhile to give up freedom; you constantly repeat to me the slogan of Saint Juste: there is no freedom for the enemies of freedom. To a certain extent, I am ready to agree. But I must know who determines the division of men into enemies of freedom and defenders of it. Always somebody who considers himself in one of the camps—that is, somebody who in a trial is simultaneously a litigant, judge, prosecutor, and, in addition, a policeman, all in one person. My engagement, to which I am constantly forced, must therefore be based on absolute confidence in that man, in his present and his future intentions. That is, I should have a total confidence in him which I can hardly have in myself. On what basis could I afford an act of that total confidence toward men who, in a conflict in which they are among the litigants, always want to be the judges, too—that is, to deny the eternal and most elementary principle of justice—and who never agree that the controversy between them and their enemies should be resolved by anybody but themselves? And nevertheless, a judge, if he is to pronounce one of the sides right, in accordance with justice, must be impartial before he comes to court— that is, he fulfills his functions properly only when he uses the same measuring rod of abstract justice on the arguments of each of the participants in the controversy. However, you refuse me this right, maintaining that I must first be on your side in order to judge justly —that is, that I have a right to be judge only when at the same time I am a participant in the trial.

"It is true that you have a separate theory to justify this abhorrent rule—namely, the theory of the non-existence of a third force in a society torn by class antagonisms—a theory according to which the office of the judge in the interpretation of modern legislation is entirely impossible. You consider your theory to be obvious, and you ask me to recognize it, and you add that by the very fact of rejecting this theory, by the very wish to take the position of judge in the controversy, I automatically place myself in the camp of your opponents. In other words, if I recognize the possibility of the existence of a third force, I am immediately classified by you as an antagonist and, as such, am morally deprived of the right to judge your arguments—because then I am a participant in the trial. I can avoid this only when I recognize the theory of the non-existence of a third force and accept your point of view. I have a right to judge and understand you only when I am one of you.

"Don't you see that in this way you use the same arguments that were used by Sören Kierkegaard in defense of Christianity, saying that in order to understand Christianity, it is first necessary to accept it? You say the same thing: in order to understand you, it is first necessary to accept your arguments. You must see that this is a demand that is unacceptable to any rationalist in the world, because rationalism, among other things, consists of refraining from choice until the arguments have been weighed. Your postulate, on the other hand, requires me to accept your arguments before granting me the right to investigate them, and it is, therefore, a manifestation of total irrationalism, against which I am warned by the whole experience of European culture. I do not deny that with such methods of action you may win many followers, but realize that you can never win them by intellectual means; your position is completely opaque, it is impenetrable to rational thought because it rejects *a priori* any criticism as an act which, by the nature of things, is hostile to you and is, of necessity—consciously or unconsciously—made from the position of the opposite camp. Your theory of the non-existence of the third force is therefore basically irrational and unacceptable to sensible beings.

"And if you say that I protect the unchanging values of culture, ridiculed by you, together with my own person, and if for this reason you want to unmask me before my audience as an aesthete in love with himself, my answer is: I have no intention of becoming a scoundrel solely in order to demonstrate that I do not care whether I am thought of as a decent man."

In turn, the Revolutionary answers: "Your defense is your indictment."

"I do not defend myself," interrupts the Intellectual. "Why does the world, for you, invariably consist of prosecutors and accused?"

"I did not invent that world," the Revolutionary continues. "One should be able to face its horrors and not lament over them. You accuse us, revolutionaries, of dividing reality into two sides and demanding engagement on one, and only one, side. This is as senseless as accusing meteorologists of causing hail and wind storms. The whole history of mankind is proof of our arguments. The second proof is the *de facto* effectiveness of our social action conducted on the basis of such an interpretation of conditions."

"History proves everything that is previously put into it by the historian," replies the Intellectual. "You analyze history, approaching it with a ready-made scheme, and at the end of the study you announce triumphantly that the same scheme emerged from your analysis—forgetting to add that you yourselves put it there first. And the practical effectiveness of this interpretation of the world has not been proved. How far this or that movement is really historically effective can be evaluated only when its era has passed, only *ex post*. Maintaining that you, for the first time in history, are free from limitations which are imposed on man's perspective by his era, you fall victim to the same mystification which you rightly notice about your predecessors."

The Revolutionary laughs mockingly: "*In qua mensura mensis fueritis, remetietur vobis.* You're trying to say that we boast of our own alleged freedom from historical limitations while you yourself are really free from them. After all, it is you who maintains that you control the world of eternal values, transcending history and free from its pressure. We, on the other hand, have a clear realization of the relativity of values; what is more, we are the only ones really to possess the skill of historical thinking which permits us also to watch the present in its constant passage."

"I know," answers the Intellectual, "that you voice the general principle of historicity, but I do not notice that you practice it. I would not accuse you of this and of inconsistency in general if you accepted my assumption as an alternative possibility—the recognition of values which under no circumstances can be erased and the negation of which is an evil in any situation. But you act differently. Your relativity is masked by appearance of fictitious immutability. You have values which essentially change every day and which are pronounced every day as final. This is the worst form of relativity because it buries both historical thinking—the value of which I do not deny—and the unchanging and lasting human achievements. It is a strange cult that professes monotheism but daily changes the god which is the object of the cult.

"You must notice that we are waging a peculiar discussion. It mirrors quite exactly that fictitious conversation between Carnot and Lavoisier, recorded by Romain Rolland. A certain naïveté, easily noticeable in that drama, does not conceal the analogy from me. Carnot demands from his interlocutor approval for sacrificing the present for the future. Lavoisier answers that to sacrifice truth, respect for oneself, and all-human values for the future, means to sacrifice the future. I cannot disagree with him. Lacking your faith —as optimistic as it is empty-headed—as to the foreseeability of future things, I cannot know what future results will follow from our present actions. Therefore, I do not agree that great moral and intellectual values should be sacrificed on the altar of objectives the outcome of which is in doubt. On the other hand, I know that, quite to the contrary, the measures used necessarily leave their mark on the ultimate outcome."

"You succumb to deceptive pictures which liberal politicians always paint about the revolutionary movement in order to denigrate it," replies the Revolutionary. "Our doctrine does not leave the whole present to be devoured. The present makes immediate use of the revolution, and thanks to this, it is possible to arrange it so that all its possibilities are not exploited, but some are renounced for the sake of greater future results. And all the measures which make you so indignant are always a defense against a greater evil. Remember that in politics a choice between two evils is more common than a choice between absolute good and evil. This is a premise of the present which was not created by either of us."

"I will never believe," says the Intellectual, "that the moral and intellectual life of mankind should conform to the laws of economic investment, that one should expect better results tomorrow by saving today—that is, to use lies for the triumph of truth and take advantage of crime in order to pave the way for nobility. I know that often it is necessary to choose between two evils. But when both possibilities are to a large extent evil, I will do everything to refrain from choosing. In this way, I also choose something, if only man's right to his own evaluation of the situation in which he finds himself. This is not so very little."

"But nevertheless, returning to your example, history made Carnot right."

"I did not notice that."

"In such a case, the condition of any further conversation is to interpret again the whole history of the world, which cannot be done, especially if we are waiting for a choice which must be made right away about the completion of this task."

"It seems that this is to the point. If we are forced to take some immediate attitude to current changes, then we cannot, of course, wait for the uncertain results of historico-philosophical discussions, which may remain unresolved for a hundred years. Therefore, our choice will always be best if it is determined by that small particle of certainty which we possess. Lasting moral values, elaborated in the long development of man up to this moment, are the surest support we have if reality demands from us a choice which, ultimately, is also of moral character. In any case, they are more worthy of confidence than any historical science. And this is the reason why, ultimately, I stick to my opinion."

"Whatever happens?"

"Whatever happens."

II. The Opiate of the Great Demiurge

I repeat that it was possible, in the difficult moments during the last war, to expect the laurel of victory to fall to the Nazis. This supposition is, in itself, not subject to moral judgment, but the practical conclusions drawn from it, and the attitude adopted as a result of such a world view, are subject to such judgment. Nobody is free of the moral responsibility for supporting a crime merely because he was intellectually convinced of its inevitable victory. Nobody is exempted from the moral duty to fight against a system of rule, a doctrine, or social conditions which he considers to be vile and inhuman, by resorting to the argument that he considers them historically necessary. We protest against such forms of moral relativism in which it is assumed that the criteria of moral judgment of human action can be deduced from knowledge of the *Weltgeist*.

This is not a protest against the thesis of the actual dependence of human moral convictions on human social conditions, but a protest solely against attempts at normative interpretation of the philosophy of history—that is, against drawing conclusions concerning duty from necessity, against seeking criteria for moral judgment in the laws of history, against a doctrine which does not confine itself to moral judgment of the past by its effects on the present, but also morally judges the present by its results in the future, imagining that it has a complete and infallible knowledge of those results. It is, finally, a protest against the contention that in historical clashes—even on a *Weltgeist* scale—victory will inevitably go to the just cause, in which "just cause" means the one that does win, thus reducing the statement that the "future belongs to the just" to a simple tautology meaning only that the just are those to whom the future belongs.

We should like to consider this problem more closely. When forecasting a hailstorm, a meteorologist does not say: "There will be a hailstorm. We can forecast it, but it is beyond our power to prevent it. The hailstorm is inevitable; therefore, enjoy the hailstorm, be enthusiastic about it, sing hymns in its praise, and convince the farmers that instead of protecting their crops against the hail, they ought to await the coming of the storm with yearning."

The historical prophet finds himself in a different situation. First, he knows in advance that human history is aimed in the direction of progress, and, while the meaning of this last word has never been really clarified, it should be understood roughly as denoting a series of situations in which each is "better" than the one preceding it. Considered on a sufficiently large scale, history is a progressive process. Practically, this means that, for the most part, man's life on earth is constantly improving.

Of course, it may be difficult to persuade "man" of this thesis. In that case, we are faced with various possibilities. Usually, one must observe that man obstinately shows a flat empiricism, that instead of penetrating to the essence of things, which is constantly improving, he occupies himself with trivialities from his own empirical life which show no such improvement. In that case, man is simply not philosophically trained. It is also possible for the "empirical I" of the man under observation to remain in complete objective contradiction to the "absolute I" of social consciousness—that is, the man simply represents an element of regression in collective life. Finally, it can also happen that what man considers a worsening of the situation is only a transitional phase which will subsequently lead to radical improvement—that is, we are dealing with the dialectical "one step backward, two steps forward." Whatever the case, man must be convinced that the world is headed for better times, at least insofar as its development is studied over sufficiently long periods of time.

As soon as anyone is convinced of this, the major difficulty ceases to exist. Now it will suffice to demonstrate with respect to any specific event that it arose on the orders of some great demiurge of history and progress, and therefore constitutes an incentive in humanity's march toward a better world. By this very fact, supporting this phenomenon or that situation is dictated as moral duty to all who have the good of humanity at heart. What better criterion of moral judgment can we find than cooperation with the secret forces of historical progress? It is enough to believe in the inevitability of progress to believe simultaneously in the progressiveness of inevitability. It is enough to believe in providence in order to bless the brick which hits one on the head. When the spirit of history assumes the difficult role of divine providence, it must accordingly demand humble gratitude for every blow it inflicts on its chosen. The demiurge of progress which guards the world demands the worship of his every creation and image. What could be easier than to prove that this or that national leader, this or that system of government or of social relations is the demiurge's anointed, even if its external appearance terrifies people with its simian hide? After all, Catholic historians also admit that God, wanting to test the faithful, sometimes ordained that Peter's See should fall into unworthy hands. The merit of the faithful is all the greater if they bow their heads down before the voice of God even when that voice comes out of the muzzle of Balaam's ass! If the demiurge of progress cares to speak in the voice of Genghis Khan, then the quicker the philosopher of history offers Genghis Khan his services, the wiser he will be. When zoologists come to the conclusion that the age of man is ended and that the age of the ants is coming, the philosopher of history can do nothing but enjoin everyone voluntarily to sit on an anthill and leave their skeletons there. This will certainly be an advantage to progress, since it has been established that progress is a law of history.

In innumerable cases during the Stalinist period, the spiritual history of the young Belinski was reconstructed. Belinski came to believe that Russian czarism was the incarnation of the spirit of history, and that it was right not to oppose history senselessly in the name of personal convictions but to affirm its essential direction against the qualms and resistances of the individual conscience. The individual's moral problem did not consist of evaluating historical events by the standards of his own sense of justice, but exclusively in adapting his sense of justice to historical inevitability. Once the individual is made aware that he constitutes only a *modus* for history, his duty is to make himself at home in the situation, not only intellectually but morally as well. That is, every instinctive movement toward moral revolt against what is presented to him as historical inevitability must be branded as the irresponsible impulse of the *modus,* which would like (what is metaphysically inconceivable) to be transformed into an independent substance in an attempt to break out of historical inevitability. This attempt is not only doomed to defeat (as demonstrated by the theory of the individual's role in history) but also deserves to be condemned as being contrary to progress. Those who accept such a philosophy of history have tried, with its help, to reconcile the existing reality of socialism with their own idea of it. *Weltgeist* was a help in bridging the gap which separated the ideological meaning of Communism from all the crimes committed in its name. This vision of reality was by no means the property of only a handful of philosophers of history, speculating on the fate of mankind, but gained sufficient amplitude to assume the proportions of a social phenomenon.

The opiate of the *Weltgeist,* applied in a more or less popularized form, effectively anesthetized consciences against the morally irritating stimuli of everyday life. The substance of history dominated the meek *modi,* who were persuaded that their hidden revulsions and the repressed reflexes of their disgusted consciences were merely normal exertions in that titanic task of pulling the chariot of history. But the *modi* who accepted the *Weltgeist* theory and, with its help, justified all the ominous stains on contemporary reality, as well as their own opportunism in the face of that reality, were by no means the innocent victims of an erroneous philosophy of history. Their initial error did not lie in the very acceptance of historical fate, but in relieving it of moral responsibility and, by so doing, relieving themselves as well of the duty of being anything but its instruments. The essential fact is that Communists have come to believe in the absolute immorality of history and simultaneously to believe in the superfluousness of any morality independent of historically inevitable conditions. And they were not at all interested in the content of the historical inevitability on whose shoulders they placed their own conformities. They did not try to think or decide independently what the content of that inevitability actually was, but instead placed the task of this difficult inquiry into the intentions of the historical demiurge on the shoulders of their superiors. They gladly agreed to let others determine for them the cunning intentions of the *Weltgeist,* and then have communicated to them the results of others' contacts with it. Each time, they passively accepted as historical inevitability all that they were told, and then willingly fulfilled its actual or alleged demands.

In the kingdom of the *Weltgeist* they were despicable underdogs who paid the taxes of history without expecting the right to vote on its decisions or even to be fully informed of them, and who consented to this role without protest. The contradictions between the world of reality and the world of recognized values was voiced only as superficial cynicism, which always provides a mild antidote for disgust with permanent conformity. This is because cynicism is no more than a clear realization of the contradictions between one's own actions and the total values recognized in a given social milieu —and silently recognized by the cynic himself. For this reason, true criminals are not cynics.

Now we touch on the sensitive point of the discussions, the point mentioned at the beginning of these reflections. How, in fact, is it possible to reconcile the conviction of the existence of historical necessity with the conviction that this necessity must be realized by brutal and terroristic means? How can this be reconciled with acceptance of any universal values—that is, with the conviction that certain actions are called for and others prohibited in all circumstances? Moral duty is the belief, perpetuated in a given social environment, that certain human actions are ends in themselves and not merely means to an end, and that other actions are counterends in themselves; that is, they are prohibited. If historical necessity is either considered as an unlimited process without a final end or an ultimate end is ascribed to it, though still unrealized and subject only to a promise of the future, and if, simultaneously, moral judgments are subject to the realization of that necessity, then there is nothing in contemporary life which can be considered an end in itself. In other words, moral values in the strict sense of the term cease to exist altogether. Can the view of the world of reality be reconciled with the view of the world of values?

This is one version of the controversy between extreme political realism and extreme utopianism, with some interpretation of these ideas. We say that realism is extreme when an individual is convinced of the fundamental inevitability of all the details of the historical process in which he must live, and consequently of the hopelessness of any endeavors which would oppose contemporary reality by means of *moral* postulates. Understood in this way, realism brands any moralizing concerning existing reality as barren and utopian, and so brands it in the name of the demiurge of history, which cannot abide moralists. On the other hand, utopianism in the sense used here is based on an assumption of permanent moral criticism of reality, the arbitrary measurement of reality by criteria of absolute good and evil, and the judgment of it exclusively from that viewpoint. The only protest of the utopian against social reality is that it is morally wrong; his only instrument for influencing the course of social reality is to tell people how the world *should* look to fulfill those criteria of absolute good and evil.

We suppose that some common assumptions do exist in the above controversy—a controversy that we do not wish to illustrate with specific examples, in order to avoid fruitless discussions of factual matters and because we wish to deal with ideal types. The realist does not question (because he doesn't have to) those moral values which the utopian juxtaposes to contemporary history: he only questions their usefulness. The utopian, in turn, does not question historical determinism at all: he only questions the right to judge events morally on the basis of their historical inevitability. He believes these moral judgments do not depend on an awareness that the fact under scrutiny fits the chain of history as interpreted in some philosophy of history.

Moreover, both sides of the controversy accuse each other of producing poor practical results with their philosophies. In the opinion of his antagonist, the realist is a theoretical opportunist with respect to history and, simultaneously, a political opportunist in any actual situation. Instead of a program of change, he only has a program of adapting to a given set of existing conditions. He accepts without question the world of things, because it is the only real world and there is only the world of values to set in contrast to it, a fiction construed *ad libitum* by visionaries, without any real roots in nature. The utopian, in turn, in the opinion of his adversary, condemns himself to sterility in practice because he builds imaginary worlds and sets himself unattainable goals out of his notions of perfection. Thus he prevents himself from achieving attainable objectives by analysis of the possibilities inherent in a world of rigid and stubborn facts.

In this fashion, the utopian-reformer-visionary and the realist-fatalist debate with each other, and have been debating that way ever since man set as his conscious goal the improvement of his social life, which is almost since the beginning of time. Actually, the discussion resembles voices calling from opposite banks of a river that cannot be crossed. Between obedience to the world of reality and obedience to the moral imperative, gapes an abyss on whose brink the great historical tragedies have been played: the tragedies of conspiratorial insurrections predesigned for disaster, and the opposite kind of tragedies, of collaboration with crime as a result of the belief in its inevitability. On both of these brinks the moral history of the revolutionary movement of recent years has also been staged.

Marx was the man who tried to bridge the abyss. On this bridge was to take place the final victory over utopian socialism. He summarized his position by saying, "The ossified relations must be forced to dance by singing to them their own tune," or by maintaining that men create their own history, not freely, but by yielding to the pressure of existing conditions. Marx devoted the greater part of his life to discovering that natural tune of history, but his disciples continually had to restate the problem. They continually had to write posthumous additions to the unfinished manuscript of *Das Kapital* and, in the face of new realities, take up the same question: what is to be done? The two men who wrote books under this title, Chernishevsky and Lenin, represent two phases of development in that relentless effort: the continual confrontation of contemporary experience with the imagined ideal, and the continuous dialogue between existing reality and imagined reality.

The difficulty of this labor is not the ordinary difficulty of a theoretical question to which a sufficiently satisfactory answer has not yet been found, but which one day may be solved once and for all. We are faced here with a problem that has no universal answer applicable to all historical circumstances, but which must be solved anew for each actual historical situation, because each one is new, each unique, and none can be analyzed solely by analogy to the past.

It follows from this that the very nature of historical determinism is vague in character. I mean "determinism" as a doctrine, describing rules of social change which can be considered valid for the future. Marx's predictions referred to a change in economic structure and were formulated in those terms. Ordinary scientific criticism did not permit going into further details so happily indulged in by Fourier and the majority of the utopians. The details of Lenin's programs, formulated before the October Revolution, went considerably further. Yet, to this very day, we cannot positively decide which part of those programs was based on peculiarly Russian conditions and which retained, or was intended to retain, universal validity for the period of transition from capitalism to socialism. We can almost certainly take for granted Marx's fundamental assumption that the development of capitalist technology creates the tendency to endow the means of production with a collective ownership; and this assumption is confirmed, in general outline, by historical experience. However, in the course of how many revolutions won and lost, how many wars and crises, how many years and decades, according to what geographical and chronological circumstances, in the course of what progress and regress, and in what diverse forms a socialist way of life will be realized cannot be deduced authoritatively from a superficial knowledge of the "laws of history." These questions are answered by the experiences of everyday life, daily shocking us with new surprises like a virtuoso magician.

In general, these facts do not hinder philosophers of history. They are happy through the years in always writing the same epitaph for capitalist society, and in composing it on the basis of their belief in "scientific prognostication." The rest—the wars, revolutions, crises, decades of struggle and suffering—fall into the philosophic category of "accident" and so do not count. They are no longer subject to penetrating historico-philosophical analysis.

From the secrets of the demiurge of history, the philosophers of history have extracted information concerning the final point at which history's wanderings will terminate, but the circuitous routes along which it wanders toward its goal escape their prophetic eyes. Every stage covered (and here the word "stage" can be most aptly defined in the sense that denotes the routes of the czarist deportation cars) can always be subjected to a cause-and-effect interpretation after it has already taken place. In many ways, then, it furnishes philosophers of history with subject material for long years of controversy and deliberation, but only rarely can any of these stages be predicted. Hence, they have gotten the name "accidents," a word which for centuries has raised human intellectual indolence to the dignity of a theory, and in our time constitutes an *asylum ignorantiae* no less effectively than in Spinoza's time. Nonetheless, the philosophy of history never lacks the courage to construct, on the basis of such knowledge of the future fate of the world, practical rules binding every human being which morally compel him to cooperate with the march of history. The philosophy of history is not offended by anything. After every turn of real history, which discloses to the world its shameful impotence, the philosophy of history blows fanfares and even composes self-criticism to the tempo of a march of trumpets and bugles. This admirable toughness displayed by the philosophy of history, in spite of all its experience with cruel defeats, comes, of course, not from its natural vigor but from the fact that it is itself a tool of the "cunning wisdom" of history, which creates it in order to mystify the social consciousness, deluding it with thoughtless opportunism and making it believe that by ridding itself of illusions, it reads reality like an open book. The debunking of consciousness has itself become a myth, and therefore, even if events give the lie to the philosophy of history at every turn, it always knows how to present its defeats as victories in the same way that the Delphic prophecies always came true.

The philosophy of history draws its strength not from itself but from the faith invested in it, and this faith is a part of political practice and has a semi-sacred character. Even the most tattered and patched-up cloak may look like a royal ceremonial gown if it is worn by a priest the people revere. Those who foretell the future from dreams will always be believed; the faithful never falter in their belief, even when it is proved to them empirically that their dreams do not come true, because believers always have one or two examples illustrating the contrary and sufficient to support their faith. And faith never requires proof—only examples and sanctions.

III. Conscience and Social Progress

In the controversy between realism and utopianism, the arguments against the latter have been formulated so many times and in such minute detail that we shall forego the task of repeating them. However, we will cite the "anti-realist" arguments which, for many reasons, seem to us to be currently of greater importance.

Our assumptions are as follows:

First assumption: *moral individualism. Only human individuals and their actions are subject to moral judgment.* This follows from the fact that there can be no moral judgment without consideration of the intentions motivating the act, because intentions are inherent in the actions of the individual man. Thus it is necessary, in turn, to conclude that moral judgment of an anonymous historical process and its negative and positive results is impossible. Social groups or classes also cannot be morally judged, in the strict sense of the term, if by "social class" we understand—and to us such an interpretation seems accurate—not only a collection of individuals but a specific social "entity" wherein the reactions of its human components are determined by the reactions of the class as a whole, and not vice versa. (We will not pursue this problem in greater detail because it is not essential to the following considerations.)

Nevertheless—and in our opinion this point is of major importance—this by no means indicates that membership in a specific group or class, and only this and no other relationship an individual has to the society he lives in, is decisive in determining his moral judgment or his behavior, which is subject to moral judgment and whose range is quite variable in history. On the contrary, we are permitted to accept the hypothesis that this determinism is absolute, as formulated in the second assumption, although there is insufficient evidence for this (I have in mind here social determinism and not determinism resulting only from membership in a class).

Second assumption: *determinism*. Opinions of what is morally good and evil, as well as good and evil in human behavior, are determined by the individual's type of participation in social life. We understand by "participation" both upbringing and the influence of tradition, as well as membership in all social groups from whose interrelations there emerges that unique thing called "personality" (tradition is, of course, also a social grouping, specifically the total number of people who remain in the sphere of influence of a certain type of consciousness shaped before them). We set aside the problem of what part various forms of social life play in shaping moral judgments: how many of them grow from universal conditions of social life as such and therefore have a *fundamental* nature universally binding; how many originate in specific conditions of class society and therefore are, in any event, extremely enduring in character; how many, finally, result from membership in a definite class, profession, and so on. (This last question constitutes a summary of all the major problems of the sociology of morality and, as such, is not suited for present consideration.)

The essential thing is that these two assumptions are not in the least contradictory, although they are so considered by many moralists. There is no logical contradiction between social determinism, interpreted even more rigorously than we would wish to do here, and the recognition of moral responsibility. From this follows the next assumption.

Third assumption: *a humanistic interpretation of value*. Although one's recognition of a certain set of moral judgments, as well as one's moral actions, is determined, one cannot, from the knowledge of the conditions shaping a man, draw conclusions about the truth or falsehood of the judgments accepted by him. In other words, from the assertion that someone knows he accepts this or that as good or evil because these or other conditions of life have induced him to do so, it does not follow that this or that is good or evil. Everyone has certain moral opinions, but no one can demonstrate the correctness of those opinions by claiming that they arose out of the influence of these or other external causes. Thus, to say that an individual may be judged morally amounts to saying that others *have a right* to judge him, and this statement has a normative character. Consequently, its antithesis is also normative.

By contending, therefore, that determinism, which is a theoretical construct, makes a moral responsibility impossible, we silently assume that moral judgments may be deduced from purely theoretical premises. If we reject the possibility of such deduction, we must recognize that the problem of determinism or indeterminism in human behavior has no logical connection with the problem of affirmation or negation of man's moral responsibility, precisely because such affirmation or negation is not a theoretical construct. Thus the third assumption eliminates the apparent contradiction between the first and second assumptions.

Nevertheless, the question with which we are concerned is by no means solved, but actually emerges as a problem. Even if it is true that individual conduct should be explained by the historical process, and not the other way around, then anyone who recognizes this truth still remains a mere individual who must at every step make a vital choice and for whom this general knowledge provides no effective instrument in making that choice. Moral choice is made no easier by the realization that it is predetermined, in the vulgar sense of the term, or by the fact that every component of the alternatives is enmeshed in a specific historical perspective. To be more exact, the choice remains difficult until we imagine that we possess infallible and final knowledge of the laws of historical development, and that we can read the future of the world as reliably as a railroad timetable. Once this insane illusion possesses us, however, we can probably choose much more easily, but at what cost! This cost is based on the fact that the idiocy of daily life is *apparently* overcome by having each of its phenomena fictitiously elevated to the dignity of a general historical category, so that it becomes a part of some "universal" of which our cosmic vision consists. For daily life is, by its very nature, tormenting because of the lack of connections between particular events. It is an accumulation of individual situations which have only one thing in common, and that is that some of them are in certain respects similar to others, thanks to which we are able to evolve some reflexes and habitual responses, selecting our reactions in what seems like an orderly fashion but actually doing so thoughtlessly and in a purely conditioned way. In fact, however, a fragment of everyday life is spent and passes so quickly that it is impossible to take note of it; together with other such moments, it creates that hideous void where nothing is real and nothing really experienced, and everything is diffused in a chaotic mass of details. This everyday life composed of separate phenomena, which lack substantial connection, searches for this connection in mythologies by happenstance, and results in what is called "the purpose of life." Any individual "purpose of life" is supposed to create that continuity with regard to which every individual fact will seem to be a *modus,* this giving the course of everyday events the appearance of meaning, while, in fact, these events disappear before they have a chance to be absorbed by the consciousness, leaving after them only a sense of meaninglessness. This act of dressing one's life up with the appearance of substance—the superficial glamor of some sort of consistency and coherence induced by subordinating one's life to a single goal—may sometimes succeed. In so doing, it silences the torments of a daily life crushed by the nightmare of one's own absurdity.

Individual life-goals, those fragile mythologies which disintegrate under any external blow, may however be replaced by the armor of the philosophy of history. The consciousness permeated by historico-philosophical knowledge (which unfailingly arranges all facts according to general "laws," and with the power of thought infallibly penetrates the future) organizes its daily life admirably, like some magnificent edifice where each small part has a perfectly defined function and each is classified in general and overestimated categories. Every fact of everyday life becomes merely an illustration of a specific abstract category. The heap of chaotic impressions of which our existence was previously composed is suddenly transformed into a paradise of pure universals. From the hell of unconnected, fragmentary events, we move to the charming symmetry of a world where only ideas and symbols exist. In that world there are no individuals, or they appear only as examples of ideas, with the mark of their species recorded on their foreheads. In that world we no longer eat bread and butter, but we reproduce labor power consciously organized for the purpose of applying it to socialist building. In that world we do not sleep, but we regenerate cerebral tissue to use it for inventive work in realizing the *Weltgeist;* we talk not to men but to carriers of ideas who themselves are only delegates of certain conflicting social forces in the gigantic advance of history. Our words are only echoes of ideas, and every step has a predetermined objective, identical with that toward which historical progress is also moving with intentions we have discovered and which we know as well as we know the palms of our hands.

In this manner, we are removed from the muck of everyday life to the madness of abstract life, as if we were moving from a brothel to a monastery. Social moral-consciousness oscillates between two extreme forms, each of which is revealed in the course of time to be the same idiotic illusion. It is also understandable that the defeat of one of these methods of interpreting life immediately pushes one into the arms of the other, a fact easily observed in the most banal experience of life.

However, because we do not intend at present to become preoccupied with all the forms of absurdity we encounter in life, we would like to call attention to only one of them: how can we free the morality of daily life from the nightmare of the philosophy of history and from those pseudo-dialectics which, by transforming morality into an instrument of history, in fact make history the pretext for disgraceful behavior? With this, we would like to make one reservation: we are not interested in that trivial criticism of the historico-philosophical world view which rejects this concept on the grounds that it "dehumanizes" the world by theoretically classifying the facts of daily life. In spite of the illusory paradise of ideas in which the historico-philosophically educated consciousness moves, it is still more human and less idiotic than the typical everyday life which, in Tuwim's words, is filled "with the torture of weekdays and Sunday boredom."

The danger of building a morality based on historico-philosophical vision and having meaning only within the framework of that vision does not consist in trying generally to interpret one's own life as a fragment of history, and thus endowing it, even by arbitrary pronouncement, with a certain meaning it does not intrinsically possess. The danger is based on a complete substitution of criteria of usefulness, which the demiurge of history derives from our actions, for moral criteria. The greater the degree of certainty we have concerning the demiurge's intentions, the greater the threat. The sectarian spirit is the natural enemy of the skeptical spirit, and skepticism is the best possible antidote, however difficult to apply generally, against the insane fanaticism of visionaries. This centuries-old truth should be refurbished from time to time whenever historical experiences which demonstrate this truth with particular clarity recur. When one achieves an absolute and unshakable certainty that the kingdom of heaven is around the corner, that the "Third Order" of which Joachim of Floris wrote is nearing its triumph and simultaneously approaching the final establishment of a new historical era—the ultimate one that *really* gives happiness and is *really* different from all the others, the only one to scotch the serpent's head and put an end to human suffering—when, therefore, we are hypnotized by boundless conviction that we are on the threshold of some kind of second coming, it is no wonder that this single messianic hope will become the sole law of life, the only source of moral precept, and the only measure of virtue. A consistent messianist must be convinced that he cannot hesitate to do anything that might help to bring about the new era. Morality then speaks in the language of the Apocalypse. It sees "a new heaven and a new earth" and knows simultaneously that before the far side is reached, the four angels will destroy a third of mankind, burning stars will fall, the abyss will open, the seven vessels of God's wrath will be poured over the world, and glory will illuminate the victor who crushes the heathen with an iron rod. The historiosophy of the Apocalypse, of Joachim of Floris, and of Thomas Munzer has been revived to some extent in the Communist movement. Although in this latter case it was supported by an honest and prolific effort of scientific analysis, it acted like a messianic vision in the operations of the mass movement. Probably it could not have been different, but awareness of this cannot provide us with a sense of security, precisely because we want to prove that out of more or less reliable knowledge of historical necessities, we still cannot deduce the rules of our conduct.

In any case, we take note of one of many practical lessons, which states that one needs a certain skepticism in the face of any prophetic philosophy of history which sees the future with excessive certainty. Experience shows that, as Marx wrote, it is still easy to enslave people by an independent historical process.

On the other hand, history is not simply an indifferent force, aloof as the gods of Epicurus, but a series of situations in which, irrespective of our will, we are really engaged. If this involvement is to be a voluntary act of individual consciousness, it is also a moral act—at least in the sense that certain other recognized values find expression in it as determining factors.

Thus, our question is as follows: if the morality of daily life cannot be deduced from knowledge of real or alleged historical necessities, should we also defend certain moral values, arbitrarily assumed or accepted by force of tradition, even when in our opinion history turns against them? Shall we, then, propagate an anti-historical morality, since we are abandoning a morality based wholly on history?

And this could be the reply: the essential social engagement is moral. Although a great political movement which aims to shape the world in its own image is created by the needs of that world and is fundamentally oriented by social developments, still every individual's access to this or any other form of political life is a moral act for which he is fully responsible. Nobody is free from positive or negative responsibility because his individual actions constitute only a fragment of a specific historical process. A soldier is morally responsible for crimes committed on the orders of his commander; even more, an individual is responsible for actions committed, allegedly or in fact, on the orders of anonymous history. If a thousand people are standing on a river bank when a drowning man calls for help, it is almost absolutely certain that someone among those spectators will rush to help the man in the water. This quasi-statistical certainty concerns a thousand people, but it does not in the least remove the necessity for moral judgment by that very individual, the one out of a thousand, who threw himself into the river. Experience testifies in advance to the fact that there will always be one such person in a crowd. The essence of this certainty may be compared to a historical prediction in the rare cases when it comes true. However, to be that one man out of a thousand potential rescuers who realizes this prediction based on large numbers, one must carry out "by oneself" an act subject to moral judgment. By analogy: if a social system exists which needs criminals for some of its tasks, one may be sure that these criminals will be found, but it does not follow that, as a result of this certainty, every individual criminal is freed from responsibility. In order to take upon oneself the role of such an instrument of the system, one must intrinsically be a criminal, one must voluntarily commit a specific act subject to moral judgment. We therefore support the doctrine of the total responsibility of the individual for his own deeds, and the amorality of the historical process. In the latter case we take advantage of the Hegelian idea, but in the former of Descartes'. It was Descartes who formulated the famous principle whose implications are not always apparent at first sight: "There is no soul so weak that it would be unable to achieve absolute power over its passions by good conduct." This means that we cannot justify any of our actions by passion, by the moral incapacity to act differently, and that we have no right to lay blame for any conscious act on any factor determining our conduct, because in each case we have the power to make a free choice. This assumption, mentioned above, can be accepted without contradiction on the basis of a deterministic world view, and also embraces all the justifications we might find for ourselves in historical necessity and historical determinism. Neither our own irresistible passions ("I was unable to resist the desire"), nor anyone's command ("I was a soldier"), nor conformity with the social customs ("Everybody did that"), nor the necessities theoretically deduced from the demiurge of history ("I thought I was acting for the sake of progress")—none of these four most typical and common rationalizations of our actions has any value as justification. By this we do not mean to say that these four types of determinism do not actually play a role in life. We only assert that none of them can relieve the individual of moral responsibility, because none destroys the freedom of individual choice. The individual act remains in the absolute power of the individual. We follow the main roads of our life on our own responsibility:

> Nor I, nor anyone else, can travel that road
>   for you,
> You must travel it for yourself. . . .

                                                    [Walt Whitman]

We wish to emphasize that we are concerned with *moral* responsibility. A soldier who executed erroneous orders from his commanders, orders which were militarily ineffective, is not for that reason responsible for a lost battle. A soldier who, on orders, participated in the mass murder of a civilian population is responsible for homicide. His moral duty is not to obey the orders. Only on that principle was it possible to judge the SS men.

Regardless of which philosophy of history we accept, we shall be

judged justly for everything we have done in its name and for everything which is subject to moral judgment.

It is not true that the philosophy of history determines our main
choices in life. Our moral sensibility does this. We are not Communists because we have recognized Communism as historical necessity; we are Communists because we have joined the side of the oppressed against their oppressors, the side of the poor against their
masters, the side of the persecuted against their persecutors. Although we know that the correct theoretical division of society is not
into "rich" and "poor," not into "persecuted" and "persecutors,"
when we must make a *practical* choice apart from the theory—that
is, a fundamental option—we are then motivated morally and not
by theoretical considerations. It cannot be otherwise because even
the most convincing theory is not by itself capable of making us lift
a finger. A practical choice is a choice of values—that is, a moral
act for which everyone bears his own personal responsibility.

IV. Hope and the Fabric of History

Thus practical choice in life is made in a world defined by "duty"
and not by "existence." These two categories, *Sollen* and *Sein,* characterize two attitudes and two visions of reality between which we
continuously but fruitlessly try to establish contact. The same question constantly arises in different forms: how to insure that the
Sollen-Sein alternative will not become the alternative between
utopianism and opportunism, romanticism and conservatism, useless madness and collaboration with crime masked by sobriety; how
to avoid the fatal choice between the Scylla of duty, casting its
arbitrary slogans into the desert, and the Charybdis of obedience to
the existing world which gradually transforms itself into a voluntary
affirmation of the world's most dreadful creations; how to avoid this
choice on the assumption, which we think essential, that we can
never really measure truly and with complete predictability the
boundaries of what we call "historical necessity," and that therefore
we shall never be able to declare definitely which of the facts of
social life are components of historical fate or which possibilities are
concealed in existing reality.

For a more detailed answer to this question, we accept the following assumptions.

Fourth assumption: *historical interpretation of value. Duty is a form of being*. That is, the very fact that a specific moral consciousness has acquired a social character means it has become a part of historical process and a factor influencing the course of that process. What is more, the awareness of a certain duty inherent in that consciousness has become an objective need of social life. Various social rules are reflected in social consciousness, not in the form of theoretical knowledge but in the form of value judgments, of a belief that this or that is morally "good" or "evil," that this or that "should" or "should not" be done. If we do not wish—following the pattern of positivist literature—to be satisfied with reflecting on the specific character of the verbal forms in which moral opinions are expressed, and to consider as the final end of our knowledge the truth that normative statements cannot be deduced from propositions derived from the rules of logic; and if, therefore, we do not wish to be content with the trivial knowledge that no world view is in itself sufficient to validate a theory of value, we must consider both the knowledge of social phenomena and the world of value as specific manifestations of collective life, reflecting in different ways its laws, tendencies, and needs. If we adopt such an attitude, we will be less concerned with the question of whether statements containing specific moral judgments are equally subject, with other statements, to the dichotomy of truth and falsehood (although we share with the positivists the negative reply to this question); we will be more interested in the type of relation that exists between consciousness pronouncing value judgment and consciousness making theory as two forms of the same social process. In reality, and it is almost shameful to repeat this truth, theories about social phenomena only too often are masked by ideology—that is, they are often (though not exclusively) a concealed collection of values imposed upon society under the guise of research altruistically serving scientific knowledge. But also consciousness which pronounces value judgments—if that consciousness assumes social dimensions (and the criteria which determine when this takes place are very difficult to formulate)—is a distorted perception of certain facts of social life, certain regularities in it reflected in the distorting mirror of interests. If a certain norm is widely accepted, then, even if it were never fully respected, by the very fact of its existence it constitutes evidence that the needs of society, or of a certain important segment of it, require that its violations be kept within limits. *"Duty" is only the voice of a social need,* and, in this sense, the world of values is not only an imaginary heaven over and above the real world but is actually a part of the real world, that part which exists only in social consciousness, though also rooted in the material conditions of social life. From this, we derive the fifth assumption.

Fifth assumption: *negation of pseudo-realistic criticism of moralizing utopias.* A social movement that has a moral basis for its program does not reveal its ineffectiveness by the mere fact that its moral postulates have little chance of realization in the foreseeable future. It is, in fact, a platitude—the truth of which all humanity has been learning from its daily experience—that social systems established by means of attractive slogans with a moral aura only faintly resemble those slogans in content. In other words, we should be wise enough not to be deceived about the speedy arrival of the kingdom of heaven. In general, however, we seem to lack this wisdom which does not apparently demand great mental effort, and because of this, from time to time, we receive from our mother—history—blows which are even more painful because they are spiced with the mockery and the realization of our own naïveté.

Sixth assumption: *the possibility of moral judgment of political choices. The basic political choices we make are subject to moral evaluation.* In a world where every particle is politically evaluated, where the struggle between parties is total, the situation described brings about a deep change in life. Our assumption rejects in essence the view, sometimes encountered, according to which group solidarity is subject to moral evaluation, but the mere act of access to some group or other, among which one makes a voluntary choice, is not subject to it. Since political elements in social life are now manifest with an intensity never before encountered, a large number of our actions which previously might have passed as neutral now carry a moral weight. For this reason, the shadow of anxiety dogs everyday life's most trivial events, because all of them contain the tormenting awareness of the connection between these events and the fundamental political conflicts. This universal system of interconnected social actions has become a fact difficult to ignore, irrespective of one's opinions of its origins and regardless of whether one likes it or not.

Doubtless there is a category of so-called "decent men." But there are so many ways one can be a decent man. And how much of this depends on the situation one finds oneself in, irrespective of one's intention? What does it mean to be a decent man in Nazi Germany, as a member of the chosen race? What does it mean to be a decent man, and a member of the Social Democratic Party conducting a policy of colonial terror? Who is a decent man during a war? And during an election? And yet there really are decent people in every situation, and there is no reason to abandon this category, vague and not clearly defined though it is, but still effective within certain limits.

If one wishes to console himself in this situation by the conviction that he may save his own soul simply by personal decency, and "the whole will be settled of itself," he will be deeply disappointed when, on the other bank of the Styx, he is handed the bill for the crimes about which he did not know at all. The entire drama consists of the fact that we are compelled to make morally binding decisions with a hopeless ignorance of their results.

The conclusions worthy of formulation which emerge from these last assumptions are the following:

To oppose existing social conditions with a program based essentially on moral demands is not in itself socially useless (or, even less, harmful), even when its practical realization is quite doubtful in view of the objective possibilities inherent in the complex of conditions. If, in this contrast, the *Sollen* and *Sein* are extremely sharply opposed and separated by a huge distance, social life itself condemns these purely moralizing programs to practical ineffectiveness by preventing them from becoming any real force whatever in the existing situation in a given community. Whenever these programs emerge as a vital element in social consciousness, whenever they make themselves known as a factor noticeably influencing public opinion, they thereby testify to being "non-utopian" —in the traditional sense of the term, which means being partially effective—and provide testimony to the fact that they arise from certain real requirements of the social consciousness.

This does not mean that thereby they become "realistic" in the sense that the possibilities exist in the society for realizing them rapidly in their pure form. If the slogans organizing the collective consciousness appeal to the moral feelings widespread at a given time, they must of necessity, as has already been stated, greatly exceed the possibilities of existing reality, yet they do not thereby prove themselves chimerical. The abstract moralizing slogan of freedom constitutes the battle cry of innumerable social movements throughout modern history. Of course, freedom could never be realized in this abstract and moralizing form. Nonetheless, it passed through many stages of fragmentary and incomplete realization, and just to ignore them because they were fragmentary and did not fulfill maximalist demands would be stupid (apart from the fact that this slogan and others also have had their deceptive and backward forms which are, however, recognizable). And yet—and we stress it once again—partial realizations succeed only when the postulates exceed the practical "potentialities" of reality, because only then are they able to mobilize and accumulate sufficient quantities of the collective energy necessary to achieve progress. This disproportion between intentions and possibilities has a certain "optimum" which is difficult to define and beyond which criticism of utopianism begins. Programs of change far exceeding the existing possibilities condemn themselves to impotence. The disproportions are necessary for any effectiveness, and for this reason they characterize all the undertakings of the left-wing social movements. *Excess of hope and excess of demands with relation to the possibilities are necessary to force reality to yield all its possibilities, to tap all the springs hidden in the actual shape of reality.* It is true that excess hope also runs the risk of disappointment, and it is also true that disappointment discourages further efforts which, in turn, prevent mobilization of the social energy necessary for exploiting existing possibilities. As a result, the potential of collective activity, in turn, becomes disproportionate to the possibilities of reality and falls below the required level.

And here is the next conclusion from the proposed assumptions:

Let us not disregard the positive role of hypocrisy. When a social system based on lawlessness, oppression, and misery masks itself with humanistic verbiage, it does not, contrary to appearances, make itself more effective in the long run. At a certain stage its façade turns against it because it was always alien to it and was imposed only under the pressure of historical circumstances. *Generally speaking, an increase in hypocrisy is a proof of moral progress* because it testifies to the fact that things previously done openly without fear of disgrace can now no longer be done without risk. In other words, the moral consciousness of society is more susceptible to incentives to which it formerly did not react. In the twentieth century, people were tortured just as effectively as in the fifteenth, but the fact that this is no longer done in public squares and that no system of government is willing to admit that it uses torture proves that the moral sensibilities of the community no longer tolerate these practices as a system. Military aggression continues to be practiced, but the fact that everyone has plenty of slogans with which to condemn any aggression indicates that no one wants to be called an aggressor and proves that the idea of non-aggression as a principle has become rooted in public life. Still, Mussolini was one of those who was not afraid to state that he conducted a policy of conquest, but no present-day politician would like to admit any purpose but defense. The principle of self-determination was a novelty when put forward by Lenin and the Bolshevik Party before World War I. After World War II, it was recognized by the United Nations—a body including governments engaged in the most reprehensible colonial oppression. The Nazis proclaimed conquests of nations in the name of the interests of a superior nation. Today, nothing can be offered to nations except liberation, freedom, and progress.

Therefore, we repeat, the façade of humanistic phraseology which disguises even criminal systems is not only a product of and a testimony to a certain progress in social consciousness, but is in itself a positive factor in this progress. The façade takes on a life of its own and, when this is incompatible with the system, breeds and nurtures the seeds of its destruction. When the system, because of excessively strong traditional ties, is unable to throw off the façade, it risks the possibility that its deceptive dress will one day become the robe of Deianira. Contradictions between façade and content transform themselves into an internal contradiction of the system each time the façade becomes alienated from the system, and this is the natural course of human history.

Thus the general conclusion derived from our deliberations is that the rules of moral behavior cannot be deduced from any theory of historical progress, nor can historical progress justifiably be used as a pretext to violate certain moral rules which otherwise remain valid for us. Apart from all the reasons presented above, two other easily observed circumstances are involved here. The idea of progress is inherently a value judgment, and there is no theory of progress which is not inconsistent—that is, which does not, when applied concretely, lead to conflicts between different values, each of which fulfills some criteria and simultaneously excludes others. (We are not presently inquiring why this is so.) Nor can moral rules be deduced from any theory of "moral progress," in the specific sense of the term, because the concept of moral progress, burdened by all the flaws and difficulties of a general concept of progress, has in addition its own flaws and difficulties which make construction of a general, rational concept of moral progress an apparently hopeless task.

In this matter, we can only formulate very general observations. The major values we accept are, according to our third assumption, unprovable in the strict sense of the term—that is, in the case of conflict between two value judgments discussion is made impossible where there is no possibility of further appeal to more general common values. This situation does not seem alarming to us. If the values—according to our second assumption—are a historical product, there is always a set of very general values universally recognized to which, in practice, we may appeal. The real difficulty lies in the permanent conflicts which arise between unquestioned values as they are concretely applied, and we are often unable to remove these conflicts. Since, according to the sixth assumption, our basic acts of political choice have a moral aspect, they must present themselves to the individual consciousness as something of a risk, because we count on the values we recognize as most probably being realized in a specific, concrete form of already-existing social action. That risk concerns the judgment of facts and not any sort of evaluation; it is a certain bet by which we assume the probability of realization of our values. But the stake is always high and is always morally binding, because it entails responsibility for the results of our acts, which are difficult to predict. Since the risk concerns judgments about facts or historical processes which must eventually take place, one thing at least remains our permanent duty: we must constantly verify our choices by investigating the facts connected with them. We must maintain a constant, watchful awareness that our choice always concerns a probability not a certainty, and that, therefore, it may always be questioned and overthrown by facts. Ignorance of the results of social actions we espoused on the basis of their values is never justifiable. We are not justified by indulging in neglect, laziness, or indolence in the face of the necessity to exercise unceasing control over our own choice. We are not justified by ignorance if, as a result of it, we condone crime. The line of demarcation between innocent ignorance and voluntary blindness cannot be drawn; ultimately, we are responsible for both. Since our choice arises from a combination of recognized values (for which we are also responsible to the society, though the act of recognition is independent of us) and from *knowledge* of the probabilities of their realization in a given set of circumstances, this knowledge must be the object of a constant, a most suspicious, and a most merciless control, taking into account everything that might prove its falsehood. We are obliged to familiarize ourselves with everything that contradicts us. Our every choice contains a risk, and no choice, by the mere fact of its realization, can be considered final and irrevocable.

Nevertheless, the greatest errors cannot be excluded. Neither can the most fateful conflicts between recognized values be thus excluded. Such conflicts cannot be removed by any moral doctrine because none of them can be free of contradictions in application. We are, therefore, equally powerless to prevent the inevitable occurrence of situations in which nobody is guilty in terms of naked intentions and yet everyone is morally responsible. In short, tragedies are a permanent possibility of this world in which we live. Contrasting skepticism with bigotry masked by loyalty, the principle of responsibility with conformism masked by theoretical relativism, the duty of individual choice with an opportunistic philosophy of history masked by realism—contrasting rationalism with the superstitious cult of unverified "laws of history," the principle of active engagement with the principle of humility and obedience—we have no intention of considering all these contrasts as any kind of solution to actual conflicting situations with which we are faced when we resort to accepted general moral rules of conduct. These moral rules, if they arise from the conflict-ridden nature of social reality itself, are solved with a risk no longer theoretical but moral, and a moral risk which everyone individually assumes.

The inevitability of the present is the inevitability of the past, because everything which really exists belongs to the past. The truth about the inevitability of the past is a tautology and gives rise to no disputes. The inevitability of what does not yet exist is always doubtful, and to predict it is generally as uncertain as roulette; in any case, the role of what depends on our decisions is difficult to determine. The poverty of prophetic philosophy of history is a daily proof of this. Therefore, decisions for which we are morally responsible cannot be based on confidence in its pronouncements. A philosophy of history worthy of consideration describes only what has existed—the past, and not the creative future of the historical process. For this reason, those who wish to subordinate their own engagement in future processes to the pronouncements of the philosophy of history are only tourists who write their names on the walls of dead cities. Everybody can, if he wishes, interpret himself historically and discover the determinisms to which he was subject in the past. But he cannot do so with respect to the self he has not yet become. He cannot deduce his own future development from the pronouncements of the philosophy of history in which he trusts. To work such a miracle would mean to become the irrevocable past oneself—that is, to cross the river of death which, the poet says, no one ever sees twice.

Nowa Kultura (Warsaw), September 1-22, 1957.

4.

PARTY, STATE, AND THE NEW CLASS

Adam Wazyk is a Pole who joined the Communist Party before World War II. During the war he served with the Soviet forces on the eastern front; his book of verse, *The Heart of the Grenade,* was published in Moscow in 1943.

"A Poem for Adults" appeared in the summer of 1955 and created an immediate success. "They drink sea water, crying: 'lemonade!' returning home secretly to vomit," writes Wazyk, summing up the bitterness and terror of the postwar decade in Poland.

Together with Pawel Hertz ("Quarantine"), he resigned from the Party in 1957 when the new journal *Europa* was suppressed.

A POEM FOR ADULTS

1.

When, by error, I jumped on a wrong bus,
people in it, as usual, were returning from work.
The bus rushed down an unknown street,
O Holy Cross Street, no longer Holy Cross,
where are your antique shops, bookstores, students?
Where are you, the dead?
The memory of you peters out.
Then the bus stopped
on a dug-up square.
Old skeleton of a four-story house
anticipated the verdict of fate.
I got off in the square
in a working district,
Where gray walls become silver,
        reminiscing.
People were hurrying home,
and I did not dare ask them the way.
In my childhood, had I not come to this house?
I returned like a man
who had gone for medicine
and come home twenty years later.

My wife asked me where I'd been.
My children asked me where I'd been.
I said nothing and sweated like a mouse.

2.

Squares turn like cobras,
houses stand like peacocks,
give me any old stone,
and I'll be back in my city.
Standing, a thoughtless pillar,
under the candelabrum,
I praise, admire, and curse
on abra- and abracadabra.
Heroically, I venture
under the splendid columns
and pay no heed to the puppets
of Gallux, painted for coffins.
Here youngsters come for ice cream!
All of them are young, and yet
their memories reach the ruins;
girls will soon have babies.
What's in the stone endures,
pathos and rubbish together,
here, future poets of Warsaw,
you'll learn your A's, B's, and C's.
Love all this most naturally,
I loved, I loved other stones,
gray and really magnificent,
sounding of reminiscence.
Squares turn like cobras,
houses stand like peacocks,
give me any old stone,
and I'll be back in my city.

3.
"Today our sky is not empty."
(from a political speech)
It was dawn, and at dawn I heard the sound of jets,
very expensive, no doubt, expensive, but still we must . . .

When we don't want to speak about our earth simply,
we say, then we say: our sky's not empty.
People walk here anyhow and dress in denim,
women grow old here early, very early. . . .
When we don't want to speak about our earth simply,
we say, then we say: our sky's not empty.
Beyond the ocean an apocalypse curls in clouds,
and here a passerby, a passerby kneels down. . . .
When we don't want to speak about the earth simply,
the kneeling man says: the sky's not empty.
Here a legion of boys lets out a cloud of pigeons,
and a girl is tying a sky-blue kerchief. . . .
When we don't want to speak about the earth simply,
we say, then we say: the sky's not empty.

4.

From villages and little towns, they come in carts
to build a foundry and dream out a city,
        dig out of the earth a new Eldorado.
With an army of pioneers, a gathered crowd,
they jam in barns, barracks, and hostels,
walk heavily and whistle loudly in the muddy streets:
the great migration, the twisted ambition,
with a string on their necks—the Czestochowa cross,
three floors of swear-words, a feather pillow,
a gallon of vodka, and the lust for girls.
Distrustful soul, torn out of the village soil,
half-awakened and already half-mad,
in words silent, but singing, singing songs,
the huge mob, pushed suddenly
out of medieval darkness: un-human Poland,
howling with boredom on December nights. . . .
In garbage baskets and on hanging ropes,
boys fly like cats on night walls,
girls' hostels, the secular nunneries,
burst with rutting—and then the "Duchesses"
ditch the foetus—the Vistula flows here. . . .
The great migration building industry,
unknown to Poland, but known to history,

fed with big empty words, and living
wildly from day to day despite the preachers,
in coal gas and in slow, continuous suffering,
the working class is shaped out of it.
There is a lot of refuse. So far, there are grits.

5.

This also happens: a brown cloud of smoke
rises above the mine that's been set afire,
the shaft's been cut off, the subterranean suffering
never will be told, the dark shaft now a coffin,
the saboteur has blood and bones and hands,
one hundred families cry, two hundred,
they write in papers or they do not write,
and only broken smoke stays in the air.

6.

At a railway station
Miss Jadzia's at the counter,
she's so nice when she yawns,
she's so nice when she pours. . .
ATTENTION! THE ENEMY PLIES YOU WITH VODKA
You'll be poisoned here for sure,
Miss Jadzia'll pull off your boots,
she's so nice when she yawns,
she's so nice when she pours. . . .
ATTENTION! THE ENEMY PLIES YOU WITH VODKA
Do not go, my boy, to Nowa Huta
or you'll be poisoned on the way,
take warning from the treacherous poster
and the national fish in your stomach. . . .
ATTENTION! THE ENEMY PLIES YOU WITH VODKA

7.

I'll not believe, my friend, that lions are calves,
I'll not believe, my friend, that calves are lions,
I'll not believe, my friend, in magic curses
or in reasons kept under glass,
but I believe that the table has four legs,
but I believe that the fifth leg is a chimera,

and when chimeras come together, my friend,
one dies slowly of heart disease.

8.

It's true,
when the brass trumpets of boredom
jam the great educational aim,
when vultures of abstraction eat out of our brains,
when students are shut off in textbooks without windows,
when our language is reduced to thirty magic formulas,
when the lamp of imagination dies out,
when the good people from the moon
refuse us the right to have taste,
it's true,
then we are in danger of becoming ignorant and dull.

9.

They fished the drowned man out of the Vistula.
They found a piece of paper in his pocket:
"My sleeve is right,
my button is wrong,
my collar is wrong,
but my strap is right."
They buried him under a willow tree.

10.

In a freshly plastered street of new buildings,
lime dust circles and a cloud rushes through the sky.
Pulverizers, rolling in the street, press the surface,
transplanted chestnut trees bloom and sing in twilight.
Little and big children scatter under the chestnut trees,
dragging wood for fuel from half-pulled-down scaffolds.
The staircase is full of names, melodious, feminine names,
fifteen-year-old whores walk down the planks to the basement,
their smiles seem made of lime, they smell of lime,
in the neighborhood the radio plays darkly for magical dances,
the night comes, hooligans play hooligans.
How difficult
it is to sleep in childhood among the singing chestnut trees. . . .

Disappear into darkness, dissonances! I wanted so much
    to be glad
of novelty, tell you about the young street,
    but not this one!
Was I deprived of the gift to see, or the gift of
    convenient blindness?
All I have is a short note, the poems of a new sorrow.

11.

Speculators took her to a quiet hell
in an isolated villa—she escaped.
She wandered drunk all night,
slept on cement till light.
They threw her out of art school
for lack of socialist morality.
She poisoned herself once—they saved her.
She poisoned herself again—they buried her.

12.

All this is not new. Old is the Cerberus of socialist
    morality.
Fourier, the dreamer, charmingly foretold
that lemonade would flow in seas.
Does it flow?
They drink sea water,
crying:
"lemonade!"
returning home secretly
to vomit.

13.

They came and said:
"A Communist does not die."
No man has lived forever.
Only the memory of him is to remain.
The more valuable the man,
the greater the pain.
They came and cried:
"Under socialism

a hurt finger does not hurt."
They hurt their fingers.
They felt the pain.
They began to doubt.

14.

They shouted at the ritualists,
they instructed,
enlightened, and
shamed the ritualists.
They sought the aid of literature,
that five-year-old youngster,
which should be educated
and which should educate.
Is a ritualist an enemy?
A ritualist is not an enemy,
a ritualist must be instructed,
he must be enlightened,
he must be shamed,
he must be convinced.
We must educate.
They have changed people into preachers.
I have heard a wise lecture:
"Without properly distributed economic incentives,
we'll not make technical progress."
These are the words of a Marxist.
This is the knowledge of real laws,
the end of utopia.
There will be no novels about ritualists,
but there will be novels about the troubles of inventors,
about anxieties which move all of us.
This is my naked poem
before it matures
into troubles, colors, and odors of the earth.

15.

There are people tired of work,
there are people from Nowa Huta
who have never been in a theater,

there are Polish apples unobtainable by Polish children,
there are children scorned by criminal doctors,
there are boys forced to lie,
there are girls forced to lie,
there are old wives thrown out of homes by their husbands,
there are exhausted people, suffering from angina pectoris,
there are people who are blackened and spat at,
there are people who are robbed in the streets
by thugs for whom legal definitions are sought,
there are people waiting for papers,
there are people waiting for justice,
there are people who have been waiting for a long time.
On this earth we appeal on behalf of people
who are exhausted from work,
we appeal for locks that fit the door,
for rooms with windows,
for walls which do not rot,
for contempt for papers,
for a holy human time,
for a safe home,
for a simple distinction between words and deeds.
We appeal for this on the earth,
for which we did not gamble with dice,
for which a million people died in battles,
we appeal for bright truth and the corn of freedom,
for a flaming reason,
for a flaming reason,
we appeal daily,
we appeal through our Party.

Nowa Kultura (Warsaw), August 21, 1955.

TWO FRAGMENTS

II.

A woman, not yet old,
an old Communist,
puts out her arms and cries,

take them off me, these rags of dogma,
give me a simple overcoat.

She awoke, her body
marked like the body of stigmatics,
the blood of those murdered
in the basements of bureaucracy
flows from her forehead.

We will not be cursed by balsams,
I bring you the simple overcoat
and the ordinary catharsis.

Still miserable,
she cries:
a farce!

V.

They lived off the dawn
and brought the night.

They lived off the idea
and lost the language of men.

They lived off the dream,
and the lie became their daily bread.

From medieval eyes,
from medieval ears,
from medieval suspicions,
from medieval brains,
from medieval methods,
the Party will liberate the sense of revolution
until it is again as Lenin saw it.

Nowa Kultura (Warsaw), April 8, 1956.

Stanislawa Sznaper-Zakrzewska is a young Polish author who is little known in her native Warsaw and virtually unknown in the West. In this brief autobiographical sketch she writes of one day and night of anguish in the life of a mother and child.

··

THE YOUNG WOMAN DOCTOR ON PREZYDENCKA STREET

The child is ill. The whole night long I hear her wheezing. The whole night long I stand over the crib. I fix the pillow and keep the child covered. The small face is flushed.

I have known for days that it would come to this. Each day she came from the day nursery, and her cold was worse. She lay on my breast, weak, hot, eyelids gluey. In the morning I carried her in my arms and kept looking at the clock. It is not easy to take a sick child from the breast. Several times I thought to let her stay home . . . but I had used the last lump of coal to feed the fire. . . .

Gritting my teeth and turning my eyes away so as not to see her struggles, I wrap her in odd scraps of woolens and flannels and carry her to the nursery. I tear my thoughts from the child and force myself to think of work. (I had finished a play to order and delivered it to the Ministry of Culture. But these were the last days of December; the fiscal books were closed. No more money for this year. Wait until next.)

I have played with danger long enough. I go to the pediatric branch of the hospital clinic. The weather is freezing, but I lift the child from her carriage because it is forbidden to bring carriages indoors. I wrap my little one in a coverlet, working fast, and carry her into the waiting room. The lazy receptionist at the window slips her nail file into a drawer; she stares at me . . . reproachfully.

"Come back for your number at eight o'clock tomorrow morning."

I explain: "I have a card from the district doctor."

"It doesn't matter. You need a number."

This is a blow. I look at the pale face of the child. "Please, Miss," I explain. "It's serious. Tomorrow is Sunday."

"Eight o'clock in the morning. Don't you hear me, Madam? One side."

And this woman, whose face is as well laundered as her starched white apron, slams the window in my face.

But I cannot leave without getting help for the child. I do not know what to do with her. After a while, I think, after a while a new patient will come. The woman will have to open the window.

That's what happens.

"Please, Miss," I say.

Ignoring me, she turns to the new visitor. I interrupt; I ask her to tell me—at least that—when the laryngologist will see patients. She demonstrates immeasurable superiority by not answering. I raise my voice. Nothing. Then I demand the Director of Staff. It works—as if I have threatened her with a whip. Very quickly, she says: "The laryngologist will be here at one."

It is freezing. I wheel the carriage aimlessly through the streets. I buy the child tea biscuits. I push them into her little hand instead of warm food. After an hour, I return to the clinic. The doctor is not there. We wait a whole hour more. Finally, we are told that he will not come at all.

What shall I do? I learn that the afternoon hours begin at three. The little one looks tired. Her cold is worse. Her fever is worse. I must get to a doctor at any cost.

Mothers waiting in the anteroom with their children will not hear of letting me get ahead. Silent and threatening, they crowd around the door, tugging at their children. I stand with the child in my arms, waiting tensely. The mothers glare at me.

The child is faint from the heat, but I am afraid to unwrap her. Through the street door, again and again, gusts of snow blow in. At last I must unwrap the child to change her diaper. The poor thing cries from thirst.

"There is no milk, there is no milk," I tell her.

To distract the child, I dangle the contents of my bag before her: a small case, a comb, a pencil. But the child is stuporous in my arms. I decide to wait out all the patients. I will enter the doctor's office last. The door slams, the blizzard spouts. White down of snowy flakes, fevered cheeks, blasts of sharp wind, the child's wet, plastered hair, the white of the snow on the door sill, the dark, sparkling eyes in which the fire of a fever burns.

I have used up all my paper tissues; now I wipe the little nose with the child's own kerchief. She breathes more and more heavily. Her eyelids are pasty. 'Once again I beg the people to let me through. No one answers.

I press the child to my breast, but this does not help. She cries desperately, clawing at her sweater. Her little mouth works as if made of rubber. She wails. No. She cannot stand this much longer.

Only later, when the carriage bumps and skids over the broken, icy sidewalks, does she fall asleep, whimpering rebelliously, eyes rheumy, a dirty, twisted kerchief on her head.

Night is coming. The old carriage threatens to fall apart. I am wet; the tension . . . I walk fast, as if flames crept after me. I stumble across broken roadways; I am frightened by small noises; I slip and once nearly fall under the wheels of a wagon.

It is one of those times when I want to cry out for help. But there is no one. I must help myself.

The child—afire. The pus flows from her nose, her eyes are swollen; the whole face swollen out of recognition. She cries no longer. She clutches my hands, breathing heavily. I lay her on the bed and try to think; I need a fire. Before I change the diaper, I must have a bowl of warm water; she is so dirty. In the meantime, I put a celluloid doll in her hand. Through the slits of her swollen eyes, she smiles at the doll, stretching out her hand.

This is the worst.

For the time being, I let her lie this way. I go to the kitchen. I chop wood, pretend that I am beating the receptionist at the clinic.

What will this night bring—I wonder. . . .

In the medicine chest I find camomile, oil of camphor, sulfa-thiazole. This must do. I will doctor the child.

After a while, the fire blazes in the stove. What luck; we are home.

Burn, burn, fire, warm the water! Smell, fragrantly healing herb!

I will say while I wash her: "How good, how pleasant, how agreeable is the water."

I will say while feeding her: "Oh, how good is the camomile. Oh, how sweet is the camomile."

I will say while rubbing her: "Now it will be warm. Now it will be good. Now it will hurt no longer."

If, during the night, I cuddle the child to my breast and listen to what her body tells me, I can give it what it needs. By morning, the child will be well.

There are no miracles. There are only medicines, herbs, the action of water, temperature, sounds, air currents, the touch of a hand.

Medicine is knowledge, but love is the greatest wisdom of all.

Do not be afraid, do not be afraid, little daughter!

In the morning the fever fell and the child gazed on the world from eyes clear of pus. I decided, however, to get the advice of a doctor. This time, of course, privately.

This is the greatest defeat of all. I am doubly depressed: for this lesson, I must pay with the health of my child, with my faith in people.

I choose the first woman doctor—her address is convenient—on Prezydencka Street. Close by.

A young, delicate blonde opens the door. This is she. Unfortunately, she does not want to see the child at home. I say something about a "private visit"; she smiles indulgently. This does not convince her. I do not want to leave. I insist that she examine the child. I explain: her condition is bad. She asks us in.

She examines the little one carefully, amusing her with a nickle-plated sterilizer. And—notwithstanding my violent arguments—she will not accept payment.

Only now do I weep, returning with the little one along Prezydencka Street. And the child weeps with me. But already I know that she will be well. The young woman doctor has given me a prescription, given the necessary instructions, and made an appointment for a checkup. The envelope, into which I had slipped a very modest fee indeed, passed back and forth between us. Finally, she tucked it into the little one's coverlet, saying: "Madam, buy her lemons and oranges."

Well, we both are weeping now in narrow old Prezydencka Street, the houses covered over with an ancient mat of wild vines. And since no one comforts us, we comfort one another. The child comforts the mother, patting her cheeks and nose. And the mother comforts the child with these words:

Don't cry.
I will buy you a doggie,
buy you a kitten,
buy you all those things that will be able
to give you joy.

Nowa Kultura (Warsaw), January 8, 1956.

There is an extraordinary quality of humorless naïveté in Wang Meng's novella of life in a Peking district Party committee which is hardly less terrible than the empty bureaucracy he deplores. "Do you smell the fragrance of the pagoda tree?" asks Chao Hui-wen, renouncing the guileless hero forever. "Those ordinary little white flowers are more delicate than peonies and stronger than plum blossoms. Do you smell them? Good night. Until early tomorrow morning when we meet again, when we both once more throw ourselves into our great but taxing work."

The hero of Wang Meng's title is a young schoolteacher who wrestles with the jaded and indefinably corrupt Han Ch'ang-hsin and Liu Shih-wu for the salvation of the Ch'ü Party Committee—a place where lethargy and error hang "like dust suspended in the air."

"A Young Man in the Organization Department" was an early bloom in the Chinese intellectuals' spring. (Minh Hoang's bitter little story, "A Heap of Machinery," dates from the same time.) Heavily censored even before publication, the novella has since come under severe attack.

Passages in italics restore cuts as later reported in the Peking *People's Daily*. Only the concluding chapters are reprinted below.

....

A YOUNG MAN IN THE ORGANIZATION DEPARTMENT

VIII.

. . . Recently, Han Ch'ang-hsin had been promoted to the position of vice director of the Organization Department. This, along with his recent marriage, seemed to make a new man of him. Shaving became a daily habit, and after he went to see a clothing exhibition, he bought himself a new suit of clothes. But he reduced his personal investigations of work going on and confined himself to signing documents and conducting interviews. Liu Shih-wu was as busy as ever.

Lin Chen frequently went to Chao Hui-wen's house, where they talked of the Ch'ü Committee and how to strengthen themselves, talked of songs, and after having finished talking, ate water chestnuts or some other inexpensive snack. Lin Chen did not ask about Chao Hui-wen's husband, and Chao Hui-wen did not speak of him. Lin Chen had become more secure than when he first arrived; he was no longer so hasty and frequently thought hard about his environment and the people he met. But his uncompromising glance became even more frank and firm.

One evening after dinner, Han Ch'ang-hsin turned to Lin Chen. Tapping the cover of the book with his finger and nodding his head, Han said: "It's fun being an author, describing everything in such extravagant ways. If in the future I ever get rheumatism or am punished for any mistakes, I think I'll write a novel."

Lin Chen took the book and tucked it away in the bottom of his drawer.

Liu Shih-wu, sitting in another corner of the room on a sofa, was wrapped up in studying the end of a chess match, but when he heard Han Ch'ang-hsin's remarks, he said: "It's not entirely beyond the realm of possibility that old Han will get rheumatism or be punished for his mistakes in the future. As for a novel, I think we can rest at ease that we won't see that masterpiece in the next week." He said these words without the slightest bit of humor, so that Han Ch'ang-hsin hastily turned his head away and pretended not to have heard them.

Then Liu called Lin Chen over, told him to sit down alongside him, and asked: "Have you read any new novels recently? If there were any good ones, I'd like to borrow them."

Lin Chen said he hadn't.

Liu Shih-wu shifted his body so that he was lying sideways on the sofa, put his hands behind his head, half closed his eyes, and drawled: "Recently I read a translation of the second part of *Freshly Plowed Virgin Soil* in *Literary Translations*—damn well written . . ."

Lin Chen asked skeptically, "Do you often read novels?"

"I'm glad to say I like to read as much as you—novels, poetry, even fairy tales. Before liberation, I liked to read Turgenev's novels best. When I was in the fifth grade of primary school, I had already read *A Nest of Gentlefolk*. I cried over the old German, Lundman, and loved Elena." Suddenly he stood up and walked closer to Lin

Chen, leaned over the back of the sofa, and continued: "I still love to read, and when I read, I'm completely entranced. Then when I've finished, I feel nothing. You know—" He sat down next to Lin Chen and half closed his eyes. "When I read a good novel I dream of a pure, beautiful, transparent life. I wish I could become a sailor, or a white-coated researcher into red blood cells, or a gardener . . ." He smiled as Lin Chen had never seen him smile before—not with his head but with his heart. "But as things are, I have to take charge of the Organization Department." He spread his fingers.

"Why do you think there is such a difference between actual Party work and fiction?" Lin Chen asked in a friendly and serious manner.

Liu Shih-wu nodded several times, coughed, stood up again, and leaned over a little further away. He said sarcastically:

"A Party worker really shouldn't read novels. *In novels one looks at the front and the bottom of life, and then you know the final result. We look at life from the side, the back, the top. We know the stages of life or, perhaps I should say, 'inside story.'* " Liu Shih-wu once more took on his confident and indifferent air. *"What do you mean?"* Lin Chen asked, staring at Liu.

"For example," he gestured in the air, "take Party recruitment: a novelist could write, 'Many new fighters entered into the front ranks of the proletariat in our great work, hurrah!' But our Organization Department is plagued by worries. An organizational member of a certain branch is found to have neglected to perform his duty in a satisfactory manner and can't even give a clear presentation of the historical background of a new recruit. Over one hundred applications are awaiting approval, but the Organization Department simply has not time to proceed with the processing of the cases. Approval of new recruits must be decided by members of the standing committee at a meeting, but when members are told that a meeting will be held for this purpose, they ask for leave. The Public Security chief often goes to sleep at meetings held to approve new members. . . ."

"You're wrong!" Lin Chen said loudly, finding this as hard to take as if he himself were being insulted. "It's very strange. *Our Organization Department director can't see the great business at hand but only a certain person taking a snooze! Maybe you were also sleeping? You have no respect for our life, and our life cannot*

*forgive you!" Lin Chen angrily finished saying this and ran out of
the office.*

Liu Shih-wu laughed lightly and called Han Ch'ang-hsin: "Come
on, look at this end game in the paper. Would it be better to move
the rook or the knight first?"

IX.

Wei Ho-ming told Lin Chen he wanted to return to the workshop
as a worker. "I can't do this work of being the organizational member of the factory Party branch and the production foreman, too."
But Lin Chen still tried to persuade him to write a report for the
Party newspaper on the opinions he had collected. Moreover, he
chided him: "You're drawing back. Don't you have confidence in
the Party and the State?" After this, Wei Ho-ming and several of
the workers with the strongest views wrote a long letter and stealthily
mailed it off to the paper. Even Wei Ho-ming had some misgivings:
"Suppose this is a 'factionalist' act? We'll only be punished!" Feeling more than somewhat guilty, he threw the letter into the mail-
box.

In the middle of May, the Peking *Daily* published the letter from
the masses exposing the bureaucratic work style of Wang Ch'ing-
ch'uan under a sharp, clear headline. The letter, over the signature
"a group of workers at the gunny sack factory," angrily demanded
that the leadership settle this question. The editor of the Peking
Daily pointed out: ". . . authorities concerned should immediately
check into the matter thoroughly. . . ."

Chao Hui-wen was the first one in the Organization Department
to discover the item and called Lin Chen over to look at the paper.
Lin Chen was so excited his hand shook, and he looked for a long
time before he could even compose a sentence. He thought: *"Good!
It's finally been exposed. And the Party newspaper has power!" He
could not wait to run and find Liu Shih-wu. When he arrived at the
door of Liu Shih-wu's office, he stopped a moment and thought:
"Why should I feel so pleased that the Party newspaper has exposed
one of our shortcomings?" He flushed with shame, but then told himself: "There's certainly nothing wrong in exposing a contradiction!"*

He handed the paper over to Liu Shih-wu, who read it over carefully and then, shaking the pages, said: "Good! The fight has begun!"

Party Secretary Chou Jun-hsiang walked into the office at just that moment. "Do you have all the information on the Wang Ch'ing-ch'uan case?"

Liu Shih-wu answered calmly: "There is no question but that certain unhealthy conditions exist in the gunny sack factory's Party branch. We have checked this matter in the past, and I've had a talk with Wang Ch'ing-ch'uan only recently. At the same time, young Comrade Lin has also made an investigation of it." He turned to Lin Chen. "Comrade Lin, tell us your findings about this case."

Someone knocked at the door. Wei Ho-ming rushed in, his face pale instead of its usual ruddy color, and said that Wang Ch'ing-ch'uan had become very angry after reading the Peking *Daily* and was trying to identify the writers of the letter.

With the publication of the case in the Party newspaper and the personal demand for a full report by the Ch'ü Committee secretary, Liu Shih-wu became a different person—a person of quick decision and drastic action—a thorough change in character that caught Lin Chen by surprise. Once Liu Shih-wu made a decision, he could work exceptionally well. He turned over all the rest of his work to other people and for several days went to the gunny sack factory every day with Lin Chen. He went into the workshop and thoroughly investigated everything about Wang Ch'ing-ch'uan and sought out the opinions of the workers. He next consulted all departments concerned in the case, and in a little over a week's time the whole case of Wang Ch'ing-ch'uan had been cleared up. He was dismissed from his administrative position and from the Party.

The meeting in which Wang Ch'ing-ch'uan's case was discussed lasted until midnight. When the meeting ended, it was raining— sometimes hard, sometimes lightly, but without stopping. The rain was cold. Liu Shih-wu and Lin Chen went off to a nearby restaurant to have some dumplings.

The restaurant was a newly opened State-Private Joint Enterprise which was both clean and comfortable. Because of the bad weather, there were few customers, and Liu and Lin were able to avoid the hot stove, on which the dumplings were boiling away in a pot, and sat down at a table in one corner.

They ordered meat dumplings, and Liu asked for wine. He took a drink and then, counting off on his fingers, said with feeling: "This is the sixth time I have taken part in disciplinary action

against responsible cadres who have committed mistakes. The first
few times my heart was very heavy." Because he had spoken intensely at the meeting, his voice was rather hoarse. "Party workers
are like doctors: their responsibility is to cure the diseases of others
while remaining unaffected themselves." He tapped the table lightly
with a finger.

Lin Chen nodded in agreement.

"What day is today?" Liu Shih-wu asked suddenly.

"May twentieth," Lin Chen told him.

"May twentieth, that's right. Nine years ago today I was hit in
the leg by the 208th Division of the Youth Army."

"Hit in the leg?" Lin Chen didn't know much about Liu's background.

Liu Shih-wu didn't say anything for a few minutes. He listened
to the sound of the rain, which just then was coming down in sheets,
and sniffed the damp air. A sopping-wet boy dashed into the shop
to avoid the rain, his hair dripping water.

"Give me a dish of pork leg," Liu Shih-wu told the waiter. Turning to Lin Chen, he continued. "In 1947, I was the chairman of the
Self-Government Association of Peking University. When we joined
the demonstration parade on May twentieth that year, the dogs of
the 208th Division shot me in the leg." He rolled up his trouser leg
and showed Lin an arc-shaped scar, then standing up, he said:
"Isn't my left leg shorter than my right?"

Lin Chen looked at Liu for the first time with admiration and
respect.

He took a few drinks from his glass, his face slightly red, and sat
down. He passed a few pieces of the meat over to Lin Chen and
then, leaning his head to one side, said: "At that time . . . how
young and zealous I was. How I wish . . ."

"Aren't you young and zealous any more?" Lin Chen asked experimentally, trying to keep Liu talking.

"Of course not," Liu Shih-wu toyed with his empty glass. "Instead, I'm terribly busy! So busy that everything has become common, wearisome. Since liberation, I haven't slept for eight full hours
on one single night. I have to deal with this man and that man, but
I have no time to deal with myself." He leaned his cheek on his hand
and looked at Lin Chen with an air of complete sincerity. "Yes, a
Bolshevik must be rich in experience but pure in mind. . . . An-

other glass of wine!" Liu Shih-wu lifted up his glass and motioned to the waiter.

By this time Lin Chen had already begun to be moved by Liu's deep and sincere confessions. Liu Shih-wu continued in a gloomy voice: "There's a common saying that a common disease among cooks is that they have no appetite; they have to cook all day and are surrounded by nothing but dishes and meals. *We, Party workers, aren't cooking vegetables, we're building a new life! As a result, this new life is incapable of arousing us. In the same way the rancidness of a kitchen affects one's stomach for food.*"

Lin Chen began to move his mouth to speak, but Liu Shih-wu waved his hand to indicate he didn't want to argue about this then. He sat quietly, leaning on his chin and staring off at nothing.

"The rain is easing off. It's very good for this year's wheat crop." Liu sighed heavily after a long pause. Suddenly he said, "You're a good cadre, better than Han Ch'ang-hsin."

Lin Chen, in his confusion, pretended to be busy with his food.

Liu Shih-wu stared at him for a while and, smiling good-naturedly, asked, "How has Chao Hui-wen been getting on lately?"

"Her state of mind seems fine," Lin said casually. He picked up a piece of meat with his chopsticks and saw Liu eying him with that familiar, flashing glance.

Pulling his chair closer to Lin Chen, Liu said slowly, "Forgive me if I'm too direct, but I feel it's my duty to tell you . . ."

"What?" Lin Chen held his chopsticks motionless in the air.

"As I see it, Chao Hui-wen's feelings toward you are not . . ."

Lin Chen laid down his chopsticks with a trembling hand.

When they walked out of the dumpling shop, the rain had already stopped. Stars appeared again from behind the clouds, and the wind was even colder. The rain water ran down the gullies on both sides of the street. Lin Chen ran back to the dormitory in a daze, feeling as if it had been he rather than Liu Shih-wu who had been drinking the wine. Everyone in the dormitory was fast asleep, and the silence was broken only by the rising and falling sound of snores. Lin Chen sat on the edge of his bed, felt the wet cuff of his pants, and felt inexplicably sad. The beautiful, pale face of Chao Hui-wen floated before his eyes. He was only a callow, inexperienced, uninformed young man. Sad, sad . . . He went over to the window and laid his face against the wet, icy glass.

X.

The members of the Standing Committee of the Ch'ü Party
Committee met to discuss the gunny sack factory problem.

Lin Chen participated as an observer. He sat in a corner, nervous,
excited, his palms wet with cold sweat. In his pocket he had an outline of his planned several-thousand-word-long statement. He was
prepared to move from the gunny sack factory over into problems
in the Organization Department's work. He felt that the exposure
and solution of the gunny sack factory problem had created an excellent opportunity to request the leadership to basically evaluate
and consider the work of the Department. The time had come!

Liu Shih-wu was just in the process of a step-by-step, detailed report on the case. Secretary Chou Jun-hsiang sat in deep thought,
using his left fist to support his soldier-like, strong, broad face. He
held down a piece of paper with his right wrist and from time to
time made a few notes. Li Tsung-ch'in was scribbling characters in
the air with his forefinger. Han Ch'ang-hsin was also there and
seemed to be concentrating on tying and untying his shoelaces.

Lin Chen wanted to speak several times, but his heart throbbed
so he couldn't catch his breath. He wondered whether for him to
make such a bold statement the first time he appeared at a Standing
Committee meeting wasn't overly presumptuous. Don't be afraid,
don't be afraid, he encouraged himself. He thought of the time he
plunged into the water at school in Tsingtao when he was eight.
Then, too, his heart pounded, and he angrily told himself: "Don't
be afraid, don't be afraid!"

Liu Shih-wu's report was finally approved by the Standing Committee, and a discussion of the next item on the agenda was about
to be started when Lin Chen raised his hand.

"If you have anything to say, don't raise your hand, just go
straight ahead and say it," Secretary Chou Jun-hsiang said, smiling.

Lin Chen stood up. His chair made a loud scraping sound. He
took out his notebook and looked at his outline. He didn't dare to
look at his audience.

He said: "Wang Ch'ing-ch'uan as an individual has been dealt
with, but how shall we guarantee that a second and third Wang
Ch'ing-ch'uan will not appear? We ought to take this opportunity
to review the shortcomings of the Ch'ü Committee's Organization
Department. First, we have only grasped Party recruitment but

have not given the attention necessary to consolidating the unity of the basic-level members in order to prevent internal conflict and aimless drifting. Second, we know there are problems that we have been putting off trying to find solutions for. Wang Ch'ing-ch'uan came to the factory a full five years ago. The problem existed from the very beginning and became more and more serious. . . . Specifically, I think both Comrades Han Ch'ang-hsin and Liu Shih-wu are responsible."

There was a momentary stir among those present. Some coughed, some put out their cigarettes, others moved their chairs.

Han Ch'ang-hsin shrugged his shoulders, ran his tongue once around the rim of his teeth, and said scornfully: "We often hear these 'second-guessers.' 'Why didn't we take care of it sooner?' Naturally, the earlier the better. When the Kao Kang-Jao Shu-shih case was made public, people asked, 'Why didn't we discover it earlier?' Neither the Organization Department nor Comrade Lin Chen is in a position to guarantee that there will be no second or third Wang Ch'ing-ch'uan."

Lin Chen raised his head and glared angrily at Han Ch'ang-hsin. Han Ch'ang-hsin only smiled coldly. Lin Chen held his anger in check and said, "Old Han knows that it is standard for there to be shortcomings, but he does not know that to progress by overcoming these shortcomings is even more proper. Old Han and Director Liu both stick to the first standard. That is why they adopt a tolerant and even indifferent attitude toward all kinds of important defects!" Finishing, he used his hand to wipe the sweat off his forehead. He himself didn't know how he had dared to speak so sharply, but, anyway, it had been said, and he felt as if a heavy load had been lifted from him.

Li Tsung-ch'in stopped painting characters in the air with his forefinger. Chou Jun-hsiang looked at Lin Chen and then shifted his eyes over to the audience. The wooden chair on which he was sitting squeaked under his heavy body as he turned to Liu Shih-wu and asked: "Do you have any comment?"

Nodding his head, Liu Shih-wu said: "Comrade Lin Chen's views are correct *and will be a new force in the Organization Department*. His spirit is an inspiration to us." Then he walked leisurely over to the side of the table, poured a cup of tea, and rubing the teacup meditatively, he said: "But coming to the gunny sack factory case, it's a little more difficult to say. We admit we haven't done enough to consolidate Party work. We have too few cadres. We aren't even able to do the work of Party recruitment satisfactorily. *Last month I wrote a report to old Li and old Chou for which even they were unable to find a solution.* But the disposition of the case of Wang Ch'ing-ch'uan was both timely and effective. The atmosphere at the meeting when the dismissal of Wang Ch'ing-ch'uan was announced was unprecedentedly exuberant. Some backward workers were made more aware of the Party's impartiality and unselfishness. One old worker broke into tears while he was speaking on the rostrum. Everyone spoke of their thanks to the Party and to the Ch'ü Committee!"

Lin Chen said quietly: "Yes, *I participated in that same meeting, and the masses expressed their limitless trust in our Party Committee's organs. We solve the problems of the masses under the brilliant guidance of the Party's policies and with the support and encouragement of the Party press and the masses. The masses embrace, applaud, and greet with tears our Party workers because they see in them the representatives of the whole Party.* It is just because of this that I feel our indifference, procrastination, and irresponsibility in our work is a crime against the masses." He raised his voice higher, "The Party is the heart of the people and the working class. We do not permit dust in the heart. We cannot permit defects in the Party organs!"

Resting his clasped hands on his knees, Li Tsung-ch'in said deliberately, as if he were speaking and deliberating how to construct his sentences at the same time: "I believe there are two main bones of contention between Lin Chen and Han Ch'ang-hsin and Liu Shih-wu. One is the question of balancing principle and practicality; the other—"

Lin Chen interrupted with incredible audacity and said: "I hope you will not only make a cold, general analysis. . . ." He was afraid if he said any more he would burst into tears.

"Why?" Chou Jun-hsiang asked. He sternly continued: "A cold, general analysis is a lot better than impulsive and high-sounding words. Comrade, you get excited too easily. The organization work of the Party cannot be properly done by reciting lyrics." Turning to the audience, he said: "Let's go on to the next item on the agenda!"

After the meeting ended, Lin Chen was so furious he was unable to eat dinner. The secretary's attitude was far from what he had expected. He was disheartened and discouraged. When Han Ch'ang-hsin and Liu Shih-wu asked Lin to take a walk with them, as if they had paid no attention to his dissatisfaction with them, he realized all the more clearly how inadequate his strength was to stand up against them. He smiled to himself bitterly and thought: "So you thought you could accomplish something great merely by speaking to the Standing Committee!" He opened his drawer and took out the Russian novel at which Han Ch'ang-hsin had sneered. He opened it at the first page and read the title printed there: *The Model Life of Anastasia!* He muttered to himself: "It's not that easy!"

XI.

After office hours the next day, Chao Hui-wen called out to him, "Come and have supper with me. I'll make meat dumplings for you." He wanted to decline, but she had already gone.

Lin Chen worried over the invitation for some time and ended by first eating in the mess hall and then going to her home. The meat dumplings were just ready when he arrived. For the first time, Chao Hui-wen wore a dark red dress and had tied a white apron around her waist. Her hands were covered with white flour, and like a diligent housewife, she told Lin Chen: "I've put fresh beans in the dumplings. . . ."

Lin Chen said nervously, "I've already eaten."

Chao Hui-wen didn't believe him and ran off to get him chopsticks. Lin Chen repeated again that he had really eaten, and Chao Hui-wen discontentedly ate by herself. Lin Chen sat down to one side and looked here and there, rubbed his hands, shifted his seat. That same warm and painful feeling welled up inside him again. His heart ached as if something had been lost from it. He simply didn't have the courage to look at Chao Hui-wen's beautiful face, shining pinkly with the reflection of her dress.

"Little Lin, what's wrong?" Chao Hui-wen stopped eating.

"N-nothing."

"Tell me." Chao Hui-wen looked at him fixedly.

"I presented all my opinions at the Standing Committee meeting yesterday, and the Ch'ü Committee's secretary didn't even notice them."

Chao Hui-wen chewed on a chopstick and thought a bit, finally saying firmly: "It can't be so. Perhaps Comrade Chou Jun-hsiang just doesn't give his views lightly."

"Perhaps," Lin Chen said, wanting, but not quite able to believe this. He lowered his head, not daring to meet Chao Hui-wen's concerned glance directly.

Chao Hui-wen ate a few more dumplings and then asked: "Anything more?"

Lin Chen's heart beat wildly. He raised his head and saw her sympathetic and encouraging eyes. He said softly, "Comrade Chao Hui-wen . . ."

Chao Hui-wen put down her chopsticks and leaned against the back of the chair a little surprised.

"I want to know if you are happy," he said in the firm, strong voice of a grown man. "I saw your tears that time in Liu Shih-wu's office. Then it was spring . . . and afterwards I forgot about it. I get by myself somehow, and I don't care about anybody else. But are you happy?"

Chao Hui-wen looked at him rather doubtfully and then shook her head. "Sometimes I also forget . . ." Then nodding her head, she said: "Yes, you can say I'm happy. But why do you ask?" She smiled quietly.

Lin Chen told her about what Liu Shih-wu had said. "Please forgive me for telling you all this nonsense of Liu Shih-wu's. I so much like to talk and listen to symphonies with you. You're wonderful, that goes without saying. Maybe there are things here which are not quite satisfactory; I may have overlooked things. I was foolishly concerned about disturbing someone." Lin Chen apologetically concluded.

Chao Hui-wen smiled gently, frowned, then raised her thin arm and rubbed her forehead. She shook her head, as if shaking off some unpleasant thought, and turned around.

She walked over to the wall and, halting in front of a new oil painting hanging there, looked at it silently. The subject was spring, and it showed the early spring sun shining brightly on a mother and her children in a Moscow street.

A moment later, she turned and quickly sat down on the edge of her bed. With one hand holding the bedrail, she said very quietly: "What is this you are saying? Really! I could not do such thoughtless, unconsidered things. I have a husband and a son. I haven't spoken to you of my husband yet, have I? We were married in 1952, when I was only nineteen, really too young to be married. He was demobilized from the army and became a section chief in a central ministry. Gradually, he became infected by a kind of wily ambition. He fought over position, quarreled over treatment, was unable to get on with his fellow workers. We were only together from Saturday night to Monday morning. His theory is that *love is just one of those things; I believed that* either love is exalted or it is nothing. We quarreled, but I'm still waiting. He's off on a job in Shanghai now, but as soon as he comes back we'll have a long talk. So what have you been talking about?" She asked again. "Little Lin, you are my best friend, and I respect you very much. But you are still a child. Perhaps it's not right to call you that. I'm sorry. We have both hoped for the same genuine sort of life. We both hope the Organization Department will become a true Party work organ. I feel as if you were my younger brother. You want to rouse me from my lethargy, don't you? Well, life ought to have the warmth of mutual help and friendship. I have always had an aversion for coldness. That is all there is. Is there any more? Can there be any more?"

Lin Chen distractedly said: "I shouldn't have been influenced by Liu Shih-wu. . . ."

"No," Chao Hui-wen shook her head. "Liu Shih-wu is a clever man. His warning was perhaps not entirely uncalled for, afterwards. . . ." She heaved a deep sigh and said, "That's that."

She collected the chopsticks and bowls and went out. Lin Chen stood up abruptly and paced back and forth. He thought and thought—as if there were something else he had wanted to say, and then it was gone. What did he want to say? Sometimes the current of some feeling flowed into one's life and both aroused and troubled one; then the current flowed out again, leaving not a trace behind. But was there really no trace? There was left a pure and beautiful memory, faint but unforgettable.

Chao Hui-wen entered the room again, bringing along her two-year-old son and carrying a briefcase. The boy had already met Lin Chen several times and affectionately greeted him as "wuncle."

Lin Chen lifted him up in his strong arms, and the gaunt room was immediately filled with the sound of a child's laughter.

Chao Hui-wen opened the briefcase and took out a sheaf of

papers. As she leafed through the sheets, she said: "This evening I want to let you read a few things. I have already written a draft on some problems in the Organization Department that I've seen in my three years here and some of my own opinions. This—" Embarrassed, she touched a piece of drawing paper. "Probably this is funny. I've set forth a competitive system for myself, setting myself today against myself yesterday. I've made out a table. If I make mistakes in my work—get a name in a notice of Party admission wrong or make a mistake adding figures on new Party members— then I enter a black cross on the table. If I have made no mistakes, then I make a red flag. If for a whole month there are nothing but red flags, then I buy a pretty scarf or something else as a reward for myself. Does this seem like a nursery game? Do you think it's funny?"

Lin Chen listened carefully and then said gravely: "Not at all, I respect your . . ."

When Lin Chen got up to leave it was already very late. Facing him at the gate, her eyes shining in the dark, Chao Hui-wen said: "It's a beautiful night, isn't it? Do you smell the fragrance of the pagoda tree? Those ordinary little white flowers are more delicate than peonies and stronger than plum blossoms. Do you smell them? Good night. Until early tomorrow morning when we meet again, when we both once more throw ourselves into our great but taxing work. Afterwards, in the evening, look for me, and we will listen to the beautiful "Capriccio." Then I'll boil water chestnuts, and we'll throw peels on the floor until it is completely covered. . . ."

Lin Chen stood leaning against the big pillar in front of the Organization Department entrance. He was excited, and yet he felt empty inside. The south wind of early summer brushed his face. When he had first arrived with The Tractor Station Manager *and the* Chief Agronomist *in his pocket, it was the end of winter. He had passed his first spring in the Ch'ü Committee.*

Although he had done very few things—really nothing at all—he had learned much and now understood much more about many things. He understood the true beauty and importance of life. He understood the difficulty and value of fighting for what you believed right. He had gradually come to understand that it was fruitless to hope to achieve anything in this ordinary yet great, many-sided, quarrelsome Ch'ü Committee merely by relying on one's own individual courage. From tomorrow on . . .

Little Liu from the office went by and called out: "Lin Chen? Where are you going? Hurry up and go see Comrade Chou Jun-hsiang; he's been looking all over for you."

Was the Ch'ü Committee secretary looking for Lin Chen? Then it was not from tomorrow on but now that he must put forth all his energy to grasp the guidance of the leadership. This was the most important thing now. He didn't know whether the Ch'ü Committee secretary intended to praise him, scold him, or only to ask him for his views on some office work. But he believed that his, Chao Hui-wen's and other young Party members' innocent troubles and loyal efforts would ultimately always gain the clear and powerful understanding, help, and support of the leadership. And when that happened, the Ch'ü Committee would become the sort of organ it really ought to be.

On the other side of a window he saw the green desk lamp and big profile of the late-working Ch'ü Party secretary. He firmly, impatiently knocked on the door of the Party leader's office.

Jen Min Wen Yi (Peking), September, 1956.

The final confrontation, Ignazio Silone has written, will be the confrontation between Communists and ex-Communists. True or not, the orthodox Communist reserves a special hatred for those who turn the analytic techniques of "scientific materialism" against the Party which claims them for its own.

"The time has . . . come," say Godek and Turski, "to apply the science of genuine, revolutionary Marxism to present conditions—above all, in an effort to explain the patterns which dominate our . . . life."

"Is This the Twilight of Marxism?" was published in *Po Prostu,* the outspoken Polish student journal banned in 1957. The two authors, once members of the editorial board, now work in obscurity. A prophetic article, it preceded the Poznan insurrection by no more than a few days.

■■■

IS THIS THE TWILIGHT OF MARXISM?

. . . The last few years have reduced Polish dialectics to the level of Hegelian idealism. Such dialectics were fertile enough when they dealt with the past, but wholly sterile when applied to the present or to the problem of the future. As such, their scientific utility ended in 1945. Invoked to explain contemporary history in the years that followed the war, they proved to be nothing more than an eclectic and idealistic instrument designed to justify the errors and distortions which began to appear in the actual process of building socialism.

The time has therefore come to apply the science of genuine, revolutionary Marxism to present conditions—above all, in an effort to explain the patterns which dominate our economic life.

The truth is that the last few years have seen persistent attempts within our bloc to use Marxism to mask existing contradictions. But the true aim and function of dialectical materialism is quite otherwise—to *reveal* contradictions, both in the past and in the present.

Five Confrontations

Popular and technical studies of historical materialism seem always to stress the following theses:

158

In socialist states a sort of harmony is said to exist between the means of production and the character of productive forces. This harmony is not complete: since socialism is merely the first step on the road to a classless society, some disproportion between the character of productive forces and production continues to exist. This disproportion, however, is not such that it can act as a brake on genuine economic progress.

Let us now test these abstract theses against the economic situation as it exists in our country. We have no wish to be tedious, and so we shall not go beyond five cases. . . .

We see that since the war our artisans and small industries have not only failed to develop: they have actually retrogressed. . . . Hundreds of thousands of acres of land lie fallow. For two years our agriculture has been at an absolute standstill; in the ceded territories, once under intensive cultivation, we have acquiesced in a sizable fall-back in production. We have hardly seized on the true possibilities inherent in our agriculture, especially in those small farms for which we have created neither a favorable social nor economic climate. But why go on? Our examples are self-evident.

Is there not a contradiction here?

Is there not a contradiction between the shortage of goods, services, and housing, on the one hand, and our inability to exploit the existing social productive capacity which ought to be able to satisfy the demand?

We continue. . . .

Under socialism, large-scale waste of raw materials and the means of production is certainly as harmful and destructive as the periodic crises of capitalism.

Is there not a contradiction between a socialist system's declared ability to pursue a rational development policy and the mass waste of public property?

We continue. . . .

In the period of the Six-Year Plan, serious disproportions developed between industry and agriculture, while the *kolkhoz* movement, which ought to have acted as the regulator and governor of our socialist economy, fell into chaos and exhibited all the symptoms of serious illness. What is the matter then? In our system, with its pretentions to scientific planning, everything in fact seems to prove that the reverse is true. Again we are forced to put the question: is there not a contradiction between the objective necessity for planning under a socialist economy and the inherent spontaneity of the economic processes themselves, the anarchic elements in particular?

We continue. . . .

Specialists who have recently visited Italy say that if we compare one hour's intensive labor by one worker at Zeran (but, of course, such intensive man-hours are rare) with one average man-hour at the Fiat Auto Works, we find that work output is roughly the same. Yet total efficiency at Fiat is five times greater than at Zeran.

Why?

A fairly simple reason. The work force at Zeran is disproportionately large as compared to real production needs. . . . Total work efficiency must therefore be small. . . .

Let us not forget . . . that inefficiency constitutes a real danger to our system. Lenin once said that the superiority of one system over another is decided, in the final analysis, by efficiency. And so we are forced to the opinion that the evidence suggests yet another contradiction.

A contradiction between the objective need of a socialist system for systematic, rapid technical progress and rising productivity, on the one hand, and relative, concealed unemployment on the other.

We continue. . . .

Overtime? For many of our workers, overtime represents a second wage. . . . But overtime is not merely a second wage. It is, of course, another job.

Two jobs, two wages! What is real about this; what is fictitious? The second wage is fictitious—the worker at Zeran who gets the equivalent of a second wage for overtime does not receive the money because he has provided the nation with further products. He needs thirteen hours to complete work which might well be done in seven. The nation does not need a further six hours of exhausting work— such work is socially unproductive. . . .

Where shall we seek the cause of this phenomenon? Will the magic formula employed by our propaganda—"difficulties common to a period of transition"—really do? Or perhaps this unnecessary and socially unproductive work is the fault of the worker himself: perhaps there is some weakness in our political and ideological backbone, on our ideological front?

The issue is exceedingly simple. The worker works very hard because he must live. He must secure for himself, for his family, the elementary needs of subsistence. He must therefore finish a job which he could easily do in seven hours in a period of time twice as long, given the present system of material incentives.

Now, does this example merely point up the absurdity of our way of doing things, or certain anti-humanitarian elements in our system as well? This is nothing new, for it often happens that economic absurdities are anti-humanitarian.

It seems to us that we have another contradiction here:

A contradiction between the fundamental purpose of socialist production—that is, service to mankind—and the anti-humanitarian elements in the present social-economic system.

There are a number of other essential contradictions, too. By way of example, we give the following:

The deepening contradiction between the economically, culturally, politically, and ideologically developed regions of our country and the backward areas.

The contradiction between the constantly increasing social demand for a varied selection of goods and the tendency of centrally directed industry to specialize in narrow fields, ignoring the problems of demand, and so on. . . .

Now, what is the source of these contradictions?

Basic Contradictions

So far, too little attention has been paid to the fertile thesis of historical materialism that development and change of productive relations take place not merely through the transformation of one type of productive relations into another, but within a definite class of productive relations as well; that, in modern systems, the process of accumulating contradictions between productive relations and productive forces is not uniform but proceeds along zig-zag lines; that this process includes temporary and relative elements of progress—that is, in certain periods of development of a given economic and social formation, productive relations do not necessarily hinder the development of productive forces.

This general sociological truth has been demonstrated in our system. It has appeared in another form than in exploitative systems. If previous formations in the process of constantly deepening essential contradictions between productive relations and productive forces were followed by periods of relative progress, then, in our opinion, they were also followed by moments of real regression.

It seems to us that we have seen such a period of relative regression in Poland in recent years, or, strictly speaking, in the period of the Six-Year Plan. . . .

What is the origin of these vital contradictions? What are the real reasons for the malfunctioning of our economy?

We are of the opinion that these vital contradictions do not really explain anything until we find the common element. What is this common element? Is it—as some of our leading economists put it— unskillful handling of the principle of value in our economy? But if we answer "yes" to this question, shall we not find ourselves employing the subjective and psychological method of treating phenomena on the basis of a free-will principle?

The common element among all the contradictions is, in our opinion, a serious and essential disagreement between actual productive relations and actual productive forces. We believe that the objective economic law of essential agreement between production ratios and creative forces has been violated in principle.

What do we mean by violation of the law? What contradiction?

We put it as follows:

It is a contradiction between the social character of production and an excessively centralized and bureaucratic system of administration of the socialist national economy.

The vital contradiction, therefore, exists in the structure of property relations—in the fact that the property relations in the socialist sector are not sufficiently socialized. It is generally known that the possibility of direct administration and disposal is an attribute of the institution of property. In this market, the actual forms of socialist state property create . . . conditions in which the group directing the national economy actually assume the right to administer and dispose of socialist state property, thus eliminating the direct producers. The objective situation of groups ruling the national economy is such that their powers exceed by far the rights of co-ownership—which, in fact, they should share with the direct producers. "Objective" here means independent of their will, of this or that subjective inclination or tendency, since the situation results from the structure of property in the state socialist sector.

This does not mean, of course, that the objective situation does not exercise a certain influence on them, or does not give rise to certain sociological consequences.

Supremacy of Administration

If the socialist economy is to progress satisfactorily, the process of socializing the economy must go deeper and deeper. It means that the number of producers must rise and take over the management and disposal of socialist wealth.

The ever-increasing central system of management is in direct contradiction to this principle of development.

This contradiction gives rise to certain sociological consequences. It puts brakes on the creation of socialist consciousness among producers, and especially among the working class. "The working class feels it owns the means of production" is a slogan often repeated, but with little relationship to reality. To what extent is the relationship between a worker and a director in charge of a socialist enterprise different from his relationship to a director in charge of a capitalistic enterprise?

The direct result is the establishment of the primacy of the administrative factor as well, of those who administer production over those who produce.

And it is not only the size of the industrial bureaucracy that is important; their quality and role are far more significant.

The development of our industrial bureaucracy in the past years is a shocking contradiction of the basic tendencies and laws of socialism. Instead of dealing more and more with the administration of things and eliminating the administration of men, our industrial bureaucracy has done exactly the opposite. It has therefore shaped itself into a purely administrative force, running the national economy, moving further and further away from realistic and complex economic problems. To an increasing extent, the institution of the bureaucracy has functioned as a panacea for all economic grievances. The tendency is a constant strengthening and multiplication of the administrative system of rule over men.

All these processes could hardly fail to exert an influence over those who staff the national economic apparatus. Administrators, frequently incompetent, have driven out experts to an ever-increasing degree. Given our system, this is natural and logical.

There has been steadily greater demand for specialists in the art of manipulating men, to the detriment of those whose skill is to deal with things or with the concrete problem of technology or economics.

The development in recent years of the supremacy of the administrative factor over the expert stems from the greater ease with which men may be ruled. The manager is thus endowed with a number of attributes of power; and, in any case, it is easier to make a flying raid on an enterprise and condemn a director and several department chiefs . . . than to give competent, matter-of-fact, and effective technical or economic aid.

We think that to claim that *all* our industrial bureaucrats favor a radical change in the present system of administering the economy would be to distort or, strictly speaking, to fake reality. Many managers are perfectly well aware that a fundamental transformation of the system would cut off their functions. They would have to become socially useful—a prospect far from attractive.

Nor would it be entirely useless to consider another sociological consequence of the supremacy of administration over those directly employed in industry and agriculture.

We must ask whether the illogical supremacy of administration over the producing factor does not also lead to certain negative social and moral consequences. Does the group in charge of the economy not develop collective and common interests?

We think the answer is "yes." No one can deny that the position of a director, for example, has ceased to be a social and skilled function and become something of a profession. In our system the directors of enterprises are not a group of men organically and personally connected with production—a group regulated by the dynamics of production. Directorship is not a function, as we have said already, but a profession sanctioned by the system of central, provincial, and district nomenclature. If a director is discharged from a certain enterprise, it does not mean that he ceases to be a director. He is transferred to a lower or higher post, but always to a directorial or managerial post. The mechanism regulating the directorial and managerial staff is chiefly located in the imminent laws of nomenclature, and is much less subject to the laws and demands of productive development.

We shall support our abstract and theoretical reasoning with a picture drawn from life. This is a picture which any reader can multiply endlessly.

And so there was a certain director in a certain district town of the Krakow province. At first he was in charge of culture. He ruined a newly established and promising municipal theater; they transferred him to the better-paid position as director of an enterprise. After a few months' time, he was jailed because money was missing from the till. After an investigation, he was released and again became a dirctor, this time in another district institution. And the same story all over: missing funds, investigation, court sentence, and a few months in jail. When the director left prison, he was rehabilitated and assigned to a new directorial post. And the same story was repeated five or six times. . . .

But "immortality" is not the only characteristic of economic managers. Universality is their other, no less significant attribute. We are not surprised when an executive is transferred, let us say, from a sports department to a department of culture and art; it has become normal. The single position of director of the district State Farm Board in a certain province was filled by a carpenter, then a man without a profession (he had started his career as the manager of an estate, a calling soon interrupted by the war), next an electrical engineer (they say he was the best), the former chief of a district security office, and so on.

The establishment of a directorial profession—more than that, the profession of manager of the national economy—multiplies dangers. We cannot review in a short article (short when the subject is taken into consideration) all the dangers involved. We restrict ourselves to one.

The crystallization of the managerial profession in the national economy raises the dangerous prospect . . . of a tendency toward increasing independence, emancipation, and even isolation of the profession of managers of national economy from the direct producers. This would lead to the possibility, and even to the necessity, of postulating contradictory interests between these two categories as well.

Po Prostu (Warsaw), June 26, 1956.

The anomaly of a new exploiting class emerging from the womb of a revolutionary movement whose aim was the abolition of classes is a painful spectacle—for Minh Hoang, who touches on the problem briefly in "A Heap of Machinery"; for Godek and Turski in their essay, "Is This the Twilight of Marxism?"; and, of course, for Milovan Djilas. The new class, *mutatis mutandis,* reminds them too much of the old.

Iurii Nagibin explores the contemporary Soviet scene. The apparent good humor of "A Light in the Window" is deceptive; it appeared in that second volume of *Literaturnaya Moskva* which Soviet critics denounced as "corrupt."

....

A LIGHT IN THE WINDOW

At the end of March, the bridge spanning the deep ravine separating the resort from the highway collapsed. The river ice broke up, cutting the frozen road which was the last remaining link with the world. The resort's supplies were cut off. For several days, the reserve stocks held out, but then even they began to run short. A few canned goods, some sugar, oil, and dried vegetables remained in the storerooms. And then the director, Vasilii Petrovich, decided to slaughter his own pig to feed the vacationers.

The pig was killed by the chief cook himself—an elderly man, sturdy as iron, from the front rank of cooks—and Vasilii Petrovich helped. It turned out to be no simple matter. When the executioners stepped across the threshold of the pigsty, the pig Mashka, enormous and clumsy, fattened to twelve *poods* on greasy, warm kitchen slops, outdid the birds in her gyrations. Obviously, she guessed why they had come to visit her, although the chef held the knives hidden behind his back. It took enormous trouble to fell her. Vasilii Petrovich and the chef, alternately and together, sprawled on the muddy boards trying to catch Mashka by the legs. But the unwieldy pig, almost blind with fat, slipped out of their determined grasp with a skill born of the fear of death and rushed about wildly uttering heart-rending squeals. Finally, they managed to tumble her on her back. The chef grabbed a long knife and thrust the keen, thin blade under the pig's left foreleg with a precise, calculated movement, and sharply jerked it back.

Then they singed Mashka to a waxy brown, skinned her, and dressed her, spooning out dark clots of blood. Vasilii Petrovich did his share as though sleepwalking. He had often had occasion to slaughter a pig, but this time the simple, everyday process seemed to him the most brutal violence against a warm, breathing, defenseless creature. He could not forget the desperate reproach in Mashka's weak-sighted, narrow, amber eyes. Not one of the pigs he had slaughtered for his own use had ever looked at him like that.

But the deed was done. The vacationers ate up Mashka with the same even appetite with which they devoured all other dishes offered in the dining hall. Vasilii Petrovich had not expected thanks. He found a certain bitter satisfaction in the fact that his selfless deed was doomed to oblivion. However, it turned out otherwise. In the eyes of the resort's employees, when they looked at their director, there was an expression which had not been there before. Vasilii Petrovich did not immediately notice it and, once he had, did not immediately guess the cause of that weak but warm gleam which shone from the eyes of the maids, waiters, nurses, and other workers. Nonrecognition has its own sad joys, but if anything gives a man happiness, it is the silent approval of those around him. The round, compact, pigeon-like director walked with a springier step.

Only one person did not esteem Vasilii Petrovich's modest deed, and that was Nastia, a housemaid in the auxiliary building. In her dark, deep-set eyes the director failed to catch the familiar warm glint. And her approval was especially valuable to him, for with Nastia he had a delicate and complex relationship.

When he took control of the resort, Vasilii Petrovich, accompanied by the former director, had made an inspection of all its services and facilities as well as the living accommodations in the main and auxiliary buildings. When they finished with this, the former director led him to a tidy one-story cottage with a glassed-in terrace.

"In this wing . . ."

Without finishing, he moved forward, opened the door, which had an English lock and was padded with thick felt and oilcloth, and invited Vasilii Petrovich to follow him. They entered a spacious, pine-scented hall from which there opened before Vasilii Petrovich's eyes a large urban-style apartment with three spacious rooms. To his right, through a doorway, the green of a billiard table was dimly visible.

In the first room—the parlor—a polished oak table held a television set; there was a soft divan along the wall, an oval table covered with a heavy fringed cloth in the middle of the room, surrounded by armchairs as heavy as lead, and above the table, sparkling with pale, reflected light, hung a crystal chandelier. Two doorways leading from the parlor to the other rooms allowed a view of frostily starched, smooth pillows in the bedroom and a corner of a writing table and the edge of a fleecy carpet in the study.

Vasilii Petrovich was silent, stunned by this magnificence.

"Our inviolable reserve," said the former director with pride. "Maintained in case *he* should come."

"Well, it's hardly likely that *that* one would come here," murmured Vasilii Petrovich, forcing a smile. In all his long life of administration he had never had any dealings with the highest authorities and therefore could not admit the possibility.

"Well, you know, you never can tell," concluded the former director, in the same curious, vaguely joking tone he had used when he crossed the threshold of the sanctuary. "So be on the alert."

The advice penetrated to Vasilii Petrovich's very heart. He had genuinely been on the alert ever since, so that the arrival of an important guest from the ministry might not catch him off guard. He assigned the auxiliary-buildings maid, Nastia, to the apartment, and she was obliged to clean the uninhabited rooms every day, wash the untrafficked floor, change the vase of flowers which purposelessly perfumed the air, brush the billiard cloth whose nap, it seemed, was beginning to grow like a neglected lawn. In addition, there were chores which fell to Stepan, the yardman; he had to chop ice off the porch, shovel piles of snow from under the windows, and keep a supply of birch logs ready in case the authority should feel like admiring the dance of flames in the fireplace.

In a word, everything was done so that the inadvertent, unexpected guest would sense how impatiently he had been awaited and how carefully his arrival had been anticipated.

Even so, these rooms were a source of endless disquiet to Vasilii Petrovich. It was difficult for him to reconcile himself as a director to the fact that such beautiful quarters went empty, senselessly devouring the people's funds and labor. At times, the ban prevailing over the rooms was even annoying to him on grounds of humanity. It took him a long time to forget the faces of two newlyweds, who arrived at the resort at the height of the July crowd and were placed in separate rooms. He almost faltered that time, imagining what untold happiness the private apartment might have meant for them. But he took himself in hand, and the young people, exchanging a look as though they were parting for life, went off to separate buildings.

Vasilii Petrovich felt no better at the arrival of a famous master builder—indeed, the builder of this very resort. The master builder arrived with his wife and a trio of indefatigable sons; even in a double apartment (two-room suite), the old people knew no single moment's peace from the turbulent rough-housing of their brats.

The director listened with grief to the incessant clacking of the billiard balls in the shabby common room, while an excellent table sat senselessly in the empty apartment. He was disturbed by the sight of the young waitresses glued to the windows of the television room, the viewing hall barely spacious enough for the vacationers. The girls shoved and pushed and quarreled, trying to catch a glimpse of the screen, the transient images distorted by the window glass. And in the private wing an excellent television set sat wasting.

All this so depressed Vasilii Petrovich that it became intolerable for him to support his grief alone. He began to share it with Nastia, the maid; he was certain that this silent, withdrawn woman with black, deep-set eyes would not gossip to anyone. He told her about the newlyweds and the master builder; but each time, what he saw in Nastia's dark eyes was not sympathy but censure. This depressed him even more, and yet again and again he would complain to her of similar woes, in the vague hope that this time, at last, she would understand. But when he became convinced that even his self-sacrificing deed, his small feat, had not extinguished the spiky little flame of reproach in Nastia's excessively intent gaze, he realized that he would have to bear his cross alone.

Vasilii Petrovich did not understand Nastia. Indeed, it was not easy to understand this quiet, slightly deaf, repressed woman, with the odd, ugly, and yet attractive face. Of course, Nastia was ugly, but when someone remarked, "You know, she has something," everyone readily agreed. Such prompting led people to notice Nastia's secret, odd charm. It is hard to understand her charm. Was it the shy and youthful—though Nastia was far beyond thirty— strangely deep and penetrating gaze of her eyes, or the proud carriage of her head, or something else? This aspect of Nastia was not constant; it would disappear abruptly, leaving perplexity behind it, and again there would be the ugly woman of undefinable age with a pale, weatherbeaten face and large, work-worn hands. Many years ago, Nastia's strange and fragile charm had attracted a young trainer from the stud farm, but the war had come, and Nastia had turned overnight from a bride into a widow. Nastia resented life for good and all, and just as the director desired to be considered good, Nastia was, above all, apprehensive that she might be suspected of kindness.

She guarded her rights: to clean from nine to ten in the morning —not a minute earlier, not a minute later; to serve hot water for shaving exactly at eight-thirty; not to make beds—that should be done by the vacationers themselves. If anyone encroached on these rights of hers, she immediately declared, "That's not my job!" But somehow, it turned out that Nastia made beds and brought hot water three times a day and did a multitude of other things that were not really her duties. She avenged herself for this in her own way, refusing point-blank to take the ten- and twenty-five-ruble notes which vacationers tried to slip her before leaving. On these occasions she made such a nasty face that the guests, mumbling apologies, clumsily wadded the money in their hands to hide it.

Nastia's entire life took a different turn when she was assigned to the special building. At first she took the director's orders to be a rude encroachment on her rights, and even the ominous word "he" did not produce the least impression on her. But then, bewitched by the unparalleled splendor of the rooms, she suddenly lost all desire to protest. And thereupon the entire meaning of her existence was bound up with these rooms.

Nastia gave herself to the new work with all the passion of her untouched heart. By degrees, the wonderful, fabulous figure of the person who was to arrive and reign amidst this splendor took shape in her mind. She believed him to be an extraordinary man, like no one else, since he was rendered such service, and since, even when invisible, he made people think of him every day, every hour. And for Nastia there was no greater joy than caring for the rooms which were to receive him. She did not, however, drop her previous responsibilities. With her usual ineradicable thoroughness, she cleaned both floors of the auxiliary building, swept the floor, emptied ashtrays, polished the bath and the washstands so that they shone like glass, changed the water in the carafes, shook out rugs, and even, grumbling to herself, made beds. But none of this touched her heart; all this belonged to that humdrum life which might easily not be. To make up for it, she lived passionately, vibrantly, and fully when the time came for the cherished private chambers. Here, her usual chores became creative work. One can simply wash a window, or one can create a wonder—make it so transparent, glittering, sunfilled, that the blue of the sky, the white of the snow, and the green of the firs are drawn into the room; that walls disappear, and the room becomes part of space. It is one thing to straighten a room. It is quite another thing when objects find their own place in the room's expanse—set the dresser at a slight angle, but not too obliquely, move the television set a little, shift the flowers from the side table to the center of the oval table, and instead of barren order, create beauty.

Almost every day brought Nastia some small contribution, and the director, inspecting the readiness of the unoccupied rooms from time to time, sensed something for which he could not himself find a name. He did not notice the changes; everything seemed the same as before, but why did the appearance of these rooms give him new joy every time and a growing sense of security?

But the days, weeks, months marched on—no one came. A year passed, and a second rolled rapidly after it; the rooms remained as before, uninhabited and cold, unwarmed by anyone's presence. The unused objects sparkled as before; the whitened eye of the blind and dumb television set stared at nothing; the billiard balls, ready for use, seemed to grow fat and plump on the grassy green table; the beautiful mirror in its carved frame reflected no human face except Nastia's dark countenance with its sharply outlined cheekbones and dark, deep-set eyes; not one drowsy head had touched the taut, fresh starch of the pillows.

The futile waiting, the useless labors, the purposeless ardor, grad-

ually gave way in Nastia to hatred. She had been deceived. Not by
the director—what did she care about him? She had been deceived
by the one for whom she had waited with such passionate urgency.

But to dwell on the thought that the expected guest had not come
meant to await him as before, and Nastia could not, did not want
to wait any longer. She stopped shifting one thing, moving another
in the rooms; and it seemed to Vasilii Petrovich that she had begun
to neglect her duties. He ran his palm across the top of the television set, along the arms of the chair, but found not a bit of dust
anywhere. He touched the glass, and his finger squeaked on a
thoroughly washed, dry surface. He stamped on rugs, vainly seeking to stir up a single puff of dust. He could seize upon nothing. But
all the same, something was wrong, and Vasilii Petrovich frowned.

Meanwhile, Nastia's contempt for the invisible inhabitant grew
and eventually enveloped her entire being. It now seemed to her the
grossest injustice that these spacious rooms, full of light and air, and
all these beautiful and desirable things were for him alone.

One night Vasilii Petrovich returned home from a solitary walk.
He was fond of the hour around midnight, when the whole resort
and all its outlying facilities were sunk in sleep, when he ceased to
be affected by the eternal, demanding urgency of people, when he
could no longer be vexed by the head nurse, the chief cook, the
bookkeeper, storekeeper, gardener, the unannounced auditor sent
from the ministry, or by phone calls from the nearby collective
farms, which always needed something from him, or by his wife,
who could never get it into her head that he was the director, not
the owner, of the resort. In fact, this simple happiness fell to his lot
rather infrequently; usually, fatigue laid him low almost as soon as
the working day ended.

The night cloaked the resort in a darkness barely penetrated by
the greenish light of the new moon. In this light, everything seemed
neat, orderly, harmonious, desirable, and lovely; even the high, icy
snowdrifts along the roads and paths, even the plaster statue of the
deer, which was unbearably clumsy by day, resembling as it did a
sheep dog wearing ludicrously lopsided antlers.

At such times, one thought pleasantly and peacefully about everything: that most of life's difficulties were behind, and now one could
slowly and sweetly slip into the warmth of bed, not fearing an
urgent call in the middle of the night; that between people the spirit

of mutual help and confidence grew steadily stronger; that one might, without fearing the ill will of the crank, try from the depths of one's heart to make the guests' lives better, more satisfying, calmer, gayer—yes, and one's own life, too.

Vasilii Petrovich turned the corner of a building and suddenly froze—in the windows of the uninhabited wing, there was a light. More precisely, lights burned in the study, the bedroom and even the billiard room, from which he heard the dry, bone-like click of billiard balls. The parlor was dark, but from it there came music, and when Vasilii Petrovich recovered himself and stepped forward, he saw a flickering, pale gray light on the wall opposite the windows and realized that the television set was working, too.

A strange sort of feeling struck Vasilii Petrovich. For the merest fraction of a second, he imagined that the objects themselves, bored with inactivity, had revolted and, without the aid of man, sprung to independent life; the lamps had lit up, the billiard balls had started rolling about on the green felt lawn, the television set had come alive, to the joy of the armchairs, side table, center table, and divan. But immediately this wild notion changed to another, more sober, but just as upsetting one: it has happened! That for which he had waited with such trepidation for more than a year, that which he had almost ceased to expect, had actually occurred. The guest, as luck would have it, had arrived in the absence of the director, when no one expected him, and in some secret and incomprehensible way, had found the quarters intended for him, got into them without a key, and with a master's confident power had brought the dead to life.

But this thought, too, only stayed for a flash—no more—and was immediately crowded out by gloomy perplexity: No, this cannot be. . . .

Standing, for some reason, on his toes, approaching almost stealthily, he crossed from the path, through the loose, thawing snow, to the window.

At the television set, on whose screen a bluish spot flickered, blotting out thin figures quickly running about, sat the maid, Nastia, her large hands folded in her lap. To her right, with eyes and mouth wide open, Klavka, the ten-year-old daughter of Stepan, the yardman, sat in stupefaction; to the left, sweetly dreaming in the deep armchair, sat her younger brother. Through the half-open door under the streaming light of two chandeliers, Vasilii Petrovich could see their father, Stepan, the yardman, laboring earnestly at the novel game of billiards.

She had dared, she had broken the ban! Openly, defiantly, she had marched into this magic world, commandeered as its rightful mistress, and even introduced Stepan into it. With an odd sinking of his heart, Vasilii Petrovich sensed that he was seeing something very good, very right, very desirable. But he immediately raised his hand, and with an abrupt gesture, rapped imperiously on the window.

And then Vasilii Petrovich shouted, threatened, and stamped his feet, beside himself with rage, drunk with his own anger. His agony was such that he almost expected his indignation to reach the ears of the *one* whose rights had been so rudely violated. It is not known whether *he* heard, but the violators remained deaf to the director's anger. Taking the children by the hand, they walked past Vasilii Petrovich with calm and measured dignity.

And looking at their severe, solemn faces, Vasilii Petrovich suddenly missed fire like a wet fuse. He fell silent, heeding an odd new feeling within him that spread to the tips of his fingers—a feeling of unbearable disgust for himself.

Literaturnaya Moskva (Moscow), Vol. II, 1956.

5.

THE SILENT LAND

The journey home is a recurrent theme in American fiction; Zhdanov's somber little story is a Soviet version, terrible and touching in its evocation of a frozen countryside and an inarticulate peasant world "which, according to all Varygin's understanding, had long since ceased to be."

Zhdanov is an authentic talent.

JOURNEY HOME

When he got home to his study after the long and tiring conference, Pavel Alekseevich Varygin set to examining the official papers which had accumulated in his absence (and had been conveyed to him in a neat folder by his secretary, Nonna Andreevna). He glanced at some questionnaires and then turned to the telegrams, which usually came from outlying districts, containing various reminders and requests. He marked them with a blue pencil as he read, putting the sheets aside, one after the other. Soon there was only one left, which for some reason had not been opened—obviously Nonna Andreevna's carelessness. Varygin broke the paper seal himself and unfolded the sheet:

"Marya Semenovna died Wednesday the twenty-fourth. Funeral Saturday," he read.

He left for the country that night, on an inconvenient train requiring two changes; the express went a day later, and he would have had to wait a full twenty-four hours.

Varygin's wife went to the door of the apartment with him, kissed him on the cheek with a mournful air, and said that, if he did not mind, she would say nothing to the children. They had not yet been given their grades for this school quarter.

"As you wish," he replied, and, as he descended the stairway in the yellow light of the hall lamp, he thought, "For her it's just an unpleasant nuisance, nothing more."

In the train he sat by the window the whole time, looking out through the muddy glass at gray stretches of fields and the dark silhouettes of trees rushing by.

The last time Varygin had seen his mother had been six years ago. She had come up from the *kolkhoz* to buy some "vittles," as his wife put it afterwards, making fun of his country birth.

The six years, it now seemed, had passed without his noticing at all. Somehow, each autumn, he intended to get to the country, but the doctor would recommend rest for his heart, and he would go to Kislovdsk.

Occasionally, very rarely, a letter came from his mother, written at her dictation by someone with an educated hand, usually on notebook paper.

"I get along, I am not so strong, but I have no complaint," his mother would inform him. He would be distressed, but then it would occur to him that his mother never had been too strong and that the formula, "I get along, I have no complaint," was essentially quite cheerful.

The train took twenty-four hours to reach Dvorik station. The slow November dawn had not yet dispersed the gray night shadows; they clung to the low, cold sky and crouched under the station shed where potatoes sat piled in mountains covered over with matting, presumably awaiting shipment.

He recalled that in his childhood a small, swampy wood adjoined the station and stretched for about eight *versts* into the country. Beyond the woods were the villages—in order, Lozhkino, Derevlevo, Kashino, Korkino, Lapshino, Pirogovo, and, finally, their own village, Tiurino. But no woods were to be seen. Varygin went across a swampy lowland, along fences built of blackened poles.

On both sides of the pathway were tall, even stacks of peat. It was evident that the marsh was now worked. Beyond the swamp there was a paved road which had not been there before. Varygin waited for a passing truck and rode as far as Lapshino. From there he went on foot to Tiurino.

They had already taken his mother to the cemetery. He was so informed at the first cottage by an elderly woman in a faded army tunic, carrying water from the well in a wooden bucket.

"And who are you?" she wanted to know, looking at Varygin's good, thick overcoat.

"Her son," said Varygin.

The woman put the bucket down and looked at Varygin again.

"Not Konstantine?" she asked. "I'm Anastasia Derevleva. Don't you remember?"

"No, Konstantine died a long time ago. I'm the other brother, Pavel," he explained.

"There, I was going to say Konstantine was dead," exclaimed the woman. "The young one took care of everything, even if she ain't family! Can you find the cemetery? I suppose you don't remember your way around. Klashka!" she shouted to a girl gathering cabbage leaves left in the beds after the harvest. "Run and show him how to get to the cemetery. It's straight across the field."

The girl ran ahead, and Varygin followed across the hard but not yet snowy fields, stumbling heavily over the uneven ground, struggling for breath, and frequently wiping sweat from his face.

They passed a field in winter crops and crossed a crooked log over a stream that meandered through the thickets. On the other side, the land rose in a gentle slope, and against the gray sky Varygin saw the old wooden church and the cemetery with the crosses set among sparse, bare trees. He remembered both the church and the stream. Only now they were considerably smaller than before. He remembered, too, the ditches full of water which they passed. They used to soak hemp straw in the ditches. The children had said that elves hid in them.

The cemetery was not fenced, and even from a distance he could see that there was someone standing at the church door.

"I'll go back now, Mister, if it's all right,' the girl said, slowing her pace. "There's the midwife, your lodger, watching. She'll tell the teacher I went to church. I'll go back now, all right?"

"Yes, go on," said Varygin.

When he drew closer, the young woman ran from the porch of the wooden church to meet him. Her face, reddened by the frosty air, was wet with tears and yet glowed with health.

"And we thought you weren't coming," she said, when Varygin introduced himself. "We waited for the express. We went to the station. We didn't know what to do. You see—perhaps you'll be angry, I myself am not a believer—only, Marya Semenovna insisted on being buried the old way, as a Christian. . . ."

Varygin took off his fur cap and, without pushing back the hair pressed down on his forehead, entered the dark church where several thin candles burned in the half-gloom and three or four figures stood at the bier.

The midwife followed him in and stood near the entrance, but he moved closer and suddenly saw the small, child-sized, dark face

of his mother, lit by the yellow glow of the wax candles. He stopped
and stood, not moving, seeing only her face before him.

An old priest, with sparse gray hair and a thin bony forehead,
chanted a prayer, addressing himself, it seemed, solely to the mother,
who lay immobile, bloodless lips compressed. The two-dimensional
faces of the saints painted on the altar screen loomed out of the
darkness. The smell of incense was oppressive, and that, as much as
the sound in the dark of the church of the Old Slavonic chant, recalled Varygin's childhood, when he had come to the church with
his mother and even sung in the choir. All this was so long ago that
possibly it had never happened at all. Once the priest passed very
close to Varygin, and his threadbare, ancient cassock reeked of
garlic.

When the funeral service ended, the women, half-hidden in the
darkness, covered the coffin and carried it outside.

Varygin left the church with the others, helped carry the coffin
across the limp grass that grew amidst the wooden crosses, and only
came to himself when his mother was buried in the ground.

Afterwards, he made it across the crooked log again, over the
little stream which in the frozen air sent up a light mist that reminded him of the incense in the church, and made his way once
more across the hard field.

It seemed to him that he had been in a world which, according
to all his understanding, had long since ceased to be.

When they reached the village and arrived at the house at last,
the midwife went up the steps to the porch and, taking a key from
her pocket, unlocked the door. Varygin remembered the wooden
porch and the door with its iron ring; only the gate to the house
was new. As he approached, he saw a sign nailed there—"Midwife
Station."

Varygin crossed the threshold. On the left, reaching to the ceiling, was the white tile stove; in a corner on the right stood a wide
wooden washtub, and above it an earthenware wash basin—probably the same washtub and the same basin which had stood there in
his childhood, and about which he had completely forgotten until
this moment.

The ceiling was much lower than he remembered. But the dark
wooden beams were the same—that he could guarantee. Here were
the old iron hooks for cradles: a first, a second, a third. His father

had lived here with his brothers. There had been three sisters-in-law dwelling in the house, and each together had rocked her own cradle. In one of them, Varygin had slept.

"I live in this half mostly and see patients here," said the midwife. "And Marya Semenovna slept here, too. This was her bed, and her towel is still hanging, as it hung."

Varygin looked at the towel, gray with age, and again, not for the first time, the thought that his mother had lived in want struck him painfully.

He took off his hat and coat and wearily lowered himself to a stool. He wanted to put his head on the table and forget everything. Once, their whole family had dined at this table. In the corner under the wooden ikon, his father had sat. Varygin remembered the smell of the thin cabbage soup and warm bread with a cabbage leaf stuck to the bottom crust. His mother had often washed the table with hot water and scraped it clean with a broken knife. This knot in the wood, with its dark center, had always seemed to resemble a horse's eye. And now the boards had yellowed and cracked with age, and the "eye" had blackened and disappeared.

A pile of notebooks lay on the table. "Regional Midwife's Course: Abstract by Antonova, A.," he read. This careful, educated hand had written the letters which had occasionally come to him from his mother.

Antonova, A., brought an armful of wood, kindled a fire in the stove, and put the teapot on to boil. Then she cleared off the notebooks, got a clean towel out of the trunk under the bookstand, wiped a cup, and poured Varygin some tea.

"I have to hurry off to Lapshino. I have a delivery there today," she said. "Please accept my apologies."

He didn't feel like tea, and he sat alone, not moving. The life which had teemed in this house in the time of his childhood had gone somewhere, and it seemed strange that now there remained only these walls and himself, Varygin. And even for him there was nothing here, and he would have to go. He did not want to think of departure, did not want to move. Where could he lie down? He looked around.

On a bench in the corner, a battered old samovar stood, foolishly leaning askew, spigot loose, grinning slyly as if it wanted to say:

"Aha, and you came apart on the road. Lie down, brother, by my side."

Varygin put his hand on the table to rise, and it seemed to him that the table, too, winked at him with its dark horse's eye. "You came back all the same!"

Varygin went to the bed and lay down.

When he opened his eyes, a line of red sunset glowed beyond the fence and was reflected in the windows. The thought suddenly came to him that he had gone to sleep in his mother's bed, in the bed where she died. He rose and sat at the table. His overcoat hung on the wall opposite; his hat lay on the bench. Behind them, in the corner, stood the samovar, serious and morose now, as though given offense.

Nearby, perhaps just outside, someone was shouting in a sharp, high-pitched voice:

"They *don't* behave in a Party manner, *that's* what I'm complaining about! Nobody, let me tell you, is allowed to oppress us rural mechanizers. Isn't it the law? The man ought to be told if order is violated."

"They'll take it up in the regional committee," a controlled, reproving voice said. "Now go on off. I tell you, the man is resting."

The voices faded; apparently the quarrelers had moved toward the gates.

A little later, a board creaked on the porch, and a stooped figure in a sheepskin jacket appeared at the door.

"You're not sleeping?" someone asked from the shadows. An electric switch clicked, and the light went on over the table. Varygin saw a wizened old man looking at him from small, gay eyes.

"And who are you?" asked Varygin.

"Me? Moshkarev, Ilya. A watchman now, but I used to work at smithing. I took to being a watchman on account of sickness. Here, with my cousin. Her guardian."

He sat on a stool at the table.

"I brought Antonina Vasilievna some wood. I saw, you were asleep. Perhaps she went off to Lapshino? Siniukhina Zoika is having another baby."

"And who was shouting?" asked Varygin, leaning back against the wall.

"Komkova Pelgeia, combine driver's wife, a bossy woman. They used to be here with us, members of the *artel,* and now they've been signed into the cadres at the tractor station. She stuck to the *kolkhoz,* but only for form, so their plot wouldn't be taken back—forty *sotki* they had. Now they've dropped her. It seems she only made twelve workdays in the year. They took the plot for themselves, and here she is, yelling 'mechanizers have been insulted!' She came to complain. Insult her, ha!"

"Isn't a plot authorized for them?"

"It's authorized. Fifteen *sotki* goes to them by law, but not from *kolkhoz* lands. From the wastelands around here, separately. In the rural *soviet,* at the session, they decided it."

He was quiet for a little and then spoke again:

"It must be you came to bury your mother. The last debt. You respected an old person. Thank you for not forgetting. And I'm assigned to the peat, but I haven't made it yet."

The old man stretched out a leg and, leaning back, pulled a half-empty bottle of vodka from his pocket.

"Here," he continued, brightening up. "If you're not too fussy for a working man, we'll drink what God sends. Don't think I'm drunk. My cousin, Maiya Ckorniakova, got married up today with Petra Dezhurov from the flax factory. They were gay there, but I had Semenovna on my mind. I stole a half-pint and left. For each his own."

He rubbed his hands, as if they were cold, glanced at the shelf, carefully got out two cups, one after the other, and poured a little into each.

"I was a friend to your father. Now you, they say, are one of the leaders. And that, you see . . . well, tastes differ. People, we're all equal. More?" he asked, indicating the cup. "Wait, I'll give you a bite of something, a little *zakuska.*"

He dug his hand into his pocket, pulled out a dark, wrinkled cucumber, wiped it clean of tobacco crumbs, and broke it carefully in two.

The vodka burned in Varygin's stomach so that he winced. He did not bite into the cucumber. The blacksmith drank and ate his own cucumber with gusto.

"Well now," he said happily, crinkling his sly eyes, under bristly, sun-bleached eyebrows. "You, it seems, are a great director of things,

and we're makers of things, and so, heh, heh, it comes out. We'll
finish this little bit, all right?"

He tipped the half-pint, and they drank again.

"Some, it seems, get funeral meats, and some a wedding feast,
heh, heh."

Varygin felt warm in his chest, and for the first time in three days
a feeling of cheer returned to him.

"And how did my mother get along here? Not too well, was it?"
he asked.

"She got along all right, one way or another, just like everybody
else."

"So? For instance, one gets enough food here?"

"No complaints. Not so bad. Our own bread doesn't last anywhere near into spring, so we go to Lapshino. And some go to the
city. The rural soviet paid her rent for the house. The midwife
station is here. Thirty-five a month. What did she need? Sometimes
she even ate white bread and let herself have real tea. This year she
got sugar whenever there was some. No, you don't have to feel
sorry."

From the frozen road beyond the gates came the sound of wheels.
A cart went past; Varygin could hear the horse stamping his hooves
and snorting. Then somewhere nearby an accordian began to play,
a gay crowd passed the house, and a piercing girl's voice, rising to
a shout, sang out:

> Through a field sown with spring crop,
> Through a rural consumers' co-op,
> Through a course on the care of the bee,
> Darling, I will stay with thee!

"Our people out walking," said the old blacksmith. "Do you want
to go join?" He rose, put the empty half-pint in his pocket, and,
without a farewell, disappeared.

Varygin also rose, put on his overcoat, and went to the door. It
was already dark, and above, in a sky swept clean of clouds, the
cold stars burned. He went a little way toward the gate, huddling
against the cold, and looked at his watch. The glowing green hands
showed all of ten past seven. The express did not leave until late at
night, and the prospect of the hours which remained before his departure seemed unpleasantly long and tiresome.

The sound of the accordian came to him from the edge of the village. Voices, girls' shrieks, and laughter rose in the night. Varygin turned and went back to the house. On the porch the soldieress Derevleva was waiting. She still wore the army tunic as before, but her head and shoulders were wrapped now in a thick woolen shawl.

"I came to fix you tea," she said melodiously, entering the cottage after him. "Antonina Vasilievna was worried about you. She sent me specially from Lapshino. Herself, she couldn't come; Zoika's keeping her, not giving birth."

She stirred up the fire on the hearth and set the teapot to boil.

Varygin heard her say:

"It's a shame Semenovna didn't wait till you came. What happiness for an old woman!"

"She expected me?" he asked.

"Well, this year, she didn't say anything. But summers, when you used to say you'd come . . . she waited eagerly. 'Everything comes to pass,' she'd say. 'Now's the time, now's the time!' Then later, she was quiet about it. But she wasn't offended, no. She understood if it wasn't easy for an important man to get away. Of all our villagers, you've gone the furthest. There's only Afanasii Berezin from Korkino that's a general maybe somewhere in Lukkhes."

Taking the tea off, she set a cup before him and sat down at the table.

"It's only that we have nothing special to brag about here. In the *kolkhoz* it's all women, and we struggle and struggle, all for nothing. Over at Borba now, they've given out four kilos again, but here at our farm . . ." She wrung her hands despondently. "At ours, things don't go well," she said apologetically. Presumably, she was embarrassed, before such a prominent and respected man as Varygin, that her *kolkhoz* had so little to boast.

"Here's what I'd like to ask you," she went on, untying her shawl. "Is it right, or not right, what they've done with us? This year we sowed seventy-four hectares of hemp. But then the hemp bloomed, and right away, we saw, the spring wheat ripened. We wanted to wait, stack the grain, but they ordered us to thresh it, deliver it: official deliveries. Now, what kind of thing is that? From here to the grain collecting station is thirty-nine *versts,* and two ferries to cross, and at the grain elevator you have to wait. And the *poskon'* hemp, if it's not harvested on time, you can be sure the *materka* won't wait! The collection agents rode us: deliver, deliver! Is it possible, we said, that our government won't wait a week? Honestly, we wouldn't have stayed in debt. As soon as we'd tended the hemp, we'd have delivered. But no, not them! Now I ask you, what's the matter with them? And they in no hurry to send it anywhere. Well, we hauled it to the elevator—and threshed it, too. And so missed the hemp harvest, and, uncut, it lost half its seed. And there we were again without bread! Now you judge, is this good, or isn't it?"

She thinks that I'm responsible for everything, Varygin thought with embarrassment, trying to remember what *poskon'* hemp and *materka* were, and the connection between them. But he couldn't recall.

"It's a political question," he said aloud. "With us, the government always comes first. Everything depends on the level of the consciousness of the masses."

He stopped, feeling that he had said something wrong.

But Derevleva heard him with an expression of satisfaction on her face.

"That's so—a political question," she exclaimed with alacrity, evidently satisfied that the conversation was reaching essential depths. "Then it's right. You explain it very well. We don't have consciousness yet here in our mass."

A motorcycle sputtered in the darkness outside the window.

"There, she's back," said Derevleva. "The MTS engineer, he brought her. He comes every Saturday. And she has next to no time for him. She doesn't know her own luck, that midwife."

Antonina Vasilievna entered first, and a young man with a ruddy complexion, high-boned cheeks, and flaxen hair followed behind her.

"Well, so you're here?" Her voice was warm. No trace seemed to remain of her sorrowful mood of the morning.

She washed her hands, sat down at the table, opened a pack of sandwiches, evidently bought at a buffet somewhere, and offering them all around, regaled them with what a strong, fine girl Siniukhina had given birth to.

It was pleasant to look at her milk-white arms, bare now to smooth elbows; to look at her soft, feminine movements as she pushed strands of damp hair behind her ears; at her warm cheeks.

She told her story and seemed to ignore the engineer, but she must have felt his gaze the whole time.

"No, she understands her good luck," Varygin decided, studying the girl's eyes, which shone brightly in spite of all the troubles and worries of her day. He thought of his own fragile wife, incessantly petulant, overfeeding the children so that Gena, at eleven, had a paunch and Sveta seemed like an old woman with a child's face mated to fat, unwieldy legs. He thought: that engineer is a happy man. If some time long ago, life had taken another turn, and he, Varygin, had stayed in the country, he would probably now still be a strong and healthy man, and his face would be taut and ruddy, like this engineer's. But one can change nothing of the past, nor, seemingly, of the future. And very likely, if a young woman with white arms and a lithe, strong body now agreed to fall in love with him, then still nothing would come of it.

"Have you been long in these parts?" he asked.

"It's already time to leave!" she laughed, but in her face there was a toughness. "Everyone tries to get out of here, out of the country places as fast as they can go to town. If possible, to the capital. Where you are, it's more civilized, even more nourishing. But it is said that we here are the more necessary."

She looked at the engineer, as though asking his support.

"Yes, there's a lot of work here," said the engineer. "In our region, out of nineteen *kolkhozes,* more than half are backward. Harvests are low, income is insignificant, people work reluctantly and eat badly."

Without looking, he got a cigarette out of the field bag hanging at his side and began to smoke nervously.

"Why is it like this?" asked Varygin.

The engineer shrugged.

"You would know best. No one wants to work without return."

The midwife silently touched the engineer's hand. He got up from the table and walked around the room.

Varygin sat resting his back against the wall and chewed on a sandwich. He had eaten nothing since morning. It seemed to him that the engineer looked at him in an unfriendly way.

"And you're not painting it too black?" he asked stiffly. "At the beginning I thought you were an optimist."

The engineer walked off to the corner and threw his cigarette into the washtub.

"Optimism," he said, turning. "Optimism is much more complicated than it seems. The country people would be better off if there weren't so many cheery souls on the public payroll. What's needed is guts enough to overcome difficulties, not hush them up. Look at our tractor station. There's a lot we could do—and nobody really cares. Come over tomorrow. You'll see."

"I have to leave today . . . business," said Varygin and looked at his watch.

The engineer also looked at his watch. His ardor had faded.

"So . . . Well, I'll be going, Tonia," he said.

She went with him into the passageway, and Varygin heard them whispering together on the porch.

"It's probably time for me to go, too," Varygin said after a while, when she had come back into the room.

"Wait a while. There's still time. Mitya will tell the tractor station to send a car."

Glancing at Derevleva, who was quietly washing dishes in the corner, she began now, with some embarrassment, to talk about the house—how it would be now. Did he want to break the lease, perhaps think of selling the house, or leave things as before?

"Leave it all as it has been," said Varygin.

A few things of his mother's remained in the dresser. He took two old family photographs which lay in the bottom of the top drawer. He did not feel in himself the desire or the strength to look into all of it, nor into what the engineer had said, nor into what he had seen here during the day.

"Please, see to it all yourself," he said, and closed the drawer.

The car came more quickly than he expected. The midwife went with him so that he would not have to bother about the ticket himself.

The road was abominable as far as Lapshino, but then, when the car reached a paved stretch and traveled with softly swishing tires along the gray ribbon illuminated by the white headlights, Varygin's usual calm mood began slowly to return. The aftertaste of resentment, left by his encounter with the engineer, seemed to fade by itself.

Of course, he thought, our local administration is not yet staffed as it should be. And for the time being they work clumsily and crudely and always cite objective causes to cover themselves. But you can't correct the situation everywhere at once. From above there is correction, prompting. But they must do it themselves, themselves!

Yes, exactly, they themselves, he thought after a minute, and was almost angry that he had not said so to the engineer.

They got to Dvorik almost an hour before the express was due and, having bought the ticket, sat together in the buffet.

The midwife, embarrassed now, awkwardly sipped the port wine he had bought her, looking around as though afraid.

"If we went together, you could become my secretary," said Varygin jokingly.

She choked and spilled wine on the oilcloth and blushed so that he himself became shy.

In the train, lying down to sleep in the half-darkened compartment where the other passengers already snored, he thought with relief that the turmoil and unpleasantness of these days were behind now. He saw with satisfaction that tomorrow he would go to his warm, well-furnished study, and sit at the table in a comfortable armchair.

But a feeling of something not unlike guilt did not leave Varygin for a long time. Sleep did not come, and in his weary fancies his imagination painted the wooden cross against the gray sky, the familiar house, the long board bench against the wall, the old samovar in the corner, leaning askew. Behind the rough deal table his mother sat, her face small and dark, as it had been in the church. She moved toward him in the darkness and asked, with hope and a kind of patient trust, as the soldieress Derevleva had asked him that day: "Is it right, or not right, what they've done with us?"

Literaturnaya Moskva (Moscow), Vol. II, 1956.

Marxism is a philosophy of cities. Karoly Jobbagy is a young Hungarian who belongs to another Central European revolutionary tradition: he speaks for the peasants.

MUD

Don't talk to me about space ships,
trips to the moon, Mars,
life in the atomic age. . . .

The oxcarts sink in a shoreless
        sea of mud.
Our roads are mud, the farmyards, the pastures.
When winter comes, the rain beats
        like this,
And men, if they only could, would turn
        to beasts
and sleep, and see nothing.
Darkness comes early; there's no electricity
        here.
We sit beside a cold lamp; the mind sputters,
        vainly sparking behind the skull.
Kerosene? Expensive, five times as expensive,
if you want to know, as gasoline.
In summer you can burn five gallons of
        gasoline on silly joy-rides.
But kerosene, sometimes there's not a drop,
        and besides,
at that price who can afford to burn a pint
        a day,
enough to light a house?

The kid? Happy he doesn't have to look
        at a book;
by the time he's fed the chickens and the pigs

(simpler to feed than read) and groped his
     way to the house,
and while the soup warms his belly,
his eyes get heavy. Stumbles to bed.

Even the radio doesn't reach us.
"They say, he said" is how we hear
     things.
Things sound so wild it could drive you
     nuts.
We don't believe much, not any more;
no point to tell us they're thinking of us,
remembering us, our needs.
We live like this. In darkness,
in mud, far away.
From Budapest to us, traveling express,
after all the changes, the trip is longer
than, let us say, shall we say,
to Moscow, by plane. . . .
In our tiny country, where I stretch my
     arms
and nearly touch the two borders.
So don't talk to me about space ships.
At least then I won't feel how far away
from you fate shoved me.
You sit around the fleshpots of Budapest
and watch with cool disdain
the poets
who would be blessed if only they sang
     your praises.

I see that big things are doing in this
       country,
and every day the papers have a new
     ersatz hero,
unparalleled in his labors.
His bench gleams under arc lights,
he sees, learns, the winter doesn't squeeze him,
goes to the movies, theater, opera.

Even the radio programs for him,
and the authorities praise him.
And we are ersatz heroes, too, all of us,
who crowded into tiny rooms,
chew pumpkin seeds and lie around like
        garbage.
Don't tell me it's worse in Africa.
I live in Europe; my skin is white.
Who will take me in his arms and make me
        feel that I am human?

                    Csillag (Budapest), April, 1956.

"The peasant," wrote Friedrich Engels, "is the barbarian of civilization." But for Peter Veres he is not: the peasant—inarticulate and slow, passionate and half a mystic in his love for the earth—is Hungary.

"Laddy" is the story of a horse—and of the Hungarian peasant. ". . . what a great thing if his anguish abates and his ears no longer ring with that everlasting terrifying 'gee-ahh!' "

Veres was born in 1897 and spent his early years among the landless peasants. After World War I, he joined the Social Democratic Party, making his living as a factory worker and later as a tenant farmer, writing all the while for left-wing journals. *Mit Ér Az Ember, Ha Magyar* ("What Is a Man Worth If He's Hungarian?") was an outspoken challenge to the Horthy regime.

In 1945 he became chairman of the Peasant Party and later Minister of Defense in the Cabinet of 1947. During the years of Rakosi's ascendency, he fell into eclipse, emerging in 1954 during the first premiership of Imre Nagy. As one of the men who made the Hungarian revolt, his present circumstances are unknown.

LADDY

I.

Laddy is not a man, or even a stripling, but a horse. And why they call him that I couldn't say, just as I don't know why they call so many horses Laddy, nor will know either—until researchers hit upon it—why so many men are named John, Jean, Hans, or Ivan.

Laddy is a light bay, gelding draft horse, but with an aristocratic strain because Count Nadhazy (from whose stud farm Laddy's sire came to Szerdahely)—according to the practice of other breeders, too, when the blood line seemed impaired—fobbed off such colts on the State stud farm (whose overseers invariably were their good friends), so that thereby the peasants' huge-bellied, chaff-eating, lumbering horses might also be ennobled. Let thoroughbred fire stir the blood of peasant horses, too! And since this—so they thought— also profited the peasant, it really wasn't cheating, even if the Count got thousands of *pengoes* for a less-than-perfect stud colt. (That the peasants needed not mettlesome mounts but sober, patient draft horses was a consideration that didn't seem to occur to anyone).

Well, no matter. Breeding is a fine thing, and perhaps that way, too, in some hundreds of years it might have been possible to raise Hungarian peasant stock to a thoroughbred level, except that we would have to wait out those few hundred years. Meanwhile, the horses come and go from market to market, district to district, even country to country. Then wars erupt from time to time, and mare and stud can be thankful they're alive, whoever their mates may be. And lest the mares go wild when their time comes, the peasants fix them with whatever stud happens to be "serving" the village—not to speak of the fact that certain farmers, and even some large land-owners, keep their own studs to which they allow random access. Also, not infrequently, sly little peasants with really fine stud colts offer them clandestinely for fewer *pengoes* than the State fee.

All this led not to blooded stock but to chaos; and so Laddy couldn't help it if he brought with him to Farmer Murvai's an English equine lady's daintiness and sensitivity, along with the wisdom and fire of man's comrade on the Arabian plain.

For all that, in his colthood no ill befell him on that account; he lived a carefree life. The farmer's stripling sons played with the colts —with Laddy, too—as they would have liked to with girls. They hugged Laddy's graceful neck and drew his head to them, looking into his fine, clear eyes, where they saw their disheveled, red-cheeked, always bristly selves reflected just as they might have been in the pupils of girls' eyes. Sometimes they even embraced the rearing Laddy, and if he playfully pretended to bite, would swat him and seize him by the mane.

Laddy loved this game, for at the time he happened to be the only small colt in the Murvai menage, his mother being always in harness, and it bored him beyond measure to see her, old Vilma, plodding endlessly up and down the furrow, back and forth, from daybreak to nightfall. Laddy sometimes ambled beside her or after her, but then, because this plodding seemed so long and senseless— for why go from one of the fields to the other, up to the wild pear tree, if you had to come back anyhow? (that this was breadwinning work for man and fed horses, too, he still didn't know)—he pre-ferred to stay by the cart or to roam the meadow munching tender alfalfa or other tidbits among the grasses. At other times he nuzzled sugar beets out beneath the hay in the cart or sought goodies in the feedbag that hung from the brace. But sometimes he also got into the Murvais' lunch, shaking loose from the bright checkered bread-cloth the fine wheat loaf and smoked bacon, too. He would munch and crumble the bread, but trample the bacon, not being a meat eater. So on this account an old soldier's chest had to be put under the seat to hide the food.

While Laddy's mother and the old horses puffed, Lou, the young and teamstering farmer boy, who happened to be home, wrestled with Laddy. The other boys—there were six—were either soldiers or had married and seldom came home, but at such times always surveyed Laddy with a trace of envy: "My, what a fine colt; I wish I had him! Why don't you give him to me, Dad? I'd raise him to be a fine saddle horse." (For the saddle horse always had to be gelded. He was the brains and soul and strength of the shaft. A saddle horse could not have a colt—let him just be concerned with the work.) Old Murvai at such times pretended not to hear, or if he did speak up, would only say: "Sure, so you can ruin and spoil him like Linda's son."

"Lou's attended to that already. Look, he's ready to jump out of his skin. If I lay a hand on him, he kicks like a thunderbolt. He'll never amount to anything in Lou's hands!"

"That's not your affair. If he doesn't pan out, we'll sell him to the military. Rosenblum will dump him for good money. . . ." For if the counts had sense enough to unload imperfect studs on the peasants, the peasant farmers also had the sense to sell handsome but ill-tempered brutes to the military. True, there, too, the sons of peasants would get the rough end of it, but they would hardly be the sons of rich farmers, who quickly become subalterns and don't curry horses, or else smoked hams and wine-filled canteens see to it that the sergeant gives them the best horses.

All this, however, was beyond Laddy's purview; he knew nothing of this, living the carefree days of colthood, enjoying food and drink aplenty. . . .

That was how Laddy's childhood passed, amid small griefs, linger-ing joys, and delightful games, right up to the moment when the veterinary came and, upon examining the studs, determined that for such and such reasons (such reasons were easy to find, since out of a hundred studs only one or two could remain stallions, mainly those belonging to counts and very large landowners) Laddy was unsuited to be a studhorse, and so they forced him to the ground, made him helpless, and despoiled him of his stallion birthright.

From then on, Laddy became another creature. They raised him as a gelding, which in itself is a special misfortune. Never could he know the tortures and sweetness of love. He had to learn and perhaps also understand (for his comprehension was not disturbed by either the stallion's instinct or the mare's desire and maternal feeling) that he was not a free animal but only the burden-beast of the tough, shrewd race called "man," that for him no more of life remained than the pain of work, the joy of eating, rare rest, and the brief refuge of sleep.

Of course, this, too, is life for a man, as for a horse, who even for such small joys accepts life's many griefs in a world of slavery and toil for others. For what can be done? A horse can't commit suicide, he still hasn't reached that point, and obviously even a man must lose his wits to some extent before spurning life.

So life must be lived, because that's the way of the world; and one must work because this is life's law. But oh, what a blow, or more than that; what a crime against nature to force upon a bright horse with fine instincts a stupid or even wicked man. This crime, of course, is spawned by greed for money and profits, but Laddy—however wise he might be in other ways—could hardly know that. Meanwhile, fate, which allegedly can take a hand, does not intervene but defaults to fortune—scatterbrained, capricious Lady Luck—to whom, it would seem, everything is one. As the peasants say: "Where it falls, there it lies." The bad man gets a good horse, the good one a bad horse, but the opposite can happen, too, because in this world, particularly at markets, blind chance, crafty scheming, and sober wisdom rule equally.

Thus, perhaps, it was also accidental that mettlesome Laddy grew into a young draft horse at Farmer Murvai's just when five sons had already left the homestead and the sixth, Lou Murvai, came to be the young master and, of course, the teamster as well on his father's holdings. . . .

Every horse must learn his job, even when not with experienced, knowing horses, learn to work in tandem and even alone—that's how he becomes a well-trained, sober horse. And since every little task—harrowing, for example—didn't require four to five horses, Laddy did such work only with Sue. Because of the old horses' lumbering gait, he couldn't keep step with them, dancing and prancing instead, which was well enough in front of a fancy carriage but ill befitted a draft team.

If they—that is, the horses—had known (or did they?) how Lou Murvai swaggered and preened himself on the two fiery colts—on their hot blood—perhaps they would have laughed him to scorn. For in Laddy's blood at times there raged a frantic excitement, impelling him to kick up his heels and run, run out into the infinite, as though these were the plains of Araby, Siberia, or perhaps the Hortobagy. (For it is a great thing, a hard thing, a real test for a young horse to grow accustomed to the long, steady pull, or even to trot quietly with a rider on his back.) At such times it didn't matter whether it was cart or harrow rattling behind him; he itched to run. If a lark sprang up from under his nose in the gray plowland—for the meadowlark is so unafraid of a horse or his master in the fields that he only takes wing at the last moment to avoid being stepped on—or if he heard a sudden shout or horn, the roar of a motor, or even if he met with those ugly black buffaloes or the gray donkey which, I don't know why, is so repugnant to a horse, he would shy and want to rush over hedge and ditch out into the wide world as if chased by a tiger.

There's no telling for certain whether it was due to a startled lark, to Lou's not holding the reins properly and the harrow's cross-piece jolting against Laddy's leg, to sheer nervous caprice, perhaps because he was tired of plodding back and forth, to gnats tickling his nose, or because Lou—showoff that he was—began putting him through his paces, but an irresistible urge for freedom awoke within him, and as the harrow slipped and Lou, as usual, yelled at him, practically gnashing his teeth—"Laddee-ee-ee! God blast you . . ."
—at that moment Laddy yanked the reins from the tips of Lou's fingers, and in an instant the colts whipped off into the blue, the harrow skipping at their heels.

Lou, of course, took fright, leaped after them, his peaked hat flew off, his boyishly matted hair fluttered in the spring breeze, but less than did the manes of the two colts; and vainly did he cry: "Whoa there, Laddy! Whoa Sue!" They didn't hear at all, or listen.

Actually, they could hardly have heard him, because the harrow bolts snapped loose and the leaves of the double harrow jiggled and clashed at the horses' heels, while the skimming shafts at every lurch slapped their legs, making the colts in flight think they were being struck at, and so the playful romp turned into equine panic. Over the hard ground clanked the harrow, while traces and harness crackled and flew, and the two colts became so crazed that they neither saw nor heard, just ran and ran, straight ahead at full gallop. But where the windrow veered off, they could no longer turn; their momentum swept them onto the plowed land that crossed their path.

Thus did they dash helter-skelter through wheat sowings, freshly plowed land, sprouting spring barley, and new-sown soft maize fields, till they reached the shallow grassy border ditch, sparsely lined by trees, and the maize fields of the neighboring estate.

In jumping the ditch, the harrow slammed into Laddy's tendons, not for the first time either, and tore the tough skin, making the blood spout. If old Murvai were here to see! Of course, he isn't; for the time being, even Lou has been left far behind, scared and out of breath from his efforts to catch up, sighing that if only the traces would break or the crosspiece, so the harrow would be left behind, because if that slashes into them or catches their hoofs in its teeth, the horses would be ruined, break their legs, or even die.

But now there's no one near enough to head off the horses. Men are working everywhere in the fields, to be sure, but they are all too far from the runaways. No one would be likely to catch them anyway, unless they fall into a ditch or the harrow catches in a tree trunk, or they get so tired of running that they can't keep it up any longer.

That is what happened. In Schlesinger's deep, soft, steam-plowed land the two crazy colts grew so exhausted, especially the more sluggish, comfort-loving Sue, that finally she let herself be dragged, and since Laddy couldn't carry her along, too, they began to calm down. So when Schlesinger's hired hands and teamsters who were planting in the neighborhood yelled: "Whoa there, whoa!" the two maddened colts suddenly halted and looked about them, trembling, thinking some such thing in horse lingo as: "God Almighty, where are we and what have we done now!"

That was how the cherished promise that was Laddy became a battered, bruised, and limping discard who was sold to Rosenblum the horse dealer and thence handed along to other dealers, lest those at Szerdahely recognize him and spread his ill-fame at the market, saying: "Ah, there's that crazy colt of the Murvais, the one that ran the loaded wagon into the ditch and shook the harrow apart. See, there's the mark on his tendon and pastern." Because with that they would scare the buyers who now are carefully appraising the colt who, despite slight faults, seems well built and bright, and good-natured, too. Why, just the sight of his head and eyes is pure delight to one who knows horses.

True, he could have become a good draft horse at the Murvais', too, but old Murvai was very angry—the two colts had cost him six hundred *pengoes* damage at the very least—and he told Rosenblum: "Take him away, Jacob. Don't let me even lay eyes on him, or I don't know what I'll do . . . I'll beat the life out of him. . . ."

That was how Laddy, only a wraith of his old self and his fire gone, came to Mezei the dwarf-holder, who had five children and half an acre of his own, rented three acres, and worked two fifty-fifty; besides which, whenever he had time and even when he didn't (because he needed money so badly for bread and fodder), he did carting. Not in town or at the railway station or on the highways, but just among the other peasants who had a little land but no draft horses. He brought hay from distant fields, helped harvest potatoes, beets, corn; when the wheat was being gathered in, he'd haul it straight to the threshing machines and then cart back the grain and straw. In a word, he always did whatever came to hand. They paid little here, but then his wagon and horse were on the frailer side, and he was alone, without even an adolescent boy to help (the children were small, the woman was nursing). In loading up, he'd bring the little ladder along, toss in a bunch of sheaves, then carefully spread them in the cart, come down, toss up more sheaves, and so forth till the load was complete. That was the only sort of carting he could undertake. . . .

Now Imre Mezei wasn't the man to let his horse stand hungry by the empty summer manger—rather, let's work till we drop! That's the kind of man he was, and so close to Laddy that he wouldn't have the heart to let the horse pine at the manger even when there was no carting. He'd be ashamed before Laddy—yes, ashamed—if he were to potter about in the yard (he couldn't bear sitting idly) and see Laddy sharpen his ears and gaze pitifully after him: was he going to the rick or to the barn for fodder? At times he might even whimper a bit, gelding fashion, for true whinnying is the province of studs and mares and the little colts, and Imre Mezei would feel upon his back Laddy's sorrowful glance if, on the pretext that now they weren't working they weren't earning, he skimped on his feed. For Mezei knows, and thinks Laddy knows, too, that for the draft horse a day or two of rest is not just a rest but a gathering of strength, that equine law stipulates that the draft horse always eat when he can, because that's when he gathers into his sinews the power which draws the plow or loaded wagon from dawn to twilight.

But Imre Mezei couldn't bear to give the horse dry chaff in the heat of summer either—it would be as if he himself were made to eat grits when the melons were ripening—because chaff is all right in its season, in dank November and during the long black nights of winter when man and beast are asleep; the fattening swine even snores, the reclining cow rests her head on her forehoof and lowers her eyelids, the hens sleep in the hayloft; only the horse, the draft horse, doesn't know what to do with so much idle time in the endless night, so he eats. If the feed in the manger runs out, he blinks a bit—luckily, in winter the flies are also asleep—puts his weight on one foot, sometimes even lies down (mostly after midnight), but soon tires of this, too, his fine equine nerves grow restless, because the horse species long ago became accustomed to either eating or working, and out in the open a horse eats while he works, foraging incessantly for his food in field and meadow.

Well, at such times during the long wintry nights the dry and tasteless chaff could be munched, too, especially if some green meadow grass, ground ivy leaves, or panic grass is mixed with the wheat stalks, or if good, juicy red squash or crunchy turnips are grated into it. But now at summer's end, when the sun blazes as if in fear that approaching autumn will not allow it to shine any more, when the flies and gnats buzz and bite as if they feel this will be their swan song in this miserable life, to make a horse munch chaff would be cruel indeed. And Imre Mezei could not be cruel to Laddy. . . .

A horse must be fed even if he isn't earning, even if his master is left without food, even if the children eat less and the woman goes ragged for the sake of the horse's belly. Anyone who balks at this shouldn't keep a horse; let him live by his own hands: that's the truth about horses, and Imre Mezei knew it well. He would have been as ashamed of cheating Laddy as of cheating a buddy on the battlefield by giving him the smaller half of their joint bread ration, the half the mouse gnawed out.

Amid the ever-present cares of their grievous toil and the rarer joys of a good morsel of food, they grew to be such friends and learned each other's ways so well (a great thing between a peasant and his horse) that Imre Mezei . . . often left it to Laddy to follow whatever rut or track he deemed best. If he disliked the jolty paved center of the highway, let him take the dusty side road or even the grassy cattle track. If Imre grew tired of sitting and jolting about on the cart, if his joints grew stiff, he'd hang the reins on the brace, stick the whip in its holder, and descend, going on foot beside the cart. That's what he did when it dawned cold, or on the blistery winter days whose ice cut to the bone. (He had no fur-lined coat; he could have bought another horse for the money.)

Yes indeed, the once-wild, shying, temperamental Laddy no longer needed to be held in constant check. He scared easily and was high-strung even now, but he hearkened to the spoken word and perhaps would be ashamed to cheat Mezei, who trusted him implicitly, confident that they'd never get stuck—however much he loaded onto the little one-horse cart, Laddy would see him through. Because what Laddy couldn't draw, the little cart couldn't carry either. . . .

And it came to pass that a miracle happened: Mrs. Mezei also came to love Laddy, though she wouldn't have admitted it to her husband for the world. For years she hid this love, never alluding to it openly, since at first she was jealous of the horse—because her husband loved him. Then, too, for a long time she hated the scurvy nag to whom she had to bring oats and maize even when they themselves ate stale bread, but later, in truth, when the husband wasn't home, she'd bring him food herself, measuring out his fodder at such times—carefully avoiding his hind legs because you can't entirely trust a horse—and she'd caress his neck and pat his face.

No need to say how much the children loved him. If the loads
were heavy, the whole family would help Laddy start up.

What feelings Laddy harbored deep in his heart for his masters
it was impossible to know, for who can see that deep? But then it
wouldn't be easy to determine even in the case of a man, a creature
who can speak—and lie—just where practical wisdom and consideration and habit end, and where love begins. Yet this much is
certain: he showed willingness, zeal, and obedience to the uttermost
limits, even unto death, and that already is almost as much, or perhaps as much, as what men call "love."

II.

Came the day when this meager but tolerable life suddenly broke
off. History, that prodigious cart doubtless drawn by bridleless horses
which confounds the fate of man and horse alike, brought Laddy
grievous trials, too. At first—in the years 1938-1940—he just had to
report frequently at requisitions, idling all day without food or drink
while the bright-collared gentlemen decided whether Laddy was to
go or stay. On two occasions he was called, and for weeks utter
strangers drove him back and forth throughout the country. In this
way he traversed a great part of upper Hungary and Transylvania,
too. Then one day his master, Imre Mezei, vanished for good from
the house, being called to the colors, and Lisbeth or the older
children went carting hither and thither—erratically and unskill-
fully enough—at which Laddy was most indignant and occasionally
showed it, too, if not by kicking, yet by stubbornness, by snapping the
traces and getting stuck. And often for weeks he would stand idle
in his stall because there was no one to go carting with him—he was
frightfully bored—besides which, the manger was mostly empty, too,
or contained only bitter mouldy odds and ends which he'd mull
over a dozen times in an effort to find something eatable. And if for
all his searching he still discovered nothing he could munch, then
finally he'd rather stand on three legs and wait, wait, wait for someone to come, woman or child, who would give him something better,
something he could eat.

Thus did the autumn of 1944 arrive when the Germans, Arrow-
Crossists, and overlords packed their things and began to run; while
the local police did nothing but distribute draft notices to men and
horses alike. Then, for the third and last time, they drafted Laddy,
too, hitched him to an unknown horse, and, at the command of a

German soldier in field-gray, speaking a prickly alien tongue, a poor Hungarian draftee drove him off toward the west. Henceforth, life became all pain and fear and gall for Laddy, who still shuddered at strange men and strange talk. Over the past few years he had become used to Imre Mezei's rarely angry, mostly good-humored chiding or mumbling, wherein the oft-recurring words, so easily translatable into horse language, were soft, like "Come now, Laddy, easy boy, whoa there," and now, from these green-uniformed fellows he had to hear only harshly staccato commands, words sharp and stabbing, such as *"Habt-acht! rechts! links! kehrt-euch! marsch!"* So it was understandable that stark terror filled his gentle eyes. These men were perhaps even worse than the horse dealers, because the latter at least, with an eye to profits, spared him to some extent, but for these a horse, too, was no more than a tool or weapon: if it breaks, throw it away!

From fall to spring, Laddy and his partner battled the mud, which here—at least during this very rainy wartime autumn—was deeper and stickier even than in the Great Lowlands. With the carts of the 69th Auxiliary Command they came and went, back and forth among the villages, because the Germans, upon seeing the Auxiliary's fine, strong horses, which the provident staff had driven off from home—they had a wide choice in the Lowlands—gave them the by-then utterly toil-worn Laddy-pair in exchange, saying that for such work they would do just as well. . . .

Along toward spring, general confusion set in again. The horrible boomings and rumbling—cannon and tanks—again came nearer; the days of wild scramble and terror were here once more, they had to flee this region, too.

On that journey occurred the second great turn of fate in Laddy's life. . . .

They didn't proceed far when the horses bogged down. And because Vilma was lazy, lumbering, and old, and because during her long life she had grown accustomed to beatings and had learnt that if she didn't pull, the other horse would—being a mare, and always with a colt she had to be spared—so it was Laddy who took to heart every encouraging word and bore on his back the lashes of the whip. Yes, but his strength isn't as of old, the horse is but skin and bones, and since fall he's been living so miserably that his muscles have only as much strength as he can get from the last morsels he has munched. . . .

So, despite all exhortation, his strength gives way. . . .

Night is already falling, and who could say how many times they've gotten stuck already, but this is the end. A cattle truck grazes Vilma. She knocks the hard-working Laddy into the ditch. Luckily, the cart remains upright, because imbedded in the mud it can't easily overturn, but poor Laddy has landed on his back like a sexton bug. He can't get up or even turn. He is so spent that he scarcely can move his limbs. . . .

The highway teems with cars and wagons whose passengers take no notice of the accident, so as to spare themselves any possible twinges of conscience for not helping, or if they do look, harden their hearts. Sorry, orders are orders; at such and such a time I must be here, I must be there. That's their excuse, even if no orders exist. Vainly do the wives wave, plead, and cry; no one stops. When people flee and have reason, or think they have reason, to fear those who follow, then precepts of brotherly love, whether those of the New Testament or the Old, are not much honored. Not only is "Love thine enemy!" omitted, but even "Love thy neighbor!" and finally also "Do not covet thy neighbor's this or that!"

And what of Laddy?

Laddy they just left there in the ditch without a word, without so much as spitting on him. . . .

Poor Laddy struggled till nearly dawn in the ditch, unable to get up. With numbed limbs, he grazed as he lay, eating the dry weeds around him right down to the roots, finding a few savory green morsels, too, beneath last season's brush. Then finally in the sharp, cold dawn, with quaking limbs, he again tried to stand—and made it! Though aching in every muscle, he moved a step or two for fresh bites of the thick, parched grasses. Slowly gathering strength— for in a horse each morsel turns at once into energy—he clambered to the meadow, instinctively edging away from the clattering tumult of the road.

At the far end of the meadow was a grove of trees near a winding rill where last year's grass still showed green below. Primeval instinct led him there, and, as he limpingly grazed, he had the luck to be discovered by a peasant who may have strolled that way to spy out, from behind the cover of the trees, whether those were still the Germans or already the Russians rumbling along the highway. He walked around Laddy as he grazed. Since the horses fed heartily (so his stomach must be good) and though he limped, nothing was broken, it looked as if the animal might survive; so he led him along the edge of the fields to his barn, which used to stable three fine strong horses: now only last season's colt remained—because he was unbroken to the harness, no one wanted him.

This peasant, Marton Baksa, became Laddy's new master.

He wasn't the worst of masters, though you couldn't compare him to Imre Mezei, whose aspect only flickered dimly in the depths of Laddy's consciousness after so much suffering; yet, were he to catch sight of him, he would surely recognize him and whinny with joy.

Marton Baksa did not love Laddy, for he was more concerned with the profit than the horse, and Laddy was ugly now into the bargain—scrawny, bent, and flattened, like the inferior fish they call "whiting." A lame nag—he'll amount to either something or nothing was what his new master thought. Maybe there'd be no more than his hide to show for all the expensive feed, as in the case of so many of his fellows. Well, in any case, by comparison with the others, Marton Baksa again was a good man. He provided food, didn't rail or shout much. That was how Laddy spent the spring and fall of 1945, in this little village by the river Raba. He recovered, lost his limp, even acquired some color from good feeding; only in the eyes of Transdanubian peasants, used to the well-cushioned form of cold-blooded horses, did Laddy seem too bony a nag. . . .

By now, refugees were streaming back from the west, bringing along quite a few good horses; so, for a huge round loaf and a few kilograms of bacon, Marton Baksa got himself a pretty fair Murakoz horse—minus papers, of course.

Simultaneously, peasants and horse dealers were appearing in Vas and Zala Counties seeking horses, because the new farmers wanted horses badly for the land they'd just received, and the old farmers needed replacements for the animals taken from them. Marton Baksa seized the opportunity, and since Laddy had no papers (nor did the former horses' papers fit him), while the purchased cold-blooded horse was just like the mare they took from him—aside from an age difference no one would look into—he sold Laddy with a light heart. . . .

He was bought by a new-fledged farmer, Francis Istenes, who had six young children and new received ten acres of land.

Here again a new life began for the gradually aging Laddy. If Istenes wasn't such a prince as Mezei, yet he was good-hearted enough to live with and to work for. Laddy managed to pull himself together a little, though of course he remained thin. He would have, even if his master had had plenty of fodder, because he was that sort; but also because Francis Istenes himself couldn't get ahead. Indeed, during Laddy's service with him and until he joined the farm cooperative, Laddy's partner was now a dappled cow, now a white heifer calf, now a lame horse, a mule left over from the war, or a small mountain horse, with whom it was always torture to draw the plow or even to pull an empty cart, because they were all slower-gaited or took smaller steps than the aging Laddy, who had to pull in their stead.

A calmer life, but few joys and much to endure; that was Laddy's lot in the new era, too, because men were gladdened by democracy and the distribution of free land, but the horses had to work the land made fallow by the war, to draw rattle-trap carts and rusty plows.

III.

History took another step. This Laddy did not know, though he felt it. In 1951 the Istenes family—after much soul searching—joined the cooperative, but of their two horses they only brought along one, the younger. They sold old Laddy and, on the proceeds, bought boots and clothes for the always ragged children. (It was little they could buy.)

What became of Laddy?

Where else could he have gone than where the swirl of history swept him? For the fate of a horse is bound up with the fate of man. There was no market for him among the peasants, who were selling their horses now: tractors and combines were taking their place, and in the villages it was the young animals that were needed. Horses were being bought by the transport and building firms, by the "Belspeds" and "Szefus."

This historic whirlwind snatched up Laddy, too, bringing him to the outskirts of Budapest as a draft horse.

But that whirlwind brought not just horses but drivers, too. In the old prewar days, when this town was built, if a sturdy peasant lad grew tired of his sixty-*filler* hire back home and of the ever-

shouting slave drivers who looked on men as dirt, he went either to
America or to Budapest as a day laborer. Or, if he had a mind to,
he could be a teamster or loader. This required no more than the
courage to undertake hard labor and the strength of an ox. Such
enterprising peasant lads now attended university or other courses,
became tractor drivers, "Combinists," skilled industrial workers or
miners, while the new teamsters—because the people of the old era
keep going as long as they can—are recruited from the former
"gentlemen." But who among them drift here? Not the real gentlemen or *bona fide* members of the middle class; they prefer illicit
frontier crossings or servile obeisance to the regime rather than
teamstering or loading, so only the former quasi-gentlemen come,
ignorant of everything in the world except issuing orders to man
and beast. (But ignorant really even of that, for, after all, only those
really command whose stupid orders it is possible to appeal. They
were former Hussar sergeants, mounted police, orderlies, and such-
like, who were too acceptable to the ruling class and too unacceptable to the people to suit the new regime now.)

So this was where Warrant Officer Csoka also found himself, and
here he might have met with Laddy, could he have recognized him,
had he been the sort of man to whom the soldier is also a man and
the horse one of God's creatures. But to him a soldier was only
cannon fodder; the horse, matériel. Laddy fell into the hands of
such a Csoka who, however, was called Gaal. In the village registry
back home he was plain Gal, but he had to differentiate himself
somehow from the other "common" soldiers. In his days as an
orderly he once saw a periodical in his master's waiting room—its
editor was listed as Moses Gaal—and this variant of his own name
pleased him no end.

But for that matter, Laddy wouldn't have fared any better with
one of the roaring, tippling teamsters either, because they had never
driven such a bright and honest horse but only lumbering, lazy,
wily nags. . . .

After sundry trials with lazy, sly, and malign beasts, they finally
harnessed him with another blooded gelding called Badar. (Where
might that colt-crazy peasant lad be, who gave him this graceful
name?) He was younger than Laddy, but more mischievous, too. If
in a good humor, he pulled; if not, he left it to Laddy and wouldn't
tense the traces though they beat him to death. A senseless and

stupid rebel he was, because by pulling once and then not pulling, he showed he could but wouldn't; and he was more obstinate, more capricious than a bad woman. For the true rebel would rather die than surrender; Badar, however, was incalculable—sheer risk for the teamster at every start, for it seemed ever doubtful whether they could even budge the loaded wagon.

Laddy had to suffer for all this. The more so, because his driver, this Gaal, was not much of an Imre Mezei. When Laddy first saw him and first opened his mouth obediently for the bit, first lowered his neck for the collar, the mysterious instinct which till now had somehow guided him in the world of men warned that this again was not a good man; here once more was an enemy. Yes, but what can a horse do, restrained as he is by bridle, bit, and collar, and getting his very food from his master's hand? What can he do? He obeys. . . .

So when he sensed, by the time that had passed and the sounds of loading behind him and also by the cart's creaking, that the load was great, a thousand devils tugged at his nerves. Though now he couldn't see just what and how much they were loading because he wore blinders—which, to be sure, were invented so that skittish horses might not see behind them or toward either side, lest they shy or bolt when someone tries to pass them, but which also serve to keep wily horses from seeing the size of the load piling up behind them. Except that in the case of such wise and experienced horses as Laddy, and such cunning ones as Badar, not even blinders are worth much; they already feel how hard it will be to start, and when they clamp the bits on them before the pull, they already are burning with fear, and thereby their strength is less, too.

For in the vast sandy loading yard the cart wheels always sink in. In rainy weather the horses and trucks gouge muddy puddles all over the big yard, but especially before the narrow-gauge railways loading ramp, while in dry weather the start is hindered by crumbly sand and a motley scattering of half-bricks, broken tiles, crumbled concrete. Because once they can move out and gain the paving by the gate and thence reach the street, even a heavy load feels comparatively good as they plod evenly toward the still-unknown goal where they will be freed of their burden and gaily rumble with the almost self-propelling empty wagon homeward bound. (How the horses can hasten toward a full manger, just as men to their dinner!)

For even that was gladness now, that at the end of a hard haul there gleamed the land of promise: the feed bag with a little fodder and pure water (plus a few kind words and one or two pats from a good driver), though this they could also rightfully expect from even a bad driver, since it was part of official regulations, even if the horses didn't know it and had no complaint book. . . . They even get their fodder ground up, yet how much better oats and maize are when they can be chewed fine. But time is precious, and some efficiency expert or other proposed that draft horses be made to eat quickly, because chewing involves time and effort, and that is a loss for the owner. (Oh dear! May the good Lord give that expert only pap for the rest of his days.)

These, however, are only minor griefs which, compared to the greater, count practically as bliss. The real misfortunes are those that must be endured if they have to stop on the way on an incline, a bridge, or a barrier and get stuck or can't start, because then, alas, it is just like when they were fleeing westward at the end of the war and were left on the road at Rabaszentkereszt. Around them roared, clanged, and screeched the toiling city, people by the hundreds of thousands and millions, concerned with their own affairs, troubles, joys. One fears that he'll be late for work; the other that they'll close the store before he gets there; a third is rushing to the beach, otherwise he'll die of the heat, and for him it's the peak of pleasure to plunge in the water; a fourth hurries to a rendezvous, fearing his darling will leave him in the lurch because the bus was delayed; and so on. Everyone bustling about his own affairs, even the teamsters passing them, because they, too, have their own aims, plans, and orders—more pay, more free time, one for one thing, and another for another—so indeed, if a team like Laddy's gets stuck, there isn't anyone likely to help, though they broil in the sun, are hungry, thirsty, and tired. At most, a passerby stops, surveys the suffering, whipped horses, saying: "Poor beasts!" or "Brutal driver!" then grumbles and goes off on his own business so he may the more quickly forget the painful scene.

The driver—whether Gaal or another—detests these curious

bystanders who are always sorry only for the horses but don't give a hang about the driver. But even if they should feel for them, he'd hate them if they didn't help. And they certainly don't. How could they when they don't know anything about it? Besides, why should they soil their clothes, what's in it for them? So most of the sympathizers melt away, saying: "Don't load them with so much!" "Feed the horses better," "What are trucks for?" or some such thing.

But that sort of trouble very often is the fault of a bad driver who stops to rest not on the level road before the incline, as Imre Mezei used to do, but before the tavern, and then seeks to make up the time at the expense of the Laddies. Because Laddy pulls with a zeal that carries Badar along, too, giving every last ounce of strength at Ulloi and Vaci Avenues, Margaret Bridge, or the sloping streets of Buda, so they can reach the level stretch above. And if the driver were as wise as Imre Mezei and liked Laddy and his fellows better than the half-liters of wine, then before each incline he'd hold a friendly little conference with his horses. But no, he almost always goes wild with rage, vents on the horses all his wrath and bitterness against the firm, the regime, his whole life, and the whole world.

At such times Laddy—the willing, obedient Laddy, loyal unto death—weeps, weeps, weeps in his soul, helplessly and innocently suffering, while again and again he puts forth all his strength a hundred times and a thousand times just to start the wagon. Because against blind cruelty and malign stupidity there's no defense, and though you expend your very soul (in human language called only "vapor" when referring to a horse), there's no such thing as appreciation or even plain common sense when a good horse falls into the hands of a bad man.

For animals with a memory less vivid—dogs, cats, oxen, and bulls—it may be easier. How good it would be, an hour later, to know nothing of how they got stuck in the factory yard, or at the railway barrier; oh, how good if the sting lasted only so long as the welts on his back. But what can Laddy do if he can't forget, if, as they approach places where they got stuck, palpitating fear besets his heart? Here's where we get stuck, here comes more beating and shouting!

And then again, Laddy can do nothing about what will probably remain the everlasting strategy of every teamster: to whip the horse that pulls the best. Laddy cannot know—his equine logic does not extend that far—that humankind is always swayed only by expediency and oblivious to justice when it's a question of getting on. And he may rage against vicious Badar—sometimes he even bites him in the neck—for, indeed, his partner is the source of most of his suffering. He knows the cart would start if they pulled together, but if Laddy pulls, while Badar just dances, the effort is vain because it just twists the wheels. Yet Badar is infected with a dogged belief that it's not worth being obedient or honest or industrious as far as the human species is concerned, and so, just for spite, he won't pull.

And this teamster, this Gaal, is a real enemy; he'd like to blast everything and everyone because of having to work, and in the lowliest state, fallen to teamstering from the rank of God Almighty in the barracks. This creature hasn't a kind word for Laddy even after they complete a fine haul and arrive somewhere. He doesn't always bother, either, to shove him his ration of chaff or, if he does, takes no notice when sly, grasping Badar seizes Laddy's feedbag to see if perchance it may contain something better than his own and then tramples it underfoot.

On such occasions Laddy, as is the wont of aging horses, goes limp and hangs his head as if he were the embodiment of measureless sorrow, sorrow over the liberty lost thousands of years ago by his equine forbears. He doesn't sleep, doesn't sleep, just hangs his head. Yet, oh how he slept in the days of his colthood. What he liked best was to sprawl in the middle of the barn, stretch out all four legs, rest his head and neck on the floor, and just lie there playing dead. He wouldn't look up, wouldn't even budge if Lou Murvai or anyone else entered the barn. Either they'd have to step over him or detour around him, because they hated to rouse him, unless they had to lead the horses to drink or hitch them up.

But where is this happiness now? What happened to those days? Gaal, ruthless Gaal is here, and beneath Laddy's hoofs he finds bricks, sand, cement, crumbly cinders or splattering slime, perhaps hard granite or concrete; and even the joy of the feedbag dies, because they smuggle rotted hay into good fodder, smuggled lest

the horses or the board of directors notice that the rick was rain-
soaked, the hay spoiled. And the directors don't notice, but Laddy
does, only he can't speak—can't speak, even though they beat him
cruelly, even though his soul weeps.

That's how it was on that hot summer's morning which—so far
as we know—marked the last turn of fate in his life. A bunch of
rolled wire netting for reinforcing concrete had been dumped before
the company office by some thoughtless teamsters, since there wasn't
space elsewhere and the warehouse supervisor was away when they
got in late at night. (They, too, had stalled somewhere.) Now it
had to be moved. Yes, but that coil of twisted steel was tricky to
handle. Not big to look at, but heavy. It hung down from the back
of the wagon, which rocked and swayed under the load. In front
of the office the yard surface was naturally cinders, because the
mud had been unbearable, squashing inside the workers' shoes and
open sandals. Cinders do absorb mud and are satisfactory under the
feet of men, because—after a good long while—they tamp it smooth
and hard. Cinders do well enough even under the wide-flagged
truck wheels, till broken up, but are hardly the thing for horses'
shoed hoofs or the sharp iron rims of the wagon wheels—are,
in fact, dangerous and worse than mud.

However, teamster Gaal had not thought of the cinders when
they loaded. He got up in the box and gave a great shout, "Gee-
ah!" as was his custom. (He had a throat of brass, tempered at
the barracks.) Laddy lunged forward in terror, but Badar, aware
through some mysterious instinct (or lucid horse sense, perhaps,
who can say?) that the load would be heavy and the terrain was
bad, simply refused to make an effort (why do they load on so
much?) and, like one who knows that now he'll get it, began
prancing desperately. Laddy, of course, dragged the wagon, but
this made it all the worse, because the front wheels, turning askew,
dug up the loose cinders, thus blocking the way.

Then began the usual uproar. Gaal didn't want to descend from
the wagon, but urged on the horses with his whip. Vainly did the
day laborer who helped with the loading—a thin little elderly man—
remonstrate: "These horses can't move the load, Comrade!"
(Neither was a Party member, but they addressed each other this
way before their superiors because the townsfolk were fed up with

the old uncle-son business, and the new titles apply just to officials and skilled workers. Yet they might be worlds apart in principle— or at least in their view of life.)

"If they don't, I'll knock them dead," replied Gaal, fanning his anger, beating the animals, and twisting the shaft right and left.

The thin little man couldn't stand this.

"That's no good. Stop beating that poor creature!"

Now Gaal flew into a rage.

"Get out of here, that's all, I say, or I'll settle with you, too, I'm in just the right mood. . . . You think this is the first time I've held a whip. . . . I know what I'm doing. That's what the blasted nags are used to. First they dance the Kallay two-step . . ."

"Look, my good fellow," insisted the thin little old man, as if he hadn't even heard the rudeness (just teamster talk), "the wheels dig up the cinders, can't get rolling. Come, let's get a few boards, stick them under the wheels; once they're rolling, the horses will draw the load if they're willing. That bay has spirit, I see; the other is a bit on the roguish side. . . ."

"Aw, quit preaching and mind your business. We've loaded the steel, so tell the foreman"—he gestured with his left thumb—"that we're ready. I don't need advice. . . ."

At this very moment the company director, Comrade Salanki, was sitting by the open window, studying the latest decree about reducing overhead, here on the spot, because over at the main office he could see nothing but figures on paper. And, among much else, it struck him—as he scanned the supply-depot budget—that they were spending huge amounts for horses, yet getting ridiculously small returns on their sale. It might be a good idea to call in the department head.

A few minutes later Comrade Kerner, who was in charge of the depot, was sitting at the end of the table, facing the window just like Salanki.

"Tell me, Comrade Kerner, what is to be done here? Expenses in every department must be reduced. We spend a lot on horses, but take in very little. How do matters stand? What do we do with the horses?"

"Comrade Director, the horses wear out, and we sell them to the horse butcher, naturally for very little. We pay four or five thousand *forints* per horse and are lucky to get back four or five hundred. Machines wear out, Comrade Salanki. Why shouldn't horses?"

"Yes, Comrade, but aren't our horses wearing out too soon? Isn't there some inefficiency here, aren't we wasting resources and public funds without reason? Listen . . ."

It was at this moment that Gaal went into his frenzied "gee-ahh-ing" and vituperation beneath their window, and the two officials looked down.

"Shh, just listen, don't say anything," said the director, because Kerner wanted to shout out the window that if the horses couldn't make it, they should get an extra team and stop wasting time. (It didn't as yet occur to him that they oughtn't to torture the horses.) And the two officials, straining their ears before the open window but without letting themselves be seen, listened to the whole altercation. "Look, Comrade Kerner, there's the answer before our eyes. They beat our horses to death, and then we go and buy others. But that's not all. Such torturing of animals is intolerable." And he recalled having read an unforgettable story about a horse written by Tolstoy. The horse, too, is a living creature—perhaps one with a soul—not a machine. Yet even a machine can't stand mishandling and abuse, though manufactured on endless belts, while horses are born only once a year, carried eleven months in the womb.

But the fracas down below continued. Stifled curses sounded. "Laddy, you . . . The devil take your stinking hide, Badar! Bada-ar! Bada—a-a-ar . . . Just wait, your hour has struck!" Then the sharp swish of the lash, blows, the rattle of shaft and chains, the creak of axles. The wagon groans, and the steel nets shift with a metallic clank, but the wagon doesn't move. "Saints in heaven!" sighed the thin little man who has been trying to push the wagon from behind—but what can one man's strength avail here? "They have the sense to pave the walk for themselves, but not this rotten yard. . . ."

Comrade Salanki, who himself used to be an electrician (maybe if he'd been a stonemason, he wouldn't have taken any notice, because they get used to the ceaseless torment of the horses around them), felt ashamed and looked at Kerner. "Listen, Comrade Kerner. That criticism down there rings true—he's right! This yard is terrible. Come, let's take a look around."

And again he glanced out the window, just as Gaal flew at the horses once more, this time whipping them from the ground.

Salanki paused.

"Comrade Kerner, look how that light bay pulls. See him stretch and strain, almost breaking in two. . . . Look how the teamster, that beast, mauls him, foaming at the mouth. Is it always this way?"

Comrade Kerner was nonplussed. He hadn't counted on an ill wind blowing the director here just when they were moving the steel nets.

"Well, no," he finally stammered, "only when they get stuck." (He wasn't going to admit it was always that way; he'd have to make him believe it was just coincidental.)

Comrade Salanki, by then, wasn't even listening but called from the window to the confounded Gaal, who now exclaimed: "Oh, my fat head! Is there someone up there?" A man, when he flies off the handle, neither sees nor hears.

"Look here, Comrade, stop beating those horses! We'll be down right away."

A few moments later they stepped out through the door that opened on the yard and headed straight toward Laddy and his partner. Gaal stood frozen in his tracks, as in his sergeant days when he saw the captain coming, who at such times always berated him whether he had done anything wrong or not. He couldn't deny his soldiering past now either. There he stood, stiffly at attention.

"Why are you beating the horses, Comrade, tell me why? Have you no heart?"

Gaal was silent at first, but then had to speak up; after all, he was the driver.

"They're bastards, Comrade. Besides, the yard is very bad here. . . ."

"Then why don't you get help? Why do you load on so much?"

"We can't take less—that's the norm. We can't go with half a load. They'll pull it all right, once we're out on the street."

"Well, why not take just half a load to the gate, then load the rest there?"

"But that's not in the norms," interjected Comrade Kerner. "There's no way of accounting for half-loads."

"No way, no way—then let's make a way! Aren't we the ones who set the loading norms?"

The thin little day-laborer who stood there beside the wagon now spoke up. "Pardon me, Comrade Director, for interrupting. All we need do is to pave the yard. There lie all those paving blocks in the corner"—he indicated the far corner of the great cluttered yard. "Iron bricks stood on end will also do. Look, there's a whole pile the stonemasons can't use anyway because they can't be worked. . . . The wheels roll easily on those, and the horses have something to grip on. . . ."

"That's true. See, Comrade Kerner? Why haven't you paved that yard? It's fantastic that every street in the whole town is paved, yet in factory yards and at supply depots the horses and cars are mired axle-deep in mud, sand, cinders."

"It's not in the Plan, Comrade Salanki."

"Not in the Plan, not in the Plan. . . . Then why don't you put it in? We've killed sixty horses in three years. Was that in the Plan?"

"I wasn't here then, Comrade Salanki"—always a good defense—"and there was talk of economizing . . ."

"Fine economizing. We save on paving blocks but beat our horses to death. Just look at these poor things. Why in heaven's name haven't I seen it till now? Sixty horses destroyed in these few years, and probably it's the same with other firms, too. . . ."

"Where will we end up at this rate?" was the thought that flashed through his mind. Then aloud, he added: "We must do it, we must pave the whole yard!"

"There are no funds," admonished Kerner.

"There'll have to be! We'll make funds."

The thin little day-laborer again spoke up.

"With your permission, Comrade Director, the whole thing wouldn't have to be done at once. It's only the loading points that should be paved right now. First of all, over by the narrow-gauge tracks, where we always load up. The men should be told to unload everything there; don't let them scatter the stuff all over the yard like they've been doing. Those three wagons loading up will start just as hard. Look, they're trying to pull out with one of them now. . . . Then too, Comrade Director, the road could slope a little, just a very little toward the street, because most of the loads are outgoing. Believe me, we'd save the expense in horses. The poor things could haul more and live longer."

This reminded Salanki of something else:

"How long do our horses serve, Comrade Kerner?"

"Well, that depends. Hungarian horses don't generally hold out long, and the Muras aren't easy to come by these days. The younger ones last as long as three years, the older do well if they hold out six months. But some can't stand it for even six weeks in our sort of work."

Comrade Salanki shook his head:

"Now tell me, Comrade, I see you know horses," he said not to the stiffly attending Gaal, whose very face was repulsive, but to the thin little day-laborer. "How long ought a horse to last?"

"Well, at hard labor, at day-by-day carting, eight or ten years; at farm work, ten or twelve, but even twenty if well treated. I once had an old mare—she died at twenty-six, but pulled to the last. And in the meantime, she raised twelve colts too—one a year, so long as her time lasted."

Salanki had still another thought: "And what do you say, Comrade Kerner? Is this the way it is at other places, too, is it this way all over the country where there's construction work?"

"Like this and worse. . . ."

"But where will we end up at this rate? Where are our eyes, Comrade Kerner? Our Hungarian horses are a thousand-year-old national treasure. We've been a famous equestrian nation and are squandering our heritage. Why, we even take account of good swineherds, shepherds, cowherds, and milkmaids; we reward them, they become Stakhanovites, Kossuth Prize winners. And what of the teamsters? How much does a teamster accomplish who drives a pair of horses ten years, Comrade Kerner? How many thousand kilometers does he cover? How many thousand carloads of material does he haul in a lifetime? Mountains, Comrade Kerner, mountains."

Comrade Kerner stared. He couldn't answer. In general, he didn't like questions that were too direct, and for several reasons. First, because in the past he was the director of a big transport company and came here as an expert, though still regarded as a bourgeois (actually, he only aspired to be one), and you never could tell what reply would be most strategic. Secondly, he never had seen where and how horses were born and raised, because for him they just came and went and in the meantime wore out. They bought them at the markets and sold them to the horse butcher or

to small-time contractors—where they might last a little longer—
and since they never considered anything except how much horses
cost, how much the teamsters' wages were, and how much the
profits, who would ever have considered the horses a national
treasure?

After a little reflection, he replied in a slightly apologetic, accom-
modating tone: "I couldn't say offhand, Comrade Salanki, but
I'll ask for a report and have statistics drawn up. . . ."

"Never mind that, Comrade Kerner, let's talk sense—this is of
national concern. I'll bring it up in the Party. Some grave neglect
has occurred here. We can't entrust our horses, either, to enemies
and evil men, so long as we can find good men. And we have
only to look for them. Once again, a question to which we were
blind . . ."

Then he considered again and turned to the thin little man
standing beside the wagon:

"You, Comrade. Were you a farmer or a teamster?" (He was
too thin and seedy looking for a farmer.)

"I was both, Comrade. Teamster and struggling farmer, too, but
I always had to do with horses."

"Well, how would you like to be in charge of them here?"

"That depends. Such torturing I wouldn't undertake for any
money. . . . After all, the horse is a feeling soul, too. He has more
sense than some stupid men. . . ." Evidently, he was thinking of
Gaal.

"Good, we'll talk about that." Then he turned to Kerner. "Have
them bring an extra team to pull out that wagon. As for you,
Comrade, may I ask your name?"

"Kereki, Michael Kereki . . ."

"I'd like to ask you, Comrade Kereki, to please come with me.
I want to talk with you awhile."

Next morning Laddy noticed that in place of the evil-looking and
alien Gaal he had a new driver—but this one seemed a man after
his own heart. It was a joy to see him fussing about with the traces
and harness, and before hitching up Laddy and Badar, he carefully looked them over, checked to see if their shoes weren't loose,
felt their tendons to make sure they weren't sore, looked into their
eyes, carefully blowing on them to see they hadn't contracted cata-

racts, because horses suddenly lose their sight in the course of terrible beatings.

And into Laddy's heart came the long-forgotten feelings of trust and tranquillity. This man would not be his executioner but a companion in toil. He felt it in his words, movements, and whole bearing; for perhaps Laddy still retained the intuitiveness of his noble ancestors, who helped their warrior masters by dragging the enemy from his mount and by kicking and biting in battle.

Even Badar settled down a bit, though in his heart there was more suspicion, and malice, too. And when the thin little man ascended the box (wonder of wonders!), the ponderous wagon surged ahead at the first pull, though some forty quintals of bricks weighted it down.

Yes, for this was an ingenious little man. Until they should lay the paving, he even put flat rocks under the wheels and in front of them, while the wagon was still empty, so the wheels could roll at once and so that he might gradually cure the horses of the paralyzing fear that each start meant curses and beating. For Laddy and his kind trembled so at starting that this sapped their strength in advance.

Yes, indeed. Teamsters must be chosen and trained just like chauffeurs or primary-school teachers. You can't entrust fine horses to lazy, unfeeling clods. And old Kereki, the thin little peasant, had a half-century's schooling in this. Why, he wasn't yet six years old when his father sat him on his first Laddy to go to the well. There wouldn't be any trouble; the horses knew where to go; all he needed was to grip the saddle horse's mane.

Badar still didn't entirely understand in what good hands, in what gentle, steady hands the reins were; but Laddy, who had already known an Imre Mezei, put his whole heart into doing each job well.

This life can no longer offer much to the aging Laddy. But what a great thing if his anguish abates and his ears no longer ring with that everlasting, terrifying "gee-ahh!"

Laci (Budapast), 1955.

6.

ART, SCIENCE, AND THE
FREE INTELLECT

The motivations of Ilya Ehrenburg are more than ordinarily obscure. At one time or another, he has been an émigré man of letters, a publicist for Stalinism in its heyday, a literary bureaucrat and bully, a virulent "anticosmopolitan" (though he is Jewish himself)—and finally, something of an impassioned defender of the freedom of creative thought.

This is an intellectual history which must have cost him dear. Even if we did not have Ehrenburg's recent novel, *The Thaw* (which added a new term to the vocabulary of post-Stalinism), and his long appreciation of Stendhal, we might still guess as much: his colleague and analogue, Fadeyev, committed suicide. But apparently Ehrenburg, through it all, has managed to keep his talent and his opinions—if not his integrity.

"The Lessons of Stendhal" is an impressive piece. Stendhal ". . . hated despotism and despised toadyism," Ehrenburg writes. " 'Even if a king is an angel, his government will destroy art—not by forbidding the subject of a picture, but by breaking the artist's spirit.' . . . discovery is not invention—it requires the development and inner freedom of the searcher. If society could have prompted Newton, Copernicus, Mendeleyev, or Einstein as to what, specifically, they should seek and find, their genius would have been unnecessary, and there would have been no discoveries."

• •

THE LESSONS OF STENDHAL

On an autumn night in 1829, a little-known French writer decided to write a novel—one without which it would be difficult for me to conceive of great world literature and my small life. . . .

On the night of October 25, in Marseilles, he did not sleep; he had conceived the book that he was to write in two sittings. He would subsequently give it a title over which literary scholars would rack their brains for a century. In this novel he was to show everything that tortured and inspired him: love and ambition, Pharisaism and spiritual courage, the black power of dogma and the red glow of conflagrations, war and revolution. He was to write about the present, the past, and the future. Naturally, he tried to cover his traces by saying in the introduction that he had written the book in 1827; he well knew the price that had to be paid for the truth. But who would believe him? Where the women whom he had loved would become indignant upon recognizing themselves in Mme. Renal or in Mathilde, the reactionaries would understand what ministers and what fanatics the book was about; one monarchy might succeed another, but for M. Guizot, Stendhal would remain the same suspicious freethinker he had been for M. de Martignac.

Stendhal played at hide-and-seek all his life. Mérimée says that he learned to do this because of the Empire police and the all-seeing eye of Fouché. . . .

Mérimée wrote in his necrology of Stendhal: "Perhaps some twentieth-century critic will select a book of Beyle from the great mass of writings of the nineteenth century and will take a more reasoned view of it than our contemporaries." Mérimée felt that the most Stendhal could hope for would be a posthumous recognition of his "subtle mind" and his "spiritual qualities."

Jules Janin, a well-known writer and critic of those days, wrote of *The Red and the Black*: "What an ineradicable demand to show everything in an abnormal light, to be coarse solely for the sake of instilling fright!" Hugo reacted to the novel with scorn: "I tried to read it but was unable to get through more than four pages."

Of the thirty-three books that Stendhal wrote, fourteen were published during his lifetime. They collected dust on the shelves of bookstores. Seventeen copies of his book *On Love* were sold in ten years. His publisher agreed reluctantly to print 750 copies of *The Red and the Black*.

Belinsky closely followed the books that caught the attention of his contemporaries; he mentions George Sand twenty times, Dumas eighteen times, Janin seventeen times, and Sue fifteen times, but he does not make a single mention of Stendhal.

Stendhal was known to very few people during his lifetime. French ministers, Papal police, and Austrian detectives knew Henri Beyle, whom they termed "seditionary," "Jacobin," and "atheistic." In their opinion, this suspicious person amused himself by writing nasty and, at times, even dangerous books. Literary scholars felt that Beyle had an incisive mind and that at times he wrote amusing pamphlets, but that he wrote novels in vain for he had no talent, no imagination, no taste. . . .

But today we are amazed at the indifference of his contemporaries, the reservations of Goethe and Balzac, and the short-sightedness of Zola. Of all the French writers of the nineteenth century, Stendhal is the closest to us. His style seems less remote than that of Balzac, and we find the exposition of the social milieu in *The Red and the Black* more profound than that in *Nana*. In the middle of the twentieth century, Stendhal's novels are read as contemporary literature within, as well as outside, France.

Henri Beyle foresaw this. He had no ambitions in literature, did not thirst for recognition, and suffered little from the mockery of the critics; but he was a long way from self-disparagement. He wrote to Balzac: "Death will make us change roles with them. When they are alive, they can do what they will with us, but when they die, they will be swallowed up forever in oblivion. In a hundred years who will remember M. de Villele or M. de Martignac? In twenty years who will remember their hypocritical rubbish? [He mentions Chateaubriand and Salvandy prior to this.] I have in mind a different lottery in which the biggest prize is to be a writer who will be read in 1935." And in actual fact, no one at present remembers the names of the all-powerful ministers of Charles X or Louis Philippe, no one reads the works of Jules Janin or Salvandy, but *The Red and the Black* or *The Charterhouse of Parma* may be numbered among the most popular books of our times. Hundreds of studies are being written about them, dozens of films are being made from them, and they are being read the world over. . . .

Stendhal is both a classic and our contemporary; he cannot be relegated to any particular literary movement; he is a realist to the extent that all great works—such as *Hamlet, Don Quixote,* and *Faust*—are realistic; he is a romantic in that, in portraying reality, he often changes the proportions, sees the heights, peers into the abysses, and thirsts for spiritual perfection (*le sublime*); this, however, does not comprise adherence to a literary school but wings, inspiration. He belongs to all, and each has the right to consider him his teacher. . . .

For me, the lessons of Stendhal lie primarily in his exceptional truthfulness. Indeed, that is the most important thing for us—not only for writers, but for all people in the middle of the twentieth century. The more ardent one's attractions and repulsions, the more insistently the conscience and the mind demand truth.

When people bothered Stendhal with questions about his profession, he would answer, half-joking and half-serious: "An observer of human hearts." This seems to correspond to the oft-heard axiom: the writer must observe what is taking place and, after interpreting his observations, describe life. Such a description of the writer's work—with the addition, "while evincing the complete objectivity required by art in the portrayal of reality" or "subjecting one's observations to social analysis and elucidating them with advanced ideology," depending on the type of society—is heard from the most varied sources. . . .

His whole life was filled with enthusiasms, work, travels, and struggle. He did not want to observe the human comedy from the first balcony, but acted in it himself. It was perhaps for that reason that some French writers considered him an incurable dilettante.

Flaubert's prescription and Beyle's life are irreconcilable. If one thinks about the work of these two writers, it might seem at first that Flaubert was an industrious master and Stendhal a superficial amateur. . . . At times Stendhal so disdained exactness of outward description that he set part of the action of *The Red and the Black* in Besançon, a town he had never visited, and calmly informed his readers of this fact. (Gogol knew Petersburg, Moscow, and the Ukraine, but had never been in the Russian town, far from all borders, that he uses as the setting for *The Inspector General*.) Does this mean that Stendhal wrote about things that he did not know? On the contrary, his novels amaze one with their inner authenticity. L. N. Tolstoy said: "I, more than anyone else, am indebted to Stendhal for a great deal. He taught me to understand war. Who before him described war as it actually is? Everything that I know about war I learned first and foremost from Stendhal." These words are worth thinking about. War in the novel *The Charterhouse of Parma* recalls anything but the traditional battle scenes. Stendhal shows the battle of Waterloo through the eyes of the young Fabrice—the small clumps of earth that the shells kick up, and the young man's feelings of fear, amazement, and naïve pride. This short chapter helped Tolstoy to understand war. Stendhal had not been at Waterloo but had encountered war in the Alps, on the Berezina, and in Germany. Old recollections helped him in 1838 to depict Waterloo, just as Sevastopol helped Tolstoy write *War and Peace*.

In tackling a novel, Stendhal "studied" nothing (only once, when he had some doubts about the intricacies of the feminine toilette, did he decide to consult Mantie—Countess Clementina Curiale). He was little concerned with props; he portrayed characters, passions, destinies. However, his characters do not live in an abstract world; we see their surroundings and understand their origins. . . .

I always enjoy rereading Flaubert's intelligent and unusually subtle writings. The author of *Madame Bovary* comes to life for me, and I see him with a book or at his desk rewriting a page for the tenth or the hundredth time; he is like a jeweler or a microbiologist. Not so with Stendhal. If he were living in our country today, he would surely have long been refused membership in the Writers' Union as a dilettante. He was a traveler, a connoisseur of music, a politician, a historian, and, least of all, a professional littérateur. . . .

As a young man, Henri Beyle had written: "My aim? To become a great poet. To do that, it is necessary to know people well. Style is something secondary for a poet." I said that Beyle did not live for literature, but his life enabled him to become a great writer.

If a writer is only an observer, he can give a beautiful description of his characters' outward appearances and acts and can show their daily life and morals, but something else is needed to lay bare the inner world of his characters and explain their actions. Talent and imagination hardly suffice for such a re-embodiment; one must have spiritual experience, for the writer's interpretation of his own experiences is clearly his key to an understanding of the experiences of others. Stendhal had such a key, and this explains the lasting quality of his novels. Conditions, dress, and morals grow old much faster than human passions. If young Communists are stirred by Shakespeare's tragedies, then why should anyone be surprised that even though there are no ultraroyalist plots, no Jesuit seminaries, and no stagecoaches today, the experiences of Julien Sorel are quite understandable in 1957?

After a great writer's death, whoever wants can make whatever claims about him he pleases. Thus, in praising Balzac, attempts

were made to disparage De Maupassant, and Eluard was abused
for the greater glory of Baudelaire. Mayakovsky was hissed in the
name of Pushkin, but twenty-five years later, singing the praises
of Mayakovsky in chorus, people condemned Martynov. At the
end of the nineteenth century, many Stendhal admirers cited his
books to denounce authors attempting to show a social cross-section
of society. These Stendhal admirers claimed that Henri Beyle was
an apologist of extreme individualism. In so doing, they often mentioned the word "egotism," which Stendhal introduced into the
French language. Stendhal first used this term in speaking of
Chateaubriand, whom he could not stand: "He reeks of egoism,
egotism, and insipid affectation." Stendhal called one of his books
of memoirs "egotism." He said: "For me, sincere egotism is describing the human heart." In his diaries, notes, and letters, Stendhal makes many observations about himself, but he is far from
being preoccupied with himself. Beyle was interested in himself
because Stendhal wanted to know people. A writer's spiritual experience depends not only on his experiences but also on his ability
to interpret those experiences. . . .

Stendhal lived unstintingly and stubbornly, and he constantly
pondered what he lived through. He was able to speak of himself as
of a character in a novel. . . .

Usually, the intrusion of the author in a novel dampens my
ardor as a reader, even when the author is more intelligent, subtler,
and more interesting than his characters. When I encounter di-
gression by the author, it seems to me as though a man has run
onstage to explain why the hero shot himself instead of getting
married or—and this is completely unbearable—to deliver the
reader a brief lecture on the antisocial nature of suicide or on the
superiority of creative labor over neurasthenia. The author's place
is behind the scenes. Stendhal, however, often appears in his novels.
Sometimes only a semicolon divides Julien Sorel's experiences from
Stendhal's commentary. Why doesn't this interference by the author
bother the reader? Probably because Stendhal was able not only
to speak of Beyle as of a character in a novel, but because he
spoke of the characters in a novel as of himself.

Gogol liked Stendhal's *Strolls About Rome,* but he would hardly
have accepted *Lucien Leuwen.* When Gogol went to France in
1837, he noted with disgust: "Everything is politics here." Stend-

hal did not feel that everything in France was politics, but he realized that politics occupied an important place in the life of his contemporaries. . . .

Formerly, French scholars ignored those chapters in his novels that were loaded with political events. Now some authors focus all their attention on precisely these chapters. It is, of course, ridiculous to show that love dramas served him only as a screen for propagandizing his civic ideas. For Stendhal, politics was one of the human passions—large, but not all-encompassing. It is not worth the effort to count how many pages of *Lucien Leuwen* are devoted to politics and how many to love. One can only note that in depicting passions, ambition, and crimes, Stendhal never forgot about politics. He could contemplate the stars and attempt to understand what night means for the one-day fly who dies before nightfall, but at the same time he read the latest issue of the newspaper; in the timeless he found the topical, and in the ephemeral the timeless or, as the poets say, the eternal. . . .

He hated despotism and despised toadyism: "Even if a king is an angel, his government will destroy art—not by forbidding the subject of a picture, but by breaking the artist's spirit . . . People want to please the minister or the deputy minister, their immediate superior. Though these ministers be the most honest people in the world, obsequiousness, flattery, and sycophancy will develop all the same . . . Suffice it to observe what happens in a small French town when a prince of the royal family passes through. Some ill-starred young man necessarily wants to join the entourage. He ultimately succeeds in doing so, not, of course, on his own merits but because he is not listed as suspect and his aunt likes to play cards with the mayor's confessor. Thus a young man is lost. He may be honest, pleasant, and, if you please, respectable, but he will forever remain a trivial soul."

Distortion of the soul by coercion, hypocrisy, bribery, and threats was a major and perhaps the main theme of Stendhal's novels. He made no attempt to hide his political sympathies; the role of a disinterested arbiter held no allure for him. The success of his novels shows that tendentiousness cannot harm a work of art if it is born of genuine passion and is in harmony with the artist's inner freedom. . . .

How does it happen that novels dictated by topics of the day

have not lost their interest for us? Beyle, who was fascinated with
political struggle, said: "I am disgusted by the mercenary and
transient political interests of the hour." He did not turn his back
on politics but was able to see further and more deeply. On the
margins of the manuscript of *Lucien Leuwen,* he wrote: "Things
must be done in such a way that adherence to certain positions
will not overshadow a man's passion. In fifty years a man with a
definite position will be able to move no one. Only that which will
remain interesting even after history has passed sentence merits
description." Stendhal showed the human traits in people involved
in political struggle and in this way saved them from an early death.
This is the difference between a novel and a newspaper, between
Stendhal and many authors of political novels, past and present,
who grow old even before the typesetters have time to set their
eloquent tirades, and, finally, it is the difference between the artist
and the one-day fly. Stendhal shows us that neither tendentiousness
nor politics can detract from a novel if the author is able to feel,
see, and think with the depth inherent in genuine art. . . .

Stendhal attacked not only a given mask but also love for masks.
Beyle's friend, Courier, was an excellent pamphleteer, and when
Stendhal wrote pamphlets he imitated Courier. Now few people
read Courier, but the political scenes in Stendhal's novels have not
faded with the passing of time. Is the tragedy of Fabrice really
limited in time and place? Beyle often said that the crux of the
matter is not the tyrant personally but the nature of tyranny. A
tyrant can be intelligent or stupid, good or evil, but all the same he
is all-powerful and powerless; he is frightened by conspiracies, he is
flattered and deceived; the jails fill up; cowardly hypocrites whisper,
and a silence settles in that is enough to stop the heart. . . .

Recalling his adolescence, Beyle said: "My passion for mathematics very likely stemmed from my hatred for hyprocrisy. Playing
the hypocrite in mathematics seemed inconceivable to me." Subsequently, Stendhal came to art; he realized that it admits of no hypocrisy. His thirst for truth coincided with his concept of the novel.
In 1834 he wrote: "In my youth I wrote biographies [Mozart,
Michelangelo]. This is something like history. Now I regret having
done it. It seems to me that one cannot attain the truth in writing
about things large and small, or in any case one cannot attain the
truth in details. Tracy said to me: 'At present one can only attain

the truth in a novel.' With each passing day I see more clearly that it is useless to seek it elsewhere. . . ."

The critics who have considered Julien Sorel an incurable careerist have often pointed out that the end of the novel is illogical, strained, and fortuitous. Why, in fact, did Julien Sorel shoot Mme. Renal? No doubt Mathilde would have had what she wanted, and despite the ill-fated letter, Julien would subsequently have become the Marquis de la Mole. All that is true, but Julien is not a cold careerist. He is seized with madness, he ceases to think rationally, and is like a lunatic. He thinks he is taking revenge on Mme. Renal, and it is only when he regains his senses in jail that he realizes that he loves her.

Of course his act is not an attractive one, but Stendhal transforms him from the accused to the accuser: the guilt rests with a society that demands hypocrisy, condemns for truth, and tramples large feelings for the sake of its many conventions. . . .

Zola felt that Stendhal scorned reality. Recalling the night scene in the garden when Julien first finds the courage to press Mme. Renal's hand in secret, Zola wrote: "One is not aware of the surroundings. It might have taken place at any time and any place, so long as it was dark." Zola noted that Stendhal described neither their clothing nor their situation and gave, in his opinion, few indications of the characters' social positions: "Naturally he knew life, but he did not show it in its true aspect. He subordinated reality to his theories and showed it in accordance with his own social ideas." In Zola's opinion, Stendhal was guilty of subjectivism and was therefore not a realist.

Stendhal's contemporaries were offended by his novels, claiming that the writer slandered French society, that the proper provincials were not like Mme. Renal, that the seminary in Besançon was a poor caricature, and that the Marquise de la Mole and Verriere's women were the fantasy of an author seeking cheap effects.

Stendhal defended himself. He was not afraid of vituperous comments, but behind the magazine critics he saw (and not without justification) the shadows of royal police. He said that his novels portrayed reality, that he was not exaggerating, not caricaturing, and by no means slandering. In *The Red and the Black* Stendhal wrote: "A novel is a mirror on a large road. It reflects now the azure sky, now filth, puddles, and ruts. And you bring an accusation of immorality against the person who has the mirror. The mirror reflects the filth, and you accuse the mirror. It is better to accuse the road with the ruts or the road inspection service." In his foreword to *Armance* Stendhal said: "Perhaps some two dozen pages are satire . . . We ask of the reader the same indulgence shown the authors of the comedy *Three Blocks*: they held a mirror up to the public, and it is not their fault if certain monsters recognized themselves. Whose side is a mirror on?"

But according to Zola, Stendhal scorned reality. His contemporaries reproached the author of *The Red and the Black* for having distorted reality. Stendhal answered: "I am a mirror." One might add to this that Zola ascribed the distortion of reality to Beyle's philosophical and political ideas, and the critic (understandably an academician) Faguet maintained that Stendhal was simply unintelligent: "In his whole life he did not have a single idea." (In our textbooks on literature, Beyle is listed as a representative of critical realism.)

The longer I study the history of literature, the less I understand the classification of schools, trends, and authors. Even Aristophanes was reproached for having distorted reality, and perhaps he spoke of a mirror in reply. Gogol tried to explain that there are various optics—for observing the stars and examining the tiniest of insects. Stendhal wrote about what he observed, and like all writers he observed far from everything. Even Zola, who claimed to be objective, scientific, and disinterested, selected subjects that corresponded to his ideas and created characters in his novels that served his purposes; he highlighted certain feelings, threw light on others in passing, and left still others in the dark. Stendhal's "mirror" was not a polished surface; he did not reflect but observed, depicted, and transformed. The perspective of Uccello's "Battles" has nothing in common with the perspective of a photograph. Hemingway's dialogues are not like a mechanical transcript of any, even the most dramatic, conversation. The chapter in *The Red and the Black* on the trial of Julien Sorel is least of all like a stenographic record of court proceedings. However detailed a social analysis of the development of a society, however much a person might be subordinated to general processes, the world of the novel is distinct from that of philosophical generalizations, state plans, and statistical data.

It is as though the writer discovers a man, but discovery is not invention—it requires the development and inner freedom of the searcher. If society could have prompted Newton, Copernicus, Mendeleyev, or Einstein as to what, specifically, they should seek and find, their genius would have been unnecessary, and there would have been no discoveries. Neither Helvetius, Rousseau, nor Saint-Simon could have prompted Stendhal's discoveries of the spirit. Tendentiousness in art is by no means the same thing as an arbitrary alteration of proportions and the subordination of the character's acts to the idea of the novel. Only bad books are made in that fashion. Under favorable circumstances, they can, of course, play a certain role, but they are topical books. In altering proportions and changing perspectives, the author is subject to the strict laws of artistic truthfulness. Only if he observes these laws will the reader accept his interpretation as a reflection and his word picture as a mirror. Stendhal created a world which, though real, was anything but a copy of the world that existed in the 1830's and 1840's. If that is critical realism, then to the end of my life I will rack my brains to discover what distinguishes it from the artistic methods of that revolutionary and humanistic realism toward which the progressive writers of the world are presently striving.

Zola felt that the lack of a meticulous description of the external aspect of characters, their clothing and situations, was a shortcoming in Stendhal. In my opinion it was a feature of his that grew out of his world view and his conception of the novel. . . .

Stendhal had great respect for the reader's imagination. He spoke of the "picture that the reader's imagination forms" and left large borders; the reader had to do a lot of filling in. Stendhal wrote the following about a novel by a mediocre writer: "It will be read, praised, and quickly forgotten . . . Everything in it is true, and everything is insipid; nothing, or almost nothing, in the book was worth writing about. This novel will please readers devoid of imagination. . . ."

He hated pseudo-poetics and false pathos: "I cannot stand it when in place of the word 'horse' an author uses the word 'stallion.' In my opinion, that is hyprocrisy. . . ."

Let us open *The Red and the Black.* Here is one of the most pathetic moments: Julien's stratagem of sending love letters to Mme. de Fervac has succeeded; the proud Mathilde has capitulated. Julien is also seized with passion. Stendhal immediately becomes laconic: "Best I omit description of such strong distraction and bliss. Julien's happiness was equaled by his self-control. 'I must leave,' he said to Mathilde, having noticed the sunrise on the chimneys to the east, far beyond the gardens." (In the Russian edition this passage is translated as follows: "But perhaps it would be more sensible to abstain from describing such a violent beclouding of the reason and such prodigious bliss. However, Julien's courage was no less great than his happiness. 'I must leave by the window,' he said to Mathilde as the sunrise glowed crimson on the distant smokestacks far beyond the gardens to the east.") The translation is almost twice as long as the original. Many explanatory words have been added, and the last sentence is broken into two sentences. I do not say this as a reproach to the translator. Stendhal felt that that was precisely the way George Sand would "translate" his novel. The translator attempted to lend a more traditional character to Stendhal's laconic style. . . .

In the Montmartre Cemetery in Paris the tourist's attention is drawn to the grave of Heine. In that same cemetery there is another grave, with an inscription in Italian. Henri Beyle requested in his will that the following be written on his gravestone:

> Arrigo Beyle
> Milanese
> Lived. Wrote. Loved.

Some visitors, taken aback by this inscription, might ask if Stendhal did not repudiate his homeland. In one of his books Beyle good-naturedly told about the amusing character in an Italian *opéra bouffe* who, in answer to the question as to what place he was a native of, answered: "Cosmopolis. You may consider me a cosmopolite." (Words have peculiar fates. In Stendhal's time the concept of "cosmopolitanism" was related to the ideals of the humanists of the eighteenth century, with their dream of a "world republic." One hundred years later the word became a term of disdain everywhere.) Some scholars of our day say that Stendhal was a cosmopolite in the modern sense of the word, that he loved Italy, ridiculed France and the French, and repudiated his homeland. Beyle, in fact, lived half his life in Italy, spent about three years in Germany, and visited England several times. . . .

When he lived in Paris, he had many foreign friends: a German doctor, a London barrister, Italian revolutionaries. He also had Russian friends: Sobolevsky, A. Turgenev, and Vyazemsky. (Stendhal did not know with what love his Russian friends spoke of *The Red and the Black* at a time when the people who bought and read Beyle's books numbered a few dozen.) Stendhal often mentioned his "Hispanophilia"; he had seen only Barcelona, and had been sent away from the city by the police, but the tragic traits inherent in Spanish genius had an unflagging attraction for him. There was nothing of the nationalistic swaggerer in him, nor had he any contempt for foreign ways of life. He saw both the good and the bad within his homeland and outside of it. . . .

Stendhal spoke of foreign things now with love, now with hatred; that which was foreign to him was his own. He was not a cosmopolite, but he was not a provincial either.

People have alleged that Heine was not a German poet because he loved France. They have alleged that Herzen was not a Russian writer because he bowed before the sacred stones of Europe. Stendhal loved his homeland, but he could countenance neither false praise nor false patriotic ostentation; he was too fine a person to beat his chest at the crossroads of Europe and proclaim the primacy of France. But, in recalling the early years of his life, Beyle wrote: "We had no religion other than the most important idea of being of service to our homeland. . . ." The controversy over Stendhal's cosmopolitanism is the old quarrel about the true nature of love for one's homeland: whether such love entails contempt for other peoples and eulogy of the faults and shortcomings of one's fellow countrymen. For maudlin patriots (and there are such patriots in France), Arrigo Beyle the Milanese was a rolling stone. But, for France, he was and remains one the clearest examples of French genius.

He said that all human unhappiness is the result of falsehood. For him the writer's work was to serve the truth. He wanted to reconcile truthfulness with the freedom that he felt was inseparable from human happiness. In jest he once said that in America the people are free to elect their streetcleaners but that they have no freedom: they cannot walk gaily along the street on Sundays because puritanical hypocrisy will not permit it. He wrote: "One must learn to flatter no one, not even the people." He knew for a fact that the happiness of one person is inconceivable without general happiness, and this explains his political passion. He also knew that social progress is not enough, that great feelings are also necessary. "More than anything and before all things, I love simplicity and goodness, especially goodness . . . That is the one thing I desire." For us, who have been raised on the Russian literature of the nineteenth century, such words are familiar and understandable. A half-century later, Stendhal's ideas about truth and art were repeated by a Russian writer who would seem to have nothing in common with him. "One can lie in love, in politics, or in medicine; one can deceive people and the Lord God himself—and there have been such cases—but in art it is impossible to deceive," said Chekhov.

Thus did Henri Beyle live, write, and love. Could any writer or, in fact, any man dream of more?

Inostrannaya Literatura (Moscow), June, 1957.

A physicist of major international reputation, Leopold Infeld lived for many years in the United States, where he worked in intimate association with Albert Einstein before returning to Poland after World War II. Among his many publications is *The Evolution of Physics,* a book written in collaboration with Einstein, which had a considerable vogue in the mid-thirties.

■■■

FOR THE DIGNITY OF SCIENCE

. . . In the first place, the aim of what I am writing here is not criticism for the sake of criticism. Brooding over the errors of the past for the sake of brooding is futile and unnecessary, but only through an open and candid discussion of errors shall we be able to get rid of the bitterness accumulated in the hearts and minds of many of us; only in this way shall we be able to remove the wall standing between many scientists and the socialist system which we want to build together.

In the second place, what I am writing here is critical. However, it does not mean that I do not appreciate the support owed by Polish science to the Party and to the government in the past period, or that I do not appreciate certain real achievements of our Polish Academy of Sciences. . . .

Since the beginning of the Polish Academy of Sciences, we have been given as models worthy of following not Copernicus, not Sklodowska-Curie, not Smoluchowski, but Lysenko and Lepieshinskaya. I am not a biologist, and I know about the work of these scientists only from my talks with biologists. Still, it is not necessary to be a biologist to be skeptical with respect to the proposition that soda baths are the fountain of youth. However, the problem itself does not matter to me now, at this moment. It does not matter now whether Lysenko was right or wasn't. For the time being, I am interested in the methods introduced by him into the world of science, and their echo in Poland.

There is an English word for which there is no equivalent in the Polish language. It is the word "bully." The verb derived from this is "to bully." A "bully" is a domestic tyrant, a petty tyrant, a brutal man who imposes his will upon others by means of shouting, and if this is not enough, by means of kicking and beating—literal beating or mental beating. . . .

When I was still on the American continent, I read the text of a lecture by Lysenko given by him in 1948 and subsequently published in English. After the lecture, a question was put: what did the Party think about his views? Lyensko answered that the Party took a stand for his views and his teachings. During my short stay in Poland in 1949 I got the impression that, after all, in Poland there was a different situation, and that in our country the Lysenko methods were not applied to scientists. Perhaps Professor Dembowski remembers the dinner we had together, during which we discussed this problem, so very painful for me then—the problem of Lysenko. How this problem subsequently rebounded in Polish biology we are told in the article by Petrusewicz and Michajlov, printed in *Nowe Drogi,* in September of last year.

I quote from this article: "What was the final result? Often it was superficiality and generality in our propaganda, sometimes it was dogmatic pronouncement instead of reasoning and proving, generally it was assertiveness. But we went still further. Not being able always to persuade, we used to have recourse to ordering people about, administrative pressure, closing the columns of periodicals to our opponents, and so on." These forms of "bully" pressure, which, according to the authors, were applied in Poland, do not need comment. However, the article itself struck me rather unpleasantly. It was written without any doubts whatsoever. On the other hand, it seems to me that there are also correct formulations in this article. I agree entirely with what the authors wrote about the relation of the Party to science. We read in this article: "It is also obvious that the Party cannot take any stand on particular scientific issues, let alone decide on scientific issues. It can only contribute to their solution by helping in the organization of research, by encouraging creative discussions based upon fundamental principles of dialectical materialism."

But the authors do not draw any conclusions from their own premises—one would like to add, in the authors' style, "the only right conclusions." These would be: those who want to decide on behalf of the Party upon the controversies between Lysenko and the

Morganists abuse the authority of the Party. Scientific controversies in biology can be solved only by experiment.

A biologist whom I consulted in these matters wrote to me:

"This sad period is about to reach its end. In the Soviet Union and in our country as well, the works of Lysenko and Boshian and Lepieshinskaya have been rejected after discussion and scientific criticism. But the effects of this period continue to endure to a great extent. And it is our duty as scientists to liquidate them in the most speedy manner. If we take biology as a science, and not as a social function, then there cannot be two biologies—the new one and the formalistic one, the Soviet one and the Western one. There is only one biology—the one created by facts taken from reality; the one based upon honest, competently managed scientific research.

"In order to insure that such a biology develops in our country, we must guarantee to all scientists in Poland a situation in which genuine freedom of research will prevail and scientific dishonesty and careerism will be unable to exist."

I will give another example. As a result of the discussion on the theory of the structure of organic particles that took place in the Soviet Union in the years 1949-1950, the Pauling theory of resonance was condemned as being idealistic.

Pauling is a great chemist, a Nobel Prize winner, one of the pioneers in the application of quantum mechanics in chemistry. . . .

It is a fact that at that time—in the early fifties—the theory of resonance was unknown to Polish chemists, because to understand it one must be thoroughly acquainted with wave mechanics. This theory was even more zealously criticized in Poland when critics were told that those parts of the theory unknown to them were allegedly "Machist." A characteristic feature of the critical opinions published in Polish periodicals, as well as in the materials of the conference of chemists held in Bierutowice in 1952, was unfamiliarity with and lack of understanding of the mechanism of the condemned theory. A well-known chemist, who participated in the discussion, said that one might as well abandon the theory of resonance, if only because it could not be experimentally demonstrated. Were we to be guided by this approach, we should have to abandon all of contemporary physics.

A colleague of mine who is well acquainted with these problems wrote to me: "The participants in the discussion at the Bierutowice conference revealed in their opinions their unfamiliarity with the elementary notions of quantum mechanics and their applications. The false views as regards the contemporary state of theory in organic chemistry are still very much alive even today."

I come now to the third problem, the one which is nearest to me personally. It is the subject of the theory of relativity and the subject of Einstein. Thus, in the *Short Dictionary of Philosophy,* a publication which will remain a monument of shame of the past period, we look in vain for an article with the heading "Einstein." Neither has this name been included in the article "Space and Time," in which, however, we find the names of Butlerov and Fyodorov.

Before I unfold this story, I must add here a very essential note. It is hardly possible to underestimate Soviet science, its gigantic development, in spite of the dark sides about which I am going to speak. The reason for this is that this science is being developed by modest and quiet people such as Wexler, Landau, and Tamm, and not by bullies of the Lysenko kind. Now the Twentieth Congress has removed the fetters imposed upon science by those bullies who thought it the proper thing to elevate Soviet science by degrading non-Russian science. Science is international, and scientists of all countries should cooperate with one another for its development.

Our friendship with the Soviet Union is a very important matter from the economic point of view, from the point of view of maintaining peace, and from the point of view of the development of science. This is known and recognized in Poland. But a very bad service was rendered to the cause of this friendship by those who have been constantly proclaiming Russian priority for every idea, whether important or not. By this officiousness, they have made ridiculous Soviet science, which has gained one of the leading positions in the world even without their shouting. Soviet science was made almost ridiculous in Poland, and a bad service was rendered to the cause of our friendship with the Soviet Union by those who in our country adopted the loudest opinions, the least objective opinions, and emphasized them with their own even louder shouting and noise. How many times was I approached by very young people with the question as to whether Mendeleyev and Pavlov were really great scientists! This is the result, and it was symbolized by writing about Butlerov and Fyodorov and not about Einstein in the article on space and time, or by attributing in this dictionary the discovery of the famous equation $E = mc^2$ to Lebyedyev and Vavilov and not to Einstein. Incidentally, this dictionary has been published in Polish, and it is being used, unfortunately, by all our postgraduate students of sciences.

In the Soviet Union some philosophers—and it might be more proper to say "quotologists"—have unleashed a storm against the theory of relativity because it is idealistic. How about this theory—they argued—and its assertion that there is no difference between the theory of Copernicus and that of Ptolemy? So, according to Einstein, Giordano Bruno and Galileo suffered needlessly from the Inquisition, and therefore Einstein should be classified, as one of the reviews has called him, a "priest-follower." This argument was repeated many times by the quotologists, but of all physicists known to me in the East or in the West there was only one serious supporter of it, and he had his own theory, not recognized by other physicists, modifying the theory of relativity.

What was the echo of these facts in Poland? The articles by quotologists were translated into Polish; generally speaking, people in Poland have been seeing Soviet physics in a crooked mirror. These problems were presented as if the quotologists were right. Great Soviet scientists such as Wexler, Landau, and Tamm have been shouted down by the stentorian voices of the bullies and quotologists.

In 1953 a scientific session was held in Poland on the 410th anniversary of the death of Copernicus. The Academy of Sciences, while preparing this session, had to choose between two paths. It could either invite someone living in Poland who had spent many years on the relativistic Copernican problem, or it could invite someone who would not say anything contrary to the opinion of the shouters and quotologists. I am anxious to say here explicitly that I accuse the Academy of having chosen this second possibility. Therefore, that solemn session became a travesty of scientific gatherings. Professor Banachiewicz, then our one living astronomer of world fame and renown, did not speak at these meetings.

And now another recollection of that period. I remember a session organized by the Academy in the Parliament building and devoted to the works of Stalin. At one point a physicist took part in the discussion. He explicitly criticized Einstein, Bohr, and Dirac as idealistic physicists. Professor Pienkowski, who was seated next to me, whispered in my ear: "Idealistic physics isn't doing badly to have produced people of that caliber." In fact, the attack by that colleague had very little—not to say nothing—in common with the defense of Marxist positions. He took his arguments from the quotologists armed with selected sentences from the works of Marx and Engels. But these great creators of dialectical materialism could not foresee the direction of the development of physics, which turned out to be so different in the twentieth century from what it had been in the nineteenth.

The period of ignorance has come to an end, let us hope forever. The Soviet Union is now going through a period of renaissance in the physical sciences because the fetters that were slowing down their development have been removed. To a great extent, public accessibility has been restored to Soviet science. Cooperation with other countries is becoming increasingly wider, increasingly explicit. For me, the symbol of Soviet science is not the discovery by Lysenko of the rye in the wheat (or perhaps it was the other way around) but Wexler's synchrotron ten-billion electron volts strong—the greatest discovery in scientific technique of our times. Let us hope that this renaissance of science will also soon take place in our country. . . .

We should fight for the democratization of our institution. We should fight against the principle of secrecy in the sciences in all cases where secrecy functions only as a screen for ignorance. We should fight for the principle that Polish science should be under the guidance of scientists and not of administrators who do not understand its needs. We should fight for educating more personnel, especially in those branches which are understaffed. We should fight against insincerity and mendacity, of which we still have, unfortunately, too much. We should fight for the rebirth of scientific thought in order that there should be no retreat toward that ignorance on the fringe of which we dwelt for the last five years. We should fight for the dignity and the future of Polish science.

Przeglad Kulturalny (Warsaw), June 21-27, 1956.

A comparatively young man, Miklos Gimes fought in the anti-Nazi underground during World War II, and later, as a Communist, joined the staff of the Hungarian daily, *Szabad Nep*. In 1952 he went abroad as Paris correspondent for his paper, returning in 1954 to join the editorial staff of *Magyar Nemzet,* the voice of the People's Front. The following year, he was expelled from the Party—a premature advocate, it seems, of "normal" relations with Yugoslavia—but was soon active in the Petöfi Circle debates which challenged the authority of the Rakosi government.

Active in the revolution, he was arrested in November, 1956. He was one of the three men executed along with Imre Nagy.

....

TWO KINDS OF TRUTH

If discussions are to have real meaning, we must be concrete. Thus, so far as the phrase "standard of living of the working class" denotes something real and measurable, it must rise, fall, or remain static. Yet in recent years when we put the simple question, "Is the living standard higher or lower at any given point in time?" it was hardly usual to get a real answer. When we wrote that the standard had risen, it was not, as some of us supposed, the "people's truth" that we proclaimed; alas, we merely lied. (The fact that some of us spoke or wrote in good faith made no difference at all.)

Let us take another example, this time from the Rajk affair. The Hungarian press declared—and it could hardly have done otherwise —that Rajk's guilt was plain as day, dark as night. And the foreign bourgeois press proclaimed—from the very first day of the trial— that the accusations were a tissue of lies, the procedures illegal, Rajk innocent. No doubt a simple regard for truth was not the sole motive of that foreign press. Yet if we ask now if Rajk was, in fact, guilty as charged, there is only a single truth: he was not guilty. He was innocent. And his innocence did not wait seven years to become fact; it was fact in 1949. Thus it was the bourgeois press which wrote the truth, and it was the Communist press which did not.

But I hear objections. What good is it to flagellate one's self?

243

What good is it to dredge up this sorry business of the standard of living and the Rajk trial?

The answer is that the pernicious theory of two kinds of truth haunts us still. Perhaps it is true to say that in the beginning we Communist journalists had no doubts; but later on our doubts grew. We began to ask ourselves if the life of the Hungarian working man was really better, if the facts of the Rajk case were really as proclaimed, if all things were really for the best in the Party and the nation. And if we suppressed these doubts, it was not merely because we lived in fear or were ignobly addicted to our creature comforts. We subscribed to the grotesque theory that only those things which aid the Party in the struggle for political objectives are true. And when objective truth contradicated the needs of Party policy, it ceased to be objective truth. . . .

Thus, little by little, we came to believe that there were two kinds of truth. Yet Party truth and the people's truth could sometimes differ, and so truth and political expediency were in the end synonymous.

However frightening such a realization may be, we must face up to its plain meaning. If there is a truth superior to objective truth, if the criterion of truth is mere expediency, then a lie itself can be true—for even a lie can be useful. In these terms, a sham political trial can be "true," since the short-term political advantages of such a trial may be compelling. And so, inevitably, we arrive at that theory which eventually served to corrupt the inventors of these sham trials—and even, at times, the victims themselves. We arrive at the theory that tainted the whole of our public life, that seeped into the innermost chambers of our souls, that degraded us, that paralyzed our critical faculties and finally robbed so many of us of the power to see the truth. This is the way it was; and it is no good denying it.

I know that these examples are elementary, that the discovery of truth is often a complex task. I know, too, that these affairs had wider implications. And I am aware, finally, that they must be studied in context. I do not wish to repudiate political and utilitarian philosophies. If there is only one truth, nevertheless, ideologies, opinions, and policies may legitimately differ. And I take it as self-evident that the Hungarian press ought to serve the ends of the

Party. But by writing *truth*. Always by respecting truth, even when that truth embarrasses our stale propaganda.

Our philosophy demands that we respect the truth, even if we may hate the reality about which we write the truth. The science of Marxism-Leninism, socialist policy, and socialist journalism all begin by proclaiming what is. Without this steadfast regard for truth, it is impossible to change what is.

It may be that I have written nothing but banalities. If this is so, these are banalities which our press has seldom found room to print. We journalists, we writers must solemnly swear never again to sacrifice ourselves to the baleful theory of two kinds of truth. Never again to permit the chasm between truth and lie to be ignored. . . .

We serve the people only. And we will defend them—but only against lies.

Bèke és Szabadsag (Budapest), October 3, 1956.

Macourek's verse is sensitive—and discreet. One of the younger generation of Czechoslovak poets, he reached maturity in the years after the *coup d'etat* of February, 1948. His first volume of poetry, *You Won't Believe Your Eyes,* was published in 1958.

....

THE PRINCIPLES OF A SHREWD CANARY

Main thing is
    to get the time right,
when to sing
Not to sing in the morning when the master shaves,
because the master
sings himself
Further,
to know what to sing
Not to sing just anything
that comes to your mind,
sing only what is proper
for a canary,
a canary in a cage
To warble, to sing lightly
and clearly,
not to sing about the cage,
but rather sing about the hempseed
Not to think selfishly only of yourself,
but sing about dried ephemera
on behalf of golden fish in the aquarium,
which cannot sing
because they are,
as is known,
dumb

Thus to sing in the most joyous way,
in the most mellow way,

    and not to turn around
    either to the blue air
    or to red flowers in the window
    or to the sun
                 Novy Zit (Prague), September, 1957.

Gyula Hay fled Hungary while still a very young man, after the collapse of the revolutionary regime of Béla Kun in 1919, and spent the next twenty-five years in Austria, Germany, and the Soviet Union, where his plays won an international success. (*God, Emperor, Peasant* was staged by the great Max Reinhardt.) In 1945, he returned to Hungary, where as a Communist he rose to a position of considerable influence in the world of politics and letters, winning the Kossuth Prize for literature more than once. But his social conscience continued to trouble him; his subsequent history is a parallel to the careers of men like Tibor Dery and Peter Veres. In 1955, he joined the reformist movement associated with the name of Imre Nagy. On the tragic morning of November 4, 1956, when Soviet tanks attacked Budapest, he broadcast an appeal to the world in the name of the Hungarian Writers' Union. He was subsequently imprisoned.

SOME OBSERVATIONS ON LITERARY CENSORSHIP AND FREEDOM

. . . I hear the anxious question: Do you really mean *absolute* freedom to write, to create? Let's face up to it. Absolute freedom is exactly what I do mean—or, that is to say, absolute freedom within the context of our social order. Let nothing be forbidden to the writer that is not, in any case, forbidden by the general laws of society. I do not ask that you permit a writer to incite to arson or murder, or to violence against the socialist system. I will not permit him to practice racial discrimination or some similar atrocity against an economic or social subclass. I do not want him to tyrannize over the rest of us. He may not slander, nor may he offend against our deepest moral sense, despite the fact that our morality has never been drawn up as a body of laws.

But a writer must be free to tell the truth. To criticize anybody or anything. To be sad. To be in love. To brood over death. To ignore the balance of light and shadow in his work. To believe in the power of God. To deny God. To doubt the wisdom and honesty of our economic planners. To think as a Marxist, or not as a Marxist, however much the originality of his thoughts may anger the dogmatists of our day. To deplore the wretched life of this or that group, though the authorities may proclaim that it is not yet their turn for better things. To consider unjust what the courts and the police say is just. To dislike certain public figures. To suggest an honorable way out of our difficulties, even though this solution be considered visionary by the political and economic pundits. To say these things even if, in fact, the pundits are right and he is wrong. To call a public building ugly, even though the government proclaims it a monument fit for eternity, justifying the millions so unwisely spent. To note that the city is shabby. To criticize a leader's way of life and habits of speech. To fight for the welfare of mankind, even when less sensitive souls see no outrage. To love the steel combine at Sztalinvaros. To hate the steel combine at Sztalinvaros. To experiment with bizarre literary styles. To hold Aristotelian dramaturgy in contempt. To hold intensely personal literary views. And so on . . . and so forth.

Who can deny that even a short time ago all these things were forbidden, that to have offended in any respect would have meant the full punishment of law? And even today, what is the situation? Perhaps now these things are grudgingly tolerated; but in no sense are writers truly free.

Writers must have freedom; they must protect this freedom to the end.

But, you say, is this *absolute* freedom? Is this *all* you mean? And perhaps those of you who are in the habit of branding writers as anarchists put the question somewhat sadly.

Our answer is: yes. In any sense that matters, this is complete freedom, just as we are truly free when we walk in the streets, though even the simple act of going for a stroll is justly regulated by the laws of society. Freedom is not license; and we do not protest that freedom to stroll in the park or through the streets means freedom to trample others, or to cross against a red light. We do not strike a bus driver when he asks for our fare. We do not slip a slingshot into our pockets for the purpose of smashing street lamps along the way. Nor do we chop down trees. But we *do* feel that our freedom is curtailed if we are fenced off from the forward section of the streetcar merely because our skins are dark, as is the case in America. We are not free if, on the way to visit a friend, a soldier stops us, ordering us to take a different route. We are not free if we are to be tormented in endless interrogation sessions (as happened to one famous author not long ago), merely because we wish to visit a little frontier town for no better reason than to satisfy a nostalgic longing for the scenes of childhood.

There are prohibitions and prohibitions. One kind—be it traffic laws or literary standards—protects our dignity. The second grossly offends against all that it means to be human.

Literature needs no special regulation.

For anything which is properly forbidden to literature—forbidden in the name of society—is forbidden in any case. The same social institutions that serve for other violations will guard us against literary offenses and punish the offenders. I must stress this because the plain truth is that it is not the open enemies of literary freedom who do the greatest damage; the greater inroads on literary freedom stem from the work of those special departments of the state that were set up in the past to supervise literature as such. These departments exist still; and since it is counter to the laws of bureaucracy that they should enjoy idleness, they lash out at writers and literature from time to time. . . .

Thus there has been a lot of talk about setting up a board of directors to govern the publishing industry. I cannot say much about the technical side of the question. Perhaps there is some need for a special commission to coordinate purchases of paper stocks, plan printing schedules, eliminate bottlenecks, and the like. But it is not to be endured that this commission should have authority over books to be published. Under no pretext would this be tolerable—not even if the fiscal argument were advanced that to publish such and such a book would be too expensive. The sad fact is that pettifogging objections are always made to anything that is new, strange, or daring, and these objections are almost always garbed in considerations of money. So long as a government department is not specifically forbidden to exercise supervisory powers, it will inevitably constitute a further barrier to freedom of literature. . . .

As for the theater, the situation is certainly the same. Innumerable official and unofficial meddlers operate under the aegis of the

Dramatics Department of the Ministry of Education. And in this office there is a most copious supply of gratuitous—and often conflicting—opinions eventually scheduled to appear in the form of interminable and capricious administrative orders and regulations. This plethora of rules, especially when combined with the bumbling efforts of the lower-level functionaries, inevitably results in the smothering of creativity and the virtual destruction of dramatic freedom. We know the outcome all too well: the Hungarian theater, which once had an international reputation, has been silent for years. . . .

But any survey of the manifold problems of censorship and literary freedom would remain incomplete without some consideration of that most terrible of all literary autocrats, the *self-censor* who sits in judgment on the very heart of the author. It is a rare man indeed who can endure an endless series of rejections and humiliations meted out by politically minded editors. Quite unconsciously and even quite against his will, the author begins to succumb: a whole network of inhibitions grows in his soul—inhibitions which, after a little time, crowd out all novelty of expression or originality of feeling, since *they* do not value these qualities. This unintentional self-mutilation will not cease until such time as we have destroyed all external barriers to literary expression—and even then, since much damage has been done, it will take time. . . .

It is a fact that conditions of literary freedom will throw new responsibilities on the critics. They will be able to meet these responsibilities only if they share with the authors in the enjoyment of such freedom. (The guiding spirit of the Party will thus best be expressed through the work of intelligent criticism; and in any case, such criticism is infinitely to be preferred as a method of determining the direction and content of literary production to mechanical censorship, a practice which can only lead to the growth of a personality cult.) Yet even real criticism cannot be achieved through the routine process of issuing orders to the critics which they obey, more or less skillfully, either out of conviction or, less honestly, out of a sense of discipline. The Party will do best to make its influence felt by subtly educating the authors, the critics, and (first of all) the reading masses in an increasingly pure and limpid Marxist understanding, thereby assuring the creation of truly progressive works conceived in the spirit of *partiinost*. Such works will outclass those of competing schools, evoking a vast popular response.

Of course, if all this is to come about, it will be necessary for some of our Party men, once and for all, to reconcile themselves to the proposition that literature is simply literature and not a vulgar extension of *agit-prop*. A true Communist will look upon literature as a wondrous tool, the creation of the human mind, through which the great voice of the people is put into words— that voice which, if not heard and understood, makes the ideal of a pure Communist policy a futility; that voice whose full meaning the people themselves only come to understand when they hear it from a sensitive author.

But how far are we still from attaining any such ideal! Let us simply look into the case of Tibor Dery and that fine short story, "Behind the Brick Wall."* Not long ago, the story cropped up in two separate conversations with Party men. I have a deep regard for both men: one is certainly an honest man, though in late years he has had little enough chance to express this sense of honesty; the other is a perceptive critic who caught the new spirit in Soviet letters long before the Twentieth Party Congress and the attack on Stalin. Yet each man, speaking quite separately, seemed to have the same thing to say. Essentially, they were so deluded as to believe that Dery had defended the idea of theft—theft of public property. They had missed entirely Dery's passionate objection to brutality, to a style of punishing offenders which çan only degrade them and, indeed, aggravate a human situation which is profoundly sad.

What was the source of this pathetic oversimplification? The answer was not hard to find. Both these Party men are well aware that pilferage is a common practice among the workers in our factories; both understand the economic causes of these thefts. But since neither knows of a good remedy to the problem of depressed living standards, they think it "untimely" and "unwise" for Dery to air the problem and most particularly wrong to suggest that measures invoked by the authorities to deal with these thefts are counterproductive.

Now I should be quite unfair to my two friends if I did not say

---

* *See* pp. 12-24.

at once that they have plenty of company in their beliefs. A good many other people misinterpreted what Dery was saying—although "Behind the Brick Wall" is fundamentally an unambiguous story and simple enough to understand. The real fault lies with the critics, our Party's literary policy, and finally the writers themselves, because it is they who have submitted to "inner censorship" and so corrupted our understanding.

Here we are squarely up against the old demand that a writer who describes evils immediately advance a practical solution. As long as an author is unable to do so, goes the argument, he must not hector the authorities. This is an absurdity: it is as if we were to demand of our authors that before concerning themselves with the troubles of the common people, who live badly, they first study economics at the university. If they prove so brilliant at economics that they are able to produce a reliable system for the speedy improvement of living standards, why then, and only then, may they proceed to their novels and poems. As long as they are not able to solve our problems, why then they must keep silence. The troubles of the people are no business of theirs.

What a tragic pessimism this is!

The tragic misunderstanding and petty degradation of the great social role of literature must come to an end. Those who still hold firmly to such archaic principles are due for some shocks. The future will not spare them. Indeed, the sounder our literature becomes, the more bitter they. . . .

Irodalmi Ujsag (Budapest), September 8, 1956.

It would be impossible to exclude Pasternak from a collection which purported to be a sampling of the new literature of protest, though Pasternak is not a revisionist even in the most latitudinarian sense of the term. But the publication of *Doctor Zhivago* in 1958 was a literary event; and the actions of the Soviet authorities who forced Pasternak to refuse the Nobel Prize for Literature inevitably linked his name with a "movement" which he transcends and which, in any case, he antedated by twenty years or more. For Pasternak is really not political. As Babette Deutsch has written: "If, as rarely, he writes . . . with political implications, it is to assert a truism that needs constantly to be reaffirmed: that the vitality and the virtue of poetry, as of every art, lies in the poet's ability to realize his own experience, large or little, in his independence of dictatorship, from the left and from the right, in his gift for linking the past with the future by work that is as old as sunrise, and as new."

Thus, in a century of vulgar certainties, Pasternak is a kind of antediluvian survival, obscure, mystical, and profound; it is as if one of the gentle creatures of Hesiod's *Theogeny* had survived into the degenerate age of iron. This is the measure of his crime in Soviet society. It is not that he is anything so simple as anti-Party or anti-state; he is an affirmation of another Russia which cannot forever be denied.

The poem reprinted below was composed late in 1958; it reflects the poet's torment in the aftermath of the Nobel Prize affair.

BEAST IN AN ENCLOSURE

I am lost like a beast in an enclosure.
  Somewhere are people, freedom, and light.
Behind me is the noise of pursuit,
  And there is no way out.

Dark forest by the shore of the lake,
  Stump of fallen fir tree,
Here I am cut off from everything,
  Whatever shall be is the same to me.

But what wicked thing have I done,
  I, the murderer and villain?
I, who force the whole world to cry
  Over the beauty of my land.

But, in any case, I am near my grave,
  And I believe the time will come
When the spirit of good will conquer
  Wickedness and infamy.

                        Moscow, 1958.

The doctrine of socialist realism is the implacable affirmative. In the years after World War II, composers like Aram Khachaturian were summarily instructed to compose music which plain people could whistle, and poets were trained in the art of the positive view. It has been said that only one man—Andrei Zhdanov—understood socialist realism, and he took the secret to the grave.

"At the Same Time" is a good-humored piece. Still, it has some of the bite of Swift.

■■■

AT THE SAME TIME

Some of Rembrandt's pictures limit themselves—and quite wrongly—to rather plain Dutch men and women. His study of an old woman's head, for example, suppresses the "positive" attributes of the female population of the Low Countries in his day, failing to stress that at the same time beauties accounted for a not negligible percentage of contemporary womanhood. In his "Kreutzer Sonata," Tolstoy libels all Russian husbands because he fails to say that at the same time the overwhelming majority of Russian husbands were not warped by a streak of morbid jealousy. There is a comparable lack of reference to the bright side in Balzac's *Père Goriot,* although it must be obvious that all the daughters of France in that age were not wanton self-seekers. Equally culpable is Shakespeare's omission in *Hamlet.* The bard fails to emphasize the favorable aspects of life in medieval Denmark and at the same time fails to record the admirable deeds of other iron-willed princes and courtiers, fastening on Hamlet's languid broodings to the exclusion of everything else. Similarly, it was a mistake to condemn the insolence of office without mentioning at the same time the good work of other government offices.

Generally speaking, the broad picture that opens before us is grim and depressing. The luminaries of the arts have steadily encroached on that golden rule of aesthetics, the law of "at-the-same-time-it-must-be-pointed-out." Even individual characterization must be sacrificed to the inexorable demands of this basic law. For suppose

256

that I choose as my hero a laboratory assistant who is not only fickle but a confirmed tippler. Would I not have to consult the various files and official directories in order to learn the names and addresses of all other laboratory assistants and, by painstaking research, make it known that while our hero may well have a weakness for women and the bottle, there are at the same time 8,734 of his colleagues whose characters would seem to be without blemish, another 648 who, while abstainers, show some measure of lightness in the matter of women, and yet another 683 who are, conversely, chaste though addicted to drink? This statistical character study would hardly take longer than ten or fifteen years. In all probability, therefore, three or four generations of writers might conceivably finish a story dealing with, say, six characters. This method should, indeed, be applied retrospectively. Shakespeare's *Macbeth,* for example, gives a patently misleading and negative portrayal of the Scottish courtiers and their womenfolk of the period. One should therefore ascertain, by delving deep into the archives, the true statistical position—and supplement the present story by the addition of five new acts containing all that "should at the same time be pointed out."

A great deal remains to be done in the field of painting. "A Summer's Dawn on Lake Balaton" or "Autumn Twilight in the Dolomites" ought to be replaced by huge tableaux demonstrating that Lake Balaton and the Dolomites at the same time can boast more than dawn and twilight or summer and autumn. They rejoice in all the seasons and hours of the day. We should, therefore, depict all these together—unless we wish to mislead the unsuspecting. Leonardo da Vinci, while basically a positive and constructive artist, merely chose to immortalize the famous Mona Lisa smile; but Comrade Giaconda was surely given to tears as well, to laughter and daydreams, and even to fury at times. These changing moods should have been recorded on a twenty-four panel Leporello print.

There is a staggering amount of sloppiness in the field of essay writing. Here, too, the more notable essayists have taken inexcusable liberties, often limiting the scope of inquiry to a single problem, process, or phenomenon, instead of dealing with both sides of the issue like good double-entry bookkeepers. How blatantly one-sided and objectionable are Zola's editorials on the Dreyfus affair, yet they are unaccountably considered works of merit! Is it not obvious on the first reading that not *every* French staff officer was wrongfully imprisoned and not *every* War Ministry official wanted to keep the innocent Dreyfus in prison? Zola says nothing of what else happened at the same time. His single purpose was to fight for an isolated cause; and though he gained ultimate victory, the articles are still deplorable. They are full of negative evidence.

Sadly enough, this excessive stress on the negative is also present in medical practice. Doctors are inveterate monomaniacs. As often as not, they do not assure the patient that, while his kidneys do leave something to be desired, his liver, heart, stomach, and spleen are at the same time working quite faultlessly—and, for that matter, that the patient does not show symptoms of diabetes or epilepsy. Accordingly, he is, on the whole, in robust health; no drastic surgery is indicated. A negative diagnosis of this kind is therefore apt to put all sorts of ideas in the patient's head; he will spare no effort to cure his diseased kidneys, and spend no time rejoicing at the positive fact that the rest of his organs are in fine condition. Members of the medical profession try to justify themselves by saying that the human system is guilty of the same one-sided reaction. If we suffer from a toothache, say, we do not feel that at the same time the 150-odd pounds of flesh that constitute our body are not in pain. Yet the size of the throbbing tooth is negligible compared to the body itself. Pain, then, is only a warning of the need to cure a minor disorder in an otherwise healthy body. But this defense on the part of doctors does not, of course, hold water. There is no doubt that they have stumbled into the error of facts torn arbitrarily from context.

When we turn to poetry, we see that whole forms of verse ought to be scrapped outright. Elegies are, as a general rule, woefully lacking in the more serene and cheerful aspects of life; odes tend to be wanting in unbiased criticism. Lyric poetry is positively—no, in fact, negatively—obsessed with love to the virtual exclusion of the major achievements of science, industry, commerce, and agriculture. The charms of a certain Laura have blinded the poet to the glorious fact that this year's country-wide average of questionnaires duly completed and returned has exceeded by thirteen million the corresponding figure for last year, and that production at the State Institute for the Supply and Completion of Inspiration has shot up to unparalleled levels.

Most celebrated poems lack the proper balance between the positive and negative; they lack an over-all statistical survey. Endre

Ady's famous poem "Blood and Gold" should have been entitled "Bodily Fluids and Metals," so as to forestall criticism of his failure to provide a complete and unabridged list of juices in the human body, and of all metals as well. Verlaine's famous couplet:

> *My soul, to what thy great sorrow hath grown—*
> *Because of one woman, of one woman alone*

would, in essence, be correct, except that it gives no indication that his soul derived pleasure from other fair ladies.

All this brings us to the total rejection of our own Attila Jozsef's "Ars Poetica." For a long time, many of us have admired this passage:

> *A would-be piper, mark you well,*
> *Must pass through the gates of hell*
> *To be taught by his descent*
> *How to blow his instrument.*

Under the "at-the-same-time-it-must-be-pointed-out" rule of aesthetics, it is not to hell that the piper must descend; it is not that he must tune his tormented and highly strung nerves to the excruciating agony of our changing times; nor is he to project his inspired self into the human spirit, to express the never-yet-expressed under the spell of compelling vision, to plunge himself, and those who succumb to his powers, into the all-redeeming catharsis of music, form, or word. No, definitely not. Instead of hell, he should withdraw to the library in search of materials. For lessons on approach and method, he is to look, not to the great men of the arts, but to the stock clerks and double-entry bookkeepers of his day.

Irodalmi Ujsag (Budapest), September 15, 1956.

Granin's ugly little story has no hero. Its bitter lesson is that "silence is the most convenient form of lie."

"A Personal Opinion" appeared along with Vladimir Dudintsev's novel, *Not By Bread Alone,* in the pages of the Moscow literary journal *Novy Mir.* Its editor, Konstantin Simonov, is the author of *Days and Nights,* an epic novel of the Russian front widely read during World War II.

■■

A PERSONAL OPINION

The young man's arrogance irritated Minayev, and yet it was strangely attractive too. Olkhovsky rejected each of his suggestions. Minayev sat at his desk, nervously shifting the inkstand to and fro, and the shrill squeak of metal on glass was unpleasantly akin to the sound of Olkhovsky's words. The young man—boy—spoke the plain truth: the academician Stroyev's tractor designs *were* expensive and inefficient. But Minayev could not allow an article like that to be printed. It was hopeless, of course, to expect Olkhovsky to understand that criticizing a man like Stroyev would compromise the institute and Minayev, too, whose own position as director had not been confirmed.

Minayev spoke gently: "Listen, I put this as a friend. Let's cut out all this about Stroyev. And the critical part of your article—it needs rewording. Then it would be easier to print."

Olkhovsky rose from his chair. His normally pallid face was flushed; his delicate hands were tightly clenched.

"If I did that, what would the article say at all? Nothing." His thin voice grated. "His designs would waste thousands of tons of gasoline. And you—how can you . . ." He broke off. "No, not at all. No revisions. It's unethical. . . . Nothing in the world . . ."

"Bravo," thought Minayev, and his mood was only half ironic. There was something in Olkhovsky's pose that seemed familiar, and all at once Minayev remembered. He had been a young man then, exactly like this, fists clenched, voice raised in anger. . . . Some time, long ago, he had stood like this, hair tousled, the Komsomol pin flaunted bravely on the lapel of his worn jacket. The memory seemed unbearably touching, but he was careful to give nothing away. His eyes remained dull, half hidden by heavy lids. His overlarge yet mobile features remained guarded, and his lips were fixed in an equivocal smile.

His voice was cold. "Ethics. You all toss the word around. Try making it something real. Try earning the right to realize your ethics. Yes, Comrade Olkhovsky," he said with a mean joy, "make your ethics real instead of a slogan. To win through, a man must sacrifice a point now and then."

Olkhovsky leaned over the desk. From under his unruly shock of hair his dark accusing eyes burned at Minayev.

"What about you, Vladimir Pakhamovich? Have you won the right to ethics?"

The puerile self-assurance grated on Minayev, but he maintained the same fixed smile that had proved his ransom in a hundred difficult situations. Casually, he said: "Be careful, or you'll knock over the inkstand." Olkhovsky flushed and stepped back. "So you see," said the urbane Minayev, "it's important to stop in time."

But when the interview ended, Minayev was left with a vague sense of unease. He thought to himself: It's all right for now . . . only one thing is important now. When I really am the director, then I can help Olkhovsky. Even Stroyev won't matter then. I'll have my own opinion, speak my mind. But it's not enough to have an opinion—you've got to have position, too. These thoughts usually calmed him. They came to him, almost unbidden, whenever he was forced to make an unpleasant switch.

Not long after, an inquiry—over the signature of Local Party Committee Instructor Loktiev—found its way to Minayev's desk. A letter from young Olkhovsky was pinned to the document. Minayev read the letter and exploded. "The cowardly policies of Minayev," read the letter, "constitute a structural archaicism. . . . If a man has a position like his, then he must permit himself the 'luxury' of defending his own opinion. . . ."

The stupid puppy, thought Minayev. The fool.

Minayev answered the letter himself. The reply was laconic, correct, and deadly, exploiting Loktiev's notoriously morbid suspicion.

Olkhovsky, it seemed, was a crank and a hothead. His cheap harangues wasted other men's time. As for his own work—not good, even regrettably mendacious.

The letter, Minayev knew, was pretty heavily weighted with these charges; but so much the better. When he came to the signature, Minayev signed with a flourish. The pen scratched, and Minayev winced at the sound. What the hell, he thought. Could he compromise his future, his hopes, for the sake of a stubborn boy? Olkhovsky had left him no choice. It's nothing, it's nothing, he thought. Later I'll set it right. And he filed *"l'affaire* Olkhovsky" under unfinished business—something to be done when his nomination came through.

Minayev stood in awe of Petrishev, the deputy minister. Probably for that reason, Petrishev's visit was less than a pleasant prospect. In Petrishev's presence, Minayev always felt an ugly and somewhat inexplicable sense of guilt. True enough, this unnecessary sensation never seemed to prevent Minayev from smiling and joking. At times, even he was astonished by the efficient mechanics of his facial muscles, his voice, his expressive hands.

On the appointed day, Minayev led the deputy minister through the institute laboratories, explaining the work in progress, noting Petrishev's every remark. If Minayev had made that very point to his staff yesterday or the day before, still he ordered his secretary to keep careful notes of all that was said, knowing that this display would please Petrishev.

In one of the laboratories Minayev saw that Olkhovsky had pushed his way through the crowd to the side of the deputy minister. The boy was paler than ever; his chin trembled, and his wide black eyes betrayed both hope and fear. Obviously, Olkhovsky's courage faded by the minute, and, understanding that, Minayev threw the switch of the great machine.

The mechanical whine rose like a fountain, broke against the ceiling, and fell back, drowning all conversation. Taking advantage of the din, Minayev glared at Olkhovsky, signaling desperately that Petrishev's inspection was not fit time to lodge complaints. Only another week, and it would all be settled.

The young man's conceit infuriated Minayev; but when Olkhovsky spoke, Minayev saw that there was no cause for alarm.

Instead of coming to the point, the boy lost himself in the maze of his own long, rehearsed phrases. The language was pompous and stiff—"the scourge of conservatism," "institutionalized irresponsibility"—no one could follow the thread of his logic. Minayev saw bewilderment in the deputy minister's eyes, and suddenly he was suffused with a sense of shame for Olkhovsky. He swore to himself in silent rage: Poor snot-nosed theoretician! Fool! Why does he drag on and on like this? It won't last long. Petrishev will shut him up.

Petrishev spoke at last: "Excuse me. Just what is it? What do you want?"

The boy was lost. Abashed, he fell silent, wordlessly moving his dry lips. Minayev dropped his eyes. God, what a little boy! Olkhovsky reached into his pocket and drew out a dog-eared manuscript and tried to push it into the deputy minister's hands. Petrishev unfolded the sheaf of papers. A *ruble* note and a few crumbs lay on the title page.

Someone in the room sniggered. Petrishev bit his lips. He held out the *ruble* note to Olkhovsky, and suddenly he burst into laughter, too. The entire crowd joined in—not unkindly. In such cases, one must laugh, too. But Olkhovsky flushed a deep, painful red. An aimless smile played on his lips, and then it seemed that he would break into tears.

"I beg of you," said Olkhovsky, speaking very fast. "See to it yourself. . . ." He spoke in a kind of numb despair, as if he knew that it was all over, that nothing mattered, and he had nothing to lose. "Otherwise. . . . Here, I gave it to Vladimir Pakhamovich . . . he . . ."

"Absolutely," said the deputy minister. "We'll clear it up. You can depend on that." He spoke soothingly, without haste.

When they were back in Minayev's office, the deputy minister asked what sort of paper it had been. What had the young man wanted?

To have confessed his fears in the matter of the academician Stroyev would have been unreasonable; for that reason, Minayev spoke as follows:

"The manuscript," he began, striking a careful pose. "Well, perhaps the boy's division chief can appraise it better than I can. He says the calculations are interesting, but he has reservations. A careful check will be necessary, free of this endless chorus of accusations, charges, complaints. . . ." In this way, he sought to save himself and at the same time maintain a scrupulous fairness to the boy.

"I never suspected he was such a troublemaker," said Petrishev, astonished.

"I studied with him at the university," said Minayev's assistant. "He was always somewhat . . ." He tapped his forehead significantly.

Minayev understood his assistant's motives perfectly well: he thought Minayev wanted it that way—but really, this was too much.

"Of course," the deputy minister said. "I know the kind. They write, demand hearings, implore—and then the whole thing turns out to be fantasy. But there's another side, too. They're not always cranks. Sometimes . . . people only make it seem that way." His face darkened; apparently Petrishev had memories of his own.

"Well," said Minayev, "in any case, the matter needs study." His manner was brusque, evidence of that rough independence Petrishev prized so much.

Petrishev agreed to leave the matter in Minayev's hands; but even if this sign of confidence was pleasing, still Minayev was troubled by a sense of guilt. He reassured himself: he had no obligation to Petrishev. The deputy minister was hardly a free agent. He could hardly question the competence of a man he was about to confirm in the post of director. The truth was—the man was helpless. You make people do things, but others force *your* hand. That was life.

Yes, now that the matter was laid to rest, he could pity Olkhovsky. The truth was that they had all imposed on the deputy minister. He had been made to believe the boy was a hothead and a crank, and that was not good. We are penalizing a boy, he thought, only because he fights so clumsily for truth. This, it seemed to him, was unacceptable.

Yes, how cheerfully he once would damn his thousand careful calculations to hell and blurt out the things he felt for. But his lips remained tightly sealed. Sitting in his armchair, he listened to the deputy minister's endless evasions, and his heavy face was the image of placid attention.

Minayev wanted to say: "Well, my fine feathered friend, how would you have phrased it, sitting in my chair?" But he knew his people, and, knowing them, he did not quite put it that way.

"It's easy for you, but if you were in Stroyev's shoes . . ."

For the first time Minayev saw how his assistant came alive and, in some strangely youthful fashion, ran his fingers through his hair, daring to spoil the carefully combed part.

"Vladimir Pakhamovich, I would have printed it without thinking twice. . . . Such an obvious economy."

"Aha," said Minayev slyly. "Then why is it you always prepare this sort of answer for my signature? Isn't that a little different from what you say? You're a regular Moltchalin."

Deliberately, his assistant smoothed his tousled hair.

"I write the way *you* want me to, so that some day I can write the way *I* consider these things should be written." He looked into Minayev's eyes.

"Aha! And you think that day will come?" Minayev smiled thinly. He chose a heavy blue pencil from the tray on his desk and signed the document with a flourish.

Olkhovsky did not speak to Minayev again. Several times Minayev met him in the corridors, but Olkhovsky ignored him, eyes downcast, ungainly arms hanging at his sides as if they belonged to someone else. Minayev was tempted to stop him, to have a heart-to-heart chat, to give him a little good advice. Patience, Olkhovsky, one must have patience. After all, Minayev would soon be attending the conference at the ministry, and there would be ample occasion to talk things over with the right people. But he felt that Olkhovsky would not understand, and this pained Minayev. He wanted to prove he was guiltless, that he was hardly a free agent, hardly figured at all in this case.

The day before his departure, Minayev was called to the district Party committee. He knew that Loktiev was moving heaven and earth to remove Olkhovsky. But, after all, who was Loktiev? What right did he have to meddle in Minayev's affairs. If it had been necessary to dismiss Olkhovsky, Minayev would have done so long ago. Why should Minayev soothe this shallow little man's wounded pride.

This is enough, he thought. The man is nothing to me. He has no authority to give orders. It would be different if the Party secretary had moved in the case—but an instructor! I have outgrown that sort of thing, Comrade Loktiev, and, besides, my position is no longer . . . Yes, he would say it. My position isn't quite as humble as it used to be. More than explicit. In his mind, he rehearsed the phrases. He would speak slowly, with condescension.

Rising up to the committee offices, his movements were automatic. He felt his clean-shaven chin, adjusted his tie—but caught himself then. He felt a kind of anger at these conditioned reflexes.

Enough of that! The time had come to allow himself a little independence; he was hardly less able than other directors. And in this case he could, and would, show Loktiev what the plain truth was.

Ascending the wide stairway leading to the district committee, walking down the long corridor, Minayev held his head high. The firm lines of his face betrayed a hard resolution in place of the furtive look of the past.

When he left the district committee an hour later, a light rain fell. The drops spattered on the asphalt. Minayev stood for a long time before his car, hand on the door. The rain quickened.

"Hurry, Vladimir Pakhamovich," said the chauffeur. "Get in."

Minayev started. "No," he said, "go on. I won't need you," and slammed the door. The ZIM pulled away. Minayev stared blankly at the dry place where the car had been parked. "Go on," he repeated, listening carefully to the sound of his voice. He began to walk. (No matter where you go, it is always supposed to be ahead.) He could walk toward the square or toward the embankment. The only thing he couldn't do was return to the district committee. No matter what he told himself; no matter how hard he tried to convince himself. It was not often that he had been forced to take stock of himself this way. No, it wasn't that he was heedless, careless. He had always tried to plan his actions, control his words; but he had never found much time to think about the *why* of things.

It was all very painful. The mechanical evasions came all too readily to mind, once again to ransom him from ugly conclusions. He found a bitter pleasure in that.

Well, all very well, he thought, but what *did* happen at the committee? And this question, inexplicably, pushed him to the wall.

Loktiev had bluntly proposed transferring Olkhovsky to an experimental station in Nikolayev.

Listening to Loktiev speak, he had asked himself what right this shadowy, ill-educated, stupid clerk—he with his dead face, he who had never created anything and would never be asked to create anything—what right did this man have to sit in judgment on the careers of men like Olkhovsky? Not even for the sake of form had he asked about the tractors that were the root of the problem—tractors, it seemed, didn't matter a damn! And it had seemed that he was quite certain that Minayev would do as he was told. The gall!

At the embankment, Minayev saw that the last ice of winter had begun to move down the river. The huge floes broke softly against the bridge piles, then fell back beneath the stone arches. Leaning over the parapet, Minayev looked down at the water. It seemed for a moment as if the ice stood still and the bridge itself moved. The black water misted in the cold air. . . . With a great effort, Minayev moved back from the parapet. He felt a pain in his chest; he was feverish. Removing his hat, he wiped his damp forehead with his sleeve. The cold rain burned on his skin.

He felt old and tired. Suddenly, he saw himself clearly—a fat, bald man with sagging jowls, walking about on the bridge, holding a hat. God, how soon he had grown old! When had it happened? He, Volodia Minayev, the leading tenor in the school choir, secretary of the faculty Party cell . . . Fright seized him. Was he really an old man?

With terrible clarity, the vision of Volodia Minayev rose before him—young Volodia Minayev, he of the bright eyes and scrawny neck, on the first day of his assignment to the tractor works. Do you remember, he thought, do you remember that fuss about engine suspension techniques? The department manager had told him: "It's too soon for you to go sticking your neck out. Listen, Minayev, do you think *you,* with your petty authority, can go tilting against a chief construction engineer? He'll blacklist you for life. What the hell do you think you are, a martyr? He'll gulp you down and never blink."

He remembered the helpless humiliation of it all. The chief engineer had listened to his impassioned harangue, slurping tea all the while, and then bluntly told him: "Listen, Lenayev"—deliberately, he had got the name wrong—"listen, if you ever come in here

again with more of this damned foolishness, I'll throw you out of
the plant. Now you may go."

There had been three of them—Minayev and two others—and
they had carried on the war. They had gone about, endlessly demonstrating and proving. But it was all for nothing. They might have
spent three, five, ten years in futile combat and accomplished nothing. First one of them had been dismissed, then a second. It was
Minayev's turn then; but he had pretended to accept facts. He had
comforted himself with the thought: It's only for a little while. A
man must learn to get around them. First I'll win a little independence, a little authority, and then I'll break these goddamned bureaucrats! And gritting his teeth, he had advanced toward his goal.

He had been made deputy to the division manager. He had
trained himself in the ways of silence and patience for the sake of
the great day when he would be able to do as he judged right. He
had voted pro when his conscience told him con. He had mouthed
words he could not really believe. He had praised things that he
knew were contemptible. And when these things were altogether
impossible, he had kept his peace. Silence is the most convenient
form of lying. Silence eases the conscience, safeguards a man's right
to a personal opinion and his hope that conscience will one day find
its voice.

But not now, not when the would-be hero is only a department
manager, only the chief of a technical division, only the chief engineer at the plant. Too soon; always too soon. And meanwhile the
list of his debts grew. Life gave birth to new ideas, threw him against
new obstacles. How many of those like Olkhovsky had remained behind! Tirelessly, like an ant, he had built the edifice of his social
position and labored to strengthen it day by day. And what? What
had he achieved? The higher he climbed, the less he was himself,
the harder it was to take risks. What stood in his way? Why was it
that other people spoke out? How was it that Petrishev had managed to triumph over unjust punishment, oppression, degradation,
and had advanced in the face of all opposition? No, nothing had
hindered Minayev. His way had actually been smoother, or at least
it had seemed smoother. And when Loktiev had taunted him, point-
ing to the words of his reply to the district committee inquiry, he
had felt shame. "You write one thing and say another," Loktiev
had said. "What, pray, shall I report to the secretary?"

Minayev had understood. Loktiev had no *need* for tact; he spoke openly. And at this point it would be better for Minayev to give in. It was easier that way.

Everything Loktiev had proposed was vile, thoroughly vile. But it seemed to Minayev that the important thing was that Loktiev said exactly what he wished. Loktiev and Olkhovsky. All the others in this sorry business thought one thing and said another. All of them, beginning with Minayev himself, and ending with his assistant. Every one of them was a complacent liar, and that, very likely, was why Loktiev did not have to lie.

Cheap bastard, he had thought angrily, looking straight into Loktiev's empty eyes. The man will have to be thrown out of the district committee. And not only the district committee—the Party as well. An evil nonentity. If he ever lost his place in the committee, he'd never find a job as a grocery clerk. But the stronger his hatred for Loktiev grew, the quieter were his spoken objections, and when Loktiev began to insist—to threaten—he merely asked that the matter be postponed for a few days. Somberly reflecting on the kind of trouble Loktiev could make if he chose, Minayev hoped to find backing in influential Moscow quarters.

"Just don't drag it out," said Loktiev. "You said yourself Olkhovsky was a hothead. We'll have to clean up the institute, make the atmosphere a little healthier."

You son of a bitch, Minayev thought to himself . . . and heartily he shook Loktiev's hand.

But at the conference in Moscow the institute came under fire—the plan had not been met—in spite of the fact that the ministry itself was responsible for the failure. The plan had been overambitious, but it was useless to complain. Minayev was a new man, and all failures were automatically his. By such ingratiating tactics, Minayev was able to win an emergency appropriation, but in this delicate situation the request for funds was supported by the academician Stroyev. After that, it was embarrassing to raise the Olkhovsky affair.

The mad whirl of the conference in Moscow overshadowed the whole business. It seemed petty, insignificant. Only on the train home, when Minayev found himself in the half-empty compartment of the sleeping car, did it come to mind again. Very likely the rain was responsible. It began to fall, unnoticed, streaking the window glass. Remembering his promise to Loktiev, Minayev sighed. He must have been mad. Nothing could be done. We'll have to transfer Olkhovsky to Nikolayev. For a while, at least, until things settle down.

Against the backdrop of the night, the double windowpane reflected the image of a stout figure dressed in striped pajamas, heavy jowls sagging, a cigarette stuck in the corner of his tight lips—and another murkier figure who seemed to stand in the darkness, in the midst of the sparkling rain drops. The cigarette smoke drifted against the cold glass, ran down the windowpane in slow swirls. Through the drifting smoke, from out of the black depths of the night, Minayev felt the gaze of the other figure, the young one, the one who wore the frayed jacket of his student days.

Little rivulets of water ran down the young one's pale cheeks, down his scrawny neck. "You see, Vladimir Pakhamovich, always putting things off, evading things, you pitiable creature. It's degrading to look at you."

"Consider the reality of the thing," Minayev replied. "It's easy enough to dream when you don't know life; but I've made it my business to learn life through and through."

"You made a promise to yourself. Once again you said: 'Just let me become director, consolidate my position'—and now . . .'"

"Listen, don't be a boy. Is a director a god? Now if I worked at the ministry, well *then* I wouldn't be at the mercy of the Loktievs. I could have . . ."

"Oh, God," said the figure. *"Loktiev*—to hell with *his* threats. You could have gone to the secretary, to the central committee . . ."

"I've done all I can. I'm doing all I can. And even with Olkhovsky, everything will be all right. You'll see, I'll get him back."

"No, you've betrayed us all," the other said. "Not only the friends of your youth, not only Olkhovsky, but yourself as well. Is it possible that I trusted you?"

"Big words, big words," Minayev said. "I can't stand big words. What I do now I only do to help *all* of them—not only Olkhovsky. I have a responsibility to the institute, to dozens like him."

And standing there in the compartment was a third Minayev, one who listened intently as the old one skillfully parried the young one's thrusts, adroitly demonstrating the inevitability of it all, promising to help Olkhovsky as soon as circumstances might permit.

Another Minayev—one who knew that this would never come to be, that he would always deceive himself, play this endless game, because he was too weak to escape the tyranny of self-deception. Minayev would always have reasons. And always he would strive to be an honest man . . . tomorrow.

The faint swirls of smoke veiled the rain-streaked features of the young one who floated there in the night. Slowly, the figure faded into the darkness, into the past. Where does the past go? All that was left was a vague feeling of yearning. It seemed now that all the years had been filled with a single, endless yearning.

In the morning, at the railroad station, his assistant brought the news. Dressing, Minayev heard the gossip of the institute.

"By the way," he asked, "did Loktiev call?"

"Several times."

"Well, that's understandable," said Minayev.

They moved slowly through the crowd. When they reached the ZIM, Minayev looked back to the train. The dusty compartment window reflected nothing. In the half-darkness that shrouded the little sleeping cubicle, all he saw was a crumpled bed and a dirty ashtray filled with cigarette butts.

Novy Mir (Moscow), October, 1956.

7.

NATIONAL COMMUNISM—
NATIONAL IDENTITY

Imre Nagy was twice premier of Hungary: the first time in 1953 and 1954, when his purpose was to stave off impending calamity by introducing a program of liberal reform; the second time, in the brief days of the revolution when the nation swept him to power.

Nagy was a veteran Bolshevik. He fought in the Russian Revolution and joined Béla Kun's abortive attempt to establish Communism in Hungary after World War I.

"Hungarian Integrity and the Five Principles of Coexistence" is one of the major essays put forward by Nagy in his defense at the time of his banishment from office in 1955. Says Nagy: "True patriotism, together with love and respect for other . . . nations is the basis and essence of proletarian internationalism."

When the Soviets put down the revolution, Nagy took refuge in the Yugoslav Embassy in Budapest. On November 22, 1956, he left that asylum under promise of safe conduct. He was abducted and later executed at an unannounced time and place.

....

HUNGARIAN INTEGRITY AND THE
FIVE PRINCIPLES OF COEXISTENCE

. . . The five basic principles are designed to regulate relations between the various countries. If, however, we try to analyze them more thoroughly, we can see that although these principles are apparent in international relationships, their significance goes much further: they include national existence, social development, and many basic questions of human freedom. If these aims are not realized, the countries and peoples will remain in slavery, at the lowest rung of social development and human civilization, emergence from which can be attained only through the principles of national independence, sovereignty, equality, non-interference in internal affairs, and the assurance of self-determination. Losing, limiting, or renouncing these rights must result in the dissolution and destruction of nations, peoples, and cultures.

The five basic principles may be considered the goal of any national liberation movement, of any transformation of colonial or

semi-colonial peoples. In principle, the problem of national liberation movements and transformation of peoples is to bring about
victory for the cause of national independence and subordination.
Attaining nationhood, national independence, sovereignty, and
equality are not always realized by various peoples simultaneously,
or through the same means or similar processes.

The centuries-old battles for national ideals and national independence, the struggle for economic, political, and cultural nationhood was carried out in Hungary under characteristic local circumstances, despite the survival of a dependence stemming from the
feudal system and foreign subjugation.

Nothing could be more erroneous than to feel that, since national
independence, sovereignty, and equality in an era of social progress
were problems of internal transformation, national principles and
ideals are also antiquated.

The nation's bourgeoisie, which could prosper only by oppressing
the working class, established its rule and subordinated the great
national interests, for which it had also fought at one time, to its
own selfish class interests. Thus the interests of the ruling bourgeoisie
clashed with the interests of the nation, to the great detriment of the
country.

The historical events of the last decade prove most convincingly
that the ideals of national independence, sovereignty, equality, and
self-determination—which from a historical standpoint became the
ideal of the masses through the national liberation movements, the
social transformation, and development—were most important factors in the period of change from capitalism to socialism. The emergence into the forefront of international life of the five previously
mentioned basic principles during the last two years prove this most
convincingly. These obvious facts also indicate other things—above
all, that the world is now living in an era of socialist transformation,
by peaceful methods or revolution; that the five basic principles are
not proving completely effective in practice; and that, therefore, the
development toward socialism, the transition from capitalism that
we are facing in the present era, is increasingly significant.

Moreover, facts indicate that the five basic principles cannot be
limited to the capitalistic system or the battle between the two systems, but must extend to the relations between the countries within
the democratic and socialist camps.

The five basic principles do not spring from differences between the two systems—capitalism and socialism—they do not express this difference, but they are factors independent of social and political relationships in the international field. Therefore, these five basic principles cannot be interpreted in a one-sided fashion, as meaning that one must fight for their realization only in the battle against the imperialist endeavors of the capitalist great powers. It must not be assumed that these principles are antiquated and therefore unnecessary in the countries within the socialist camps.

There exist erroneous views to the effect that clinging to these five principles and enforcing them in the relationships between the countries belonging to the democratic and socialist camps is contrary to proletarian internationalism and nationalism, and indicative of a deviation toward chauvinism, thus weakening the democratic and socialist camps.

On the contrary: they strengthen them, because the socialist camp can become the rallying point of independent sovereign countries possessing equal rights. Moreover, close cooperation within the socialist camp in the economic, political, and cultural fields can insure a healthy relationship if the five basic principles are mutually respected. Therefore, close cooperation among the countries of the socialist camp and realization of the five basic principles do not contradict one another. At the same time, however, these connections are based on new principles which conform to the demands of a development toward socialism. It cannot be considered accidental that these five basic principles became apparent and greatly significant in connection with laying the foundation for the relationships between countries belonging to the democratic and socialist camps. It must also be taken into consideration that the five basic principles were put forward by the economically underdeveloped countries who participated in the Bandung Conference. For them, the adoption of these principles was the prime requisite for their economic, political, and cultural development, and for the assurance of their national existence.

The principles that govern the relationships between countries and peoples do not touch the interests of only one or another social stratum, but affect the fate of the entire nation; therefore, they are considered the basis of all-inclusive national policies. Such national policies can be carried on only by a nation that possesses national independence and sovereignty, and thus can protect its liberty and equality against other peoples and does not permit interference in its private affairs. National independence, which is the most important factor of all in the five basic principles, has as its basic requirement national unity, creation of national loyalty, and winning the support of the masses for the cause of national independence. In such a way, the support of the widest possible masses is won to participate actively in the solution of decisive national problems. These events are taking place before our very eyes, not only in certain countries but on entire continents. This is the role of people creating history, carrying on the battle that is based on the ideals of the five basic principles.

The noble traditions of these five basic principles have roots in our country also, which were formed during our historical development. There were periods in history when the light of these principles and ideals of ours shone brightly in all of Europe. The noble traditions of battles for independence are still alive today and have their effect, nurturing these principles as our greatest national virtue. Attaining national independence and sovereignty where it is nonexistent, or preserving it, has always been the greatest national problem in past periods, as it is today and will be in the future, even under the socialist system's development. While nations and national states exist—and on this score we face an entire historical era—the five basic principles will remain the motivating power of the development of the socialist system. That is why the nation clings to its independence, sovereignty, and freedom. That is why it cannot and does not yield to force or "voluntary" relinquishing of these ideals. There were and are difficult times in the life of a nation, when those in power, alluding to the best interests of the people and the nation, accept dependence, subordination, humiliating slavery— betraying the cause of national independence. There are many instances in history that show that the former ruling classes accepted slavery for the nation—instead of independence, sovereignty, liberty, and equality—to insure their own specially privileged status. However, according to the lessons of history, these betrayals of the nation do not end with the destruction of the nation but with that of the traitors, following which the ideals of freedom and independence burn with a stronger and brighter flame in the hearts of the masses.

The ideals of national independence and sovereignty that in our time have been so emphatically set forth by the five basic principles —which in the old Hungary had never been fully realized—were left as a legacy to the working classes. The working class must become a more consistent fighter for the ideals of independence and freedom than were the bourgeoisie. The working class cannot clash with the cause of national independence, sovereignty, freedom, and equality. It cannot subordinate the universal interest of the nation to its own class interests, because the working class can liberate itself and has done so only in conjunction with the other working classes, and can stabilize its power only by cooperating fully with them. Thus the interests of the working class and the nation are identical and cannot come into conflict with the universal national interests. Historical developments have made the working class the supporter and guardian of the future fate of the nation and the embodiment of national ideals.

With the emergence of the five basic principles, the greatest problem in the development toward socialism came to the forefront. So far, in the transition from capitalism to socialism, little was said about these principles. The scientific theory of Marxism-Leninism, the foreign policy of the countries in the socialist camp applied these five basic principles only to the imperialist great powers and capitalist relationships. Neither from the theoretical or practical political standpoint is it correct to view the five basic principles as a schism between the two systems, limiting it exclusively to the capitalist world. This would not agree with the Marxist-Leninist viewpoint either. The five basic principles are undoubtedly powerful motivating factors in the struggle against imperialist, capitalist conquest and its efforts to subjugate. But they are also a powerful factor in the building of a socialist society. Minimizing this or denying this may have serious consequences, and, as facts show, the danger does not recede but grows. These situations arise from improper, anti-Marxist views which declare that socialism supersedes nationalism, denying the national characteristics of socialism, falsifying international proletarianism—in reality, this means a cosmopolitan distortion of Marxism. The working class, if it wants to fulfill its historical role and accept, as it must, the burden of solving national problems, must above all insure its independence and sovereignty. In this it will inescapably find itself in opposition to those cosmopolitan views which declare that the dogmas remaining from the ideological, autocratic rule of Stalin are binding principles of socialism in general. By this, they place obstacles to the spreading of socialism in all parts of the world. It is understandable that under these circumstances the five basic principles play such an important role, gaining ground so swiftly in those countries that are taking their first steps toward socialism. The remnants of ideological, autocratic rule, the binding dogmas and patterns, are in sharp contrast to the realization of the five basic principles, making it more difficult for the working class to fulfill its leading role. Through such actions, the working class is separated from the workers' movements of the world. Its international character, stemming from its class role, becomes limited, and as a result proletarian internationalism is falsified. The working class is hindered in creating national unity and prevented from lining up the majority of the nation to support and accept the aims and leadership of the working class. In carrying out this goal, acceptance of the five basic principles is inescapable. Only through such acceptance can national ideals and problems be solved. The working class cannot be international, in the interpretation of the idea by Marxist socialism, if its internationalism does not lie in devotion and faithfulness to its own nation—and if it does not rest on accepting responsibility for its own national independence, sovereignty, and equality. . . .

The question arises: can the working class be at one and the same time the chief pillar and vanguard in building socialism *and* in putting national ideals and aims into practice? Can the ideals of socialism, proletarian internationalism, and national independence be reconciled? These questions must without doubt be answered by an unqualified "yes." The national ideals embodied in the five basic principles do not point toward a separation between nations, but indicate the drawing together of nations that are speeding up and smoothing the course toward socialism. The five principles are guarantees that while advancing together inside the socialist camp and continuing social, economic, and cultural development under nationally specific situations, the independence, sovereignty, and equality of the individual nations can be preserved.

This circumstance makes it possible for countries and peoples in which there are Marxist workers' parties, other progressive nationalist parties, or patriotic forces to approach and develop socialism, which is impossible along Soviet lines. It opens up wide vistas of possibilities with regard to developing socialism along specifically national roads. These are based on the past unequal development of countries under capitalism, a logical result of which is unequal development under socialism. Since the five basic principles are so closely connected with this theory, we find that this view is diametrically opposed to ideological dogmatism. In answering the questions that have been posed here, one cannot ignore the fact that, under situations that govern the building of socialism, the working class which is in power as the embodiment of national aspirations *can* become the true fighter for proletarian internationalism *only* on the basis of nationalistic principles. . . .

Only thus, along the only correct basic Marxist principles and upon the principle of peaceful coexistence of countries having different social and political systems, can there evolve a socialist society that consists of countries traveling different roads under particular national patterns but independent, free, and equal. It cannot be doubted that it is more difficult to enforce these five principles against the imperialist great powers than between countries of a democratic and socialist type. But from this it does not in the least follow that among the latter these guiding principles have become "superfluous," or that they should be interpreted differently. On the contrary, there they are more easily realized and offer wider possibilities for application. The decisive question is: who does respect these basic principles, and who does not? . . .

Today in Hungary the Party and the country are led by those who, with their anti-Marxist, sectarian, "leftist" policies, have moved into opposition to the majority of the Party membership and to the widest strata of the country's population. Lacking mass support, they cannot stand on their own feet, nor can they enforce the basic principles in relations with friendly countries or kindred parties. These are the people who, because of their cowardice and their spiritual poverty, cannot do without the Stalinist autocratic rule and the dogmas that outline for the Party and the country the policies and directives that must be followed in international and internal politics, as well as in the economic, political, and cultural life of the nation. They not only voluntarily accept such a dependent and humiliating role but cling to it, because this is the only solid support to insure their power. But the more they try to enforce the application of these dogmas and schemes and their imitation here at home, the further away they get from Hungarian reality, the Hungarian peoples' aims and national aspirations, which cannot be disregarded.

The leaders of the Party and the country must understand that the fate of the nation and that of the people are identical. The people cannot be free if the nation is not independent, if it does not possess complete sovereignty, if foreign influences prevail in its internal affairs, as no nation can be independent and sovereign whose people do not possess completely the right to freedom.

National independence and freedom of the people can be realized together under socialism. Independent and sovereign national existence and freedom of the people are equal factors in the development of a socialist society, just as important as economic and political factors or the peaceful coexistence of nations and the theory of economic rivalry on the international level. If a nation does not possess its sovereign rights or is unable to attain them, the dependency and subjugation of the country will result in the rule of poverty and backwardness for the nation. Only in an independent, sovereign, and free country are the people rich and prosperous. Therefore, the fate of the people depends very much on the way in which national independence develops. In a country lacking independence, prosperity is non-existent. People do not struggle ceaselessly for national independence, sovereignty, and equality merely for the sake of economic well-being or merely because of their enthusiasm for ideals. These two ideals are closely intertwined in the national aspirations of the people.

We are living in an age and we are facing times when the realization of the five basic principles in countries having different systems and those having identical systems will be crucial for the future of nations possessing national independence, sovereignty, and equality. The country and Party must be led by those who are completely reliable and able to lead the country along democratic lines and attain the greatest possible national support, so that the country may be assured of complete possession of its sovereign rights.

The five basic principles of peaceful coexistence and the mutual relations of the great powers—and of the economically backward small nations as well—is of primary importance from the standpoint of preserving peace and the formation of power groups. The policies of the power groups are contrary to the ideals of national independence and sovereignty that are based on the five principles, as well as to the ideal of peaceful coexistence between various states. The separation of states into various power groups must lead sooner or later to armed conflict. For this reason, the only feasible path for peaceful development and the avoidance of war is not the creation of power groups but the liquidation of such groups as may exist. For small countries, such as Hungary, it is a question of vital importance to decide properly on our position in relation to the various states. The country must strive to uphold the peace in every possible way. It must avoid becoming an active participant in any of the clashes between power groups or becoming embroiled in war—to serve as a field of battle or an area of troop passage. It must also assure that in all such questions the nation will decide for itself, in full possession of its sovereign rights. Our country, as an independent nation, must align itself with the countries and people who are fighting for peace. But can a small country exist without belonging to a power group? Peaceful coexistence of nations demands the liquidations of power groups. In the fight against aggressive power politics, the most potent force is the great and solid strength of the socialist nations, headed by the Soviet Union, which at present constitute the basis of the greatest anti-war group in the world. The five conditions of peaceful coexistence, which are the basis of cooperation of the small and economically backward countries and of the fight against the power groups—and they are the general rules of international coexistence—can therefore become the guarantee of realizing socialism peacefully.

The liquidation of the power groups is in the interest of all progressive mankind, the socialist camp included, transcending national interests. Therefore, the countries of the socialist camp must endeavor to liquidate the policy of power politics. Their foreign policies must be carried on in this direction by aiming for the liquidation of all power groups as soon as possible. Gaining a socialist victory is possible only in this way. For this reason, taking a stand against such power groups, whether that of neutrality or active coexistence, will mean the realization of consistent representation of the basic principles of cooperation within the countries of the socialist camp. The correctness of this principle cannot be denied. However, in regard to the policies of putting this into practice, there are serious considerations. The main question is: which is the most practicable way of liquidating the power groups and power politics? According to present experiences, the rivalry of the power groups and their battle against each other will hardly lead to the cessation of power politics and will hardly be responsible for attaining peaceful coexistence. It is more likely that differences will be aggravated and international tensions will increase. The most practicable plan, seemingly, is the active coexistence of progressive Democratic Socialist or similar countries with those other countries having a different system, through a coordinated foreign policy and through cooperation against the policies of the power groups, through neutrality or active coexistence. This path is made easier for Hungary by its geographical location through its neighboring states, neutral Austria, and countries building socialism, among them the Soviet Union, and neighboring Yugoslavia, which stands on the principle of active coexistence. It is the sovereign right of the Hungarian people to decide in which form they believe the most advantageous international status will be assured, and in which form they think that national independence, sovereignty, equality, and peaceful development will be attained. Joining forces with the five basic principles of peaceful coexistence is most advantageous because the Soviet Union has already accepted these principles as guiding principles in international politics. Hungary must choose this path all the more, because historical experience decisively proves that economic, political, military, and other power groups are built on quicksand and cannot entice the masses of the people into the service of their cause or win their allegiance. The Hungarian people have become convinced by the terrible experiences of the two world wars that they cannot and must not become participants in the rivalries of free power groups. The country cannot undertake obligations that transcend its capabilities, that will draw away its forces or divert its attention from solving its own national problems, or that endanger the independence and sovereignty of the country with the possibility of a new war and its devastating consequences.

On the basis of all these logical assumptions, the Hungarian nation must keep in mind the particular national interests and the general interests of the socialist countries. The Hungarian nation must follow the policy of active coexistence in the field of international politics, which is in the national interests of Hungary, and of the successful spreading of socialism and the peaceful coexistence of the two systems, including economic competition. This policy would create a much firmer and more lasting basis for Hungarian-Soviet relations and would make the connections between the socialist countries a closer one. For this reason, it is our duty, which cannot be postponed but is the command of history. On the basis of the experiences and lessons learned during the long, stormy, centuries-old battle for the independence and sovereignty of our nation, we must lay the foundation of an independent national foreign policy that will, despite the buffeting received through political tactics, show for our country the way and the clear goal and will preserve us from again becoming the plaything of historical storms. Hungary has for centuries stood in the focal point of hostile world forces, and thus could not find for itself a place in the family of nations. For this we have paid a very heavy price in a series of national catastrophes. After our glorious freedom fight was crushed, our great national genius Louis Kossuth summarized the great historical lessons—unhappily, too late—and designated the path to be followed. He envisioned the assurance of an independent, sovereign, self-governing Hungary, not through alignment with a great power or through joining a power group but by close cooperation with neighboring peoples within the framework of a federation of free and independent nations.

We must return to the ideals which have been revived under new historical circumstances, of the peaceful coexistence of peoples and their cooperation—the true conditions for which are created by the realization of socialist ideals. The ruling classes in Hungary did not follow the ideals of Kossuth in the sphere of international relations. Their realization, together with so many other great national problems—among them, national independence and re-allotment of land—was left as a legacy to us Communists. Since the Hungarian nation for the first time since 1849 has become again a factor in forming history and in the relations and cooperation between nations, the forms and framework of political law—the Kossuth ideals —must be accepted. And we do accept these ideals, taking into consideration the changed historical situation for building socialism. The peace of independent, sovereign, and free peoples, their friendship and their dependence on each other, as well as their common desire to create a socialist society, is a firm and lasting basis upon which an independent Hungarian national foreign policy can be formed—one that would point toward the future and open up wide vistas for establishing an independent national foreign policy. Absence of this makes the internal and external situation of our country very precarious and wavering. No lasting harmony can be attained in internal and external policies, nor can any decided line of direction toward various countries or relationships to power groups emerge, if a clear stand is not taken in regard to the various important international problems. The main reason for this is that on these questions the Party and the government are not guided by their own particular circumstances but by dogmas. Such a situation is unworthy of a free, independent, and sovereign country.

This situation, which did not develop in the Marxist-Leninist spirit of proletarian internationalism or in the relations between independent, sovereign, and equal socialist countries, must undoubtedly be changed—all the more as this is not a question of an isolated occurrence, but one that must be solved *generally* within the socialist camp. In fact, the problem is even more far-reaching. Occurrences that are repeated often in the Communist parties of the capitalist countries—the cleavages in the international Socialist movement, the disunity of forces, the disorder in relations and cooperation between the Socialist and Social Democratic parties within the international and national framework, and so on—all show that the principles laid down at the Bandung Conference and the Soviet-Yugoslav declaration at Belgrade are of historical importance. Their realization cannot be deferred without serious consequences for the Communist parties and the cause of socialism. . . .

The scientific Marxist evaluation of the international situation and the objective deductions derived in relation to the internal and external politics of the country so far have not been considered to be the task of the Party leadership. We never examined the international situation thoroughly in the light of our own country's interests or from the viewpoint of its effects on our country. Our own activity in the field of international politics was restricted to some equalizing efforts which were deemed necessary to insure homogeneity inside the socialist group. For this reason, questions of the international situation and external policies played an insignificant role in the politics of the Party and the government, especially where these questions touched on the problems of our own country. In general, we used the international situation only to prove an economic or political aim, which was determined beforehand, and ignored the actual situation or often distorted it. We always explained it arbitrarily as the given situation happened to require it.

This was the reason why changes in the international situation often clashed sharply with internal politics. In the years 1949 to 1952, incorrect evaluation of the international situation, overemphasis on the war danger, and the actions resulting from these assumptions played a very serious part in those grave mistakes that were made by our Party leadership with regard to the economic activities of the people. These mistakes were made public by the resolution of the central leadership in June, 1953. In consequence of these mistakes, the country was brought to the brink of catastrophe. The events in June, 1953—in East Germany, Czechoslovakia, Hungary, and elsewhere—clearly show how an incorrect evaluation of the international situation and a resulting unsound foreign policy brought about grave crises in the internal life of the countries mentioned. The great importance of the June policy, the policy of the "new era," and of the political changes that occurred in 1953 in the Soviet Union and in the People's Democracies is that they have brought the objective international situation into harmony with internal and foreign policy.

During the fall and winter of 1954, as a consequence of the mistakes committed in the field of foreign policy in the countries of the socialist group—and in our country also, which overshot the mark —the Party leadership aimed at the liquidation of democracy and the sharpening of the dictatorship of the proletariat. The deterioration of the internal situation and the allegations about the increased danger of war played the main roles in those attempts, which aimed . . . at the return to the old policies. . . .

Hungary at present is a weak unit in the socialist camp. It is an uncertain factor which contributes to the deterioration of the united socialist front, because in the midst of lessening tension in the international situation, internal tension is rapidly growing in our country. Partly because of this, and partly because of the serious mistakes of the past and the rigid rejection with regard to the liquidation of mistakes, and also because of the general distrust with which we are regarded in international life, the present policy of Hungary is a serious obstacle to the rapprochement between the West and the East, and especially between socialists and Communists.

The inner tension of Hungary, which is chiefly political, is caused by the fact that the leadership is opposing the ideals of national independence, sovereignty, and equality as well as Hungarian national feeling and progressive traditions.

This growing tension must be weighed from the viewpoint of the security and defense of the socialist countries, because the unrest of the masses undermines our ability to defend the country.

The contention that to change the present policies and leadership would cause internal shock and strengthen reaction is not true. As a matter of fact, it is not true that there is danger of a counter-revolution. On the contrary, the country and the cause of socialism are being brought to the brink of a catastrophe if radical political and personal changes are not carried out quickly. Nothing will aid international imperialism more than the policies of the present leadership, which drives the people into the arms of reaction. The lessening of tension in the field of international relations makes possible the radical liquidation of this inner tension without having to fear the consequences of the political machinations of international reaction. On the contrary, they would lose ground as a result, all the more because the Communist and People's Democratic forces are standing firm in Hungary. They have every political and personal basis for finding a solution in a new policy based on the Belgrade declaration. This would make it possible for the country to progress toward socialism on a path compatible with the particular Hungarian situation, on the basis of national independence, sovereignty, and equality, without any type of interference. Such a change would make Hungary a firm supporter of socialism and close brotherly cooperation within the socialist camp.

Our country cannot progress toward socialism in a vacuum of social development. Around us in the world, near and far, there are countries of varying social orders, in various stages of development, which show their diversity in their language, traditions, economy, culture, and whole way of life. We are one of the countries within this circle. We must therefore recognize that we are members not only of the socialist camp but of the great community of nations, to the countries and peoples of which we are bound by countless ties which we cannot and indeed must not sever, because we do not want to be disbarred from the great community of nations, and also because we could not then successfully progress toward socialism through social and economic improvement. The barriers between the countries of the socialist camp and the great community of nations must be torn down, and the ties that bind them together must be developed.

This Marxist-Leninist lesson must be learned as a consequence of the experiences of the past ten years.

It is the historical mission of the Soviet Communist Party to liquidate the burdensome legacy of the Stalinist era, to which task the Hungarian Communists and the Communists of all other countries, as well as the progressive democratic and socialist forces, will in all probability add their far-reaching support.

Proletarian internationalism, national independence, international solidarity, in harmony with national feeling and deep patriotism, together with the unity of ideologies and principles, will widen the path for all mankind toward creating a socialist society. We Hungarian Communists will faithfully cultivate and always profess the historical Marxist Communist motto: "Workers of the world, unite!"—to which we will also add the motto expressed in the "Szózat," representing deep national feeling and love of country: "Oh Magyar, keep forever thy native country's trust." For us Hungarians in the great struggle for the victory of socialism, and in our daily work and lives, these two mottoes have been welded together indissolubly. The principles and ideals which they express will serve as the guiding principles for our activities in internal as well as foreign policy.

Budapest, 1955.

The history of the twentieth century is the history of triumphant nationalism. Against the inroads of this passionate ideology, the Soviet empire has proved no sturdier than any other: in a sense, the Titoist defection, the East German riots, the Hungarian and Polish revolutions have no greater significance than this.

Wolfgang Harich is a dissident East German Marxist. A young man, until March, 1957, he held the chair of social sciences at East Berlin University. He numbered among his friends men like the late Bertolt Brecht, German poet and playwright of renown.

"The Soviet pattern of socialism cannot be a model for every other country," writes Harich. "Indeed, the U.S.S.R. itself will have to change . . ." This is the essence of Harich's position, and the position of thousands of others who think like him.

Early in 1957, Harich was arrested on charges of treason and sentenced to ten years' penal servitude. The document reprinted below was composed in great haste on the eve of his arrest and passed to Social Democrats in the West.

••

THE TESTAMENT OF A PARTY REBEL

Who We Are

We are a group of functionaries of the Socialist Unity Party, which represents a broad articulate and an even broader inarticulate following. This following has grown particularly in the cultural institutions of the German Democratic Republic—universities, technical and other colleges, newspaper offices, publishing houses. . . .

Bertolt Brecht sympathetically cooperated with our group up to his death and regarded it as the best hope of the Party; in our frequent discussions with him we learned of the bitterness and disappointment with which he viewed present conditions in the German Democratic Republic.

We have gone through a long process of ideological classification which began shortly after the death of Stalin and received strong impulses through the events of June 17, 1953. After the Twentieth

Party Congress, we worked out a platform on the special German road to socialism for internal Party discussion.

We tried to acquaint the Party leadership with this platform but found them unapproachable. . . . Hence we felt compelled to hand our "platform" to the Soviet Ambassador, Comrade Pushkin, in order to reach our Party leaders through his good offices.

Our platform was meant to form a basis for internal discussion about the reformation of the Party. It is not our intention to break with the Party and to become renegades in the manner of, say, Arthur Koestler. We do not intend to repudiate Marxism-Leninism but to liberate it from Stalinism and dogmatism and to restore its basis of humanist, non-dogmatic thought.

We wanted, in a completely legal manner, to discuss and to realize our ideas inside the Party and the German Democratic Republic. Our legality, however, finds its limits when the present Party leadership itself acts illegally. This is, in our opinion, happening now. Despite official assurances to the contrary, our Party is systematically returning to the cult of personality.

Internal Party discussion is being strangled, the press muzzled; working-class discontent is, in a completely un-Marxist manner, explained as resulting from the work of imperialist agents. In such a situation, Party discipline cannot be an end in itself. We take as our model Karl Liebknecht, who in 1914 and again in 1918 violated Party discipline so as to save the Party.

Our break with the present Party leadership, therefore, does not mean a break with the Communist Party. The two are not identical. Nor do we intend to turn our backs on the German Democratic Republic or to shirk our citizens' responsibility for its present state.

We all share the guilt for the condition to which our Party has brought the German Democratic Republic. Hence it is our duty to change this condition and to fight for the change.

Part of this duty is change in our attitude toward the Social Democratic Party, which is the strongest working-class party in Germany and has made working-class unity in West Germany a reality. We disagree with the Social Democratic Party in many points of detail, and we do not share certain bourgeois democratic and opportunist tendencies within it. But we agree with the Social Democratic Party in fundamentals. This agreement in fundamentals may make it possible to overcome the division of Germany.

Our Ideological Conception

We hold that capitalism in Western Europe is obsolescent and socialism inevitable, but we do not think that victory of socialism in Western Europe demands a revolution. We think West European socialism will take over from capitalism in a peaceful manner.

We are, moreover, of opinion that the transformation process from capitalism to socialism in Western Europe will not everywhere take place under the auspices of the Communist Party, but that in many countries the Communists will have no part whatever in its direction.

The transition to socialism is an objective historical process; no party has a monopoly in it. We hold that in Western Germany only the Social Democratic Party can bring about socialism because the Communists have lost all influence on the West German working class. For the same reason, in Britain only the Labor Party, in Italy only the Socialist Party can bring about socialism. In a reunited Germany, socialism can be the work only of the Social Democratic Party in alliance with the genuinely socialist forces within the Socialist Unity Party or (about which, more later) of a new workers' party which might arise from a fusion of the Social Democratic Party with a reformed Socialist Unity Party purged of Stalinism and Stalinists. In any case, we reject, as far as Germany is concerned, the exclusive Communist claim to leadership in the building of socialism, because this conception is sectarian, unrealistic, and doomed to failure.

The realistic possibilities of a socialist development in Europe as a whole we view as follows:

The countries of Eastern Europe are in need of radical political reforms but are in their economic structure ahead of most of Western Europe. Given radical de-Stalinization, both the U.S.S.R. and the People's Democracies will gradually influence economic developments in Western Europe by their example. Simultaneously, Western conceptions of liberal democracy will influence the East and step by step enforce a retreat from political totalitarianism.

In its mutual influence and interpenetration we see the true meaning of coexistence, which should end by giving the East political liberty and democracy and the West structural economic changes, which, at least in the basic industries, will prove indispensable. We intend to accelerate this process in the German Democratic Republic so as to blunt the edge of East-West antagonism and to contribute to the peace of Europe.

Our relations to the U.S.S.R. are determined by the following considerations: the U.S.S.R. is the first socialist state in the world. Not even Stalinism can change this fact. But the Soviet pattern of socialism cannot be a model for every other country; indeed, the U.S.S.R. itself will have to change it, since in its present shape it has, even internally, become an impediment to further socialist progress.

This shape which socialism has taken in the U.S.S.R. is historically conditioned. Apart from Russian backwardness and lack of democratic traditions, the overgrowth of the Party and State apparatus which marks it resulted from the need to catch up rapidly with the West in industrial development. This first industrialization of the U.S.S.R. was necessary: to this extent, Stalin was right, and Trotsky was wrong.

But the methods and forms by which it was achieved implied a political degeneration of the Bolshevik Party and the Soviet State, and in seeing this Trotsky was right while Stalin, in denying it, was wrong. It is this degeneration of Party and State which has led the Twentieth Party Congress to criticize the methods and forms of Stalinism. However, such criticism of Stalin was not a Marxist analysis: it did not even touch the basic reasons for the degeneration of the Soviet system.

Neither did it touch the basic questions of the relations between the U.S.S.R. and the People's Democracies.

Since 1945, the Soviet Union has been both a progressive and a reactionary factor in East Europe. It was progressive in ending capitalism and feudalism. But at the same time the Soviet Union exported a political system which had already become an impediment to further progress in the Soviet Union itself: in this, it played a reactionary role. Even worse, it proceeded to exploit the People's Democracies and to disregard their sovereign equality and national independence.

Today it is plain that the policy of the U.S.S.R. toward the People's Democracies is a total failure. It has led to the disintegration and threatening dissolution of the socialist camp. The resistance of the People's Democracies against the hegemony of the U.S.S.R.

is part and parcel of the popular masses against the Stalinist Party
and Government apparatus and its methods. Wherever the healthy
forces of the Party take the lead in this class struggle, it leads to re-
generation and renewed progress toward socialism. Poland is the
clearest example.

In the U.S.S.R. itself, the Stalinist apparatus has become aware
since the death of Stalin that it is facing a dead end. It resolved to
make concessions to the popular masses. Hence both the Malenkov
line of economic policy and the Khrushchev criticism of Stalin. The
Twentieth Party Congress was an attempt to anticipate threatening
revolution from below by revision from above, and to keep control
in the hands of the apparatus. It could not succeed in practice because the existence of the apparatus is itself the chief obstacle to
revision.

In its relations to the People's Democracies, the Soviet Union
tried after the Twentieth Party Congress to impose de-Stalinization
as mechanically as it had imposed Stalinization before. This produced friction and attempts on the part of the People's Democracies
to carry out de-Stalinization in their own manner. This, in turn, im-
pelled the Soviet Union to react with Stalinist and, indeed, Fascist
methods. Examples: reaction to the Togliatti interview after the
Twentieth Party Congress; the circular of the Soviet Communist
Party to all Communist parties about Yugoslavia; reaction to
Poland and Hungary; maintenance of Stalinism in the German
Democratic Republic.

The only possible comment on this relapse of the Soviet Union
into Stalinism is that it deprives of all justification the claim of the
U.S.S.R. to a leading role in the socialist camp, notwithstanding the
fact that the U.S.S.R. is the strongest socialist country on earth. The
Soviet Communist Party today stands for nationalism and Stalinism;
to get out of this position, it must be forced back at least to the
Malenkov line and the position at the Twentieth Party Congress.

Our Plan

From this reading of the present situation, we draw the following
conclusions for the Socialist Unity Party and the German Democratic Republic:

1. The Party. We want to reform the Party from inside. We stick
to Marxism-Leninism. We reject Stalinism. This means, as regards

the theory of Marxism-Leninism, that it must be complemented and broadened by taking account of the thought of Trotsky, and even more of Bukharin, of Rosa Luxemburg, and, partly, of Karl Kautsky; it must be enriched by a critical reception of the thought of Fritz Sternberg and other Social Democratic theorists. Marxist-Leninist theory must also come to terms with the experience gathered in Yugoslavia and with the new ideas thrown up in recent theoretical discussion in Poland and China; the Eighth Party Congress of the Chinese Communist Party has produced particularly important material in this respect.

As regards organization, the following measures are called for: the domination of the Party members by the Party apparatus must be radically broken; "democratic centralism" must be made really democratic; the principles of Marx, Engels, and Lenin must be restored in the practice of Party life; the Stalinists must be expelled from the Party.

2. The State. The following reforms are necessary: production to be replanned with a view to raising the mass standard of living (Malenkov line). No more raising of working norms. Profit sharing to be introduced in socialist industries and trade. Old-age pensions for workers to be put on the same principles as for working intellectuals. No more privileges for leading functionaries; workers' councils on the Yugoslav model in all socialist enterprises.

Equality of treatment for big nationalized and small private industries.

Ending of forced collectivization, which is not appropriate to the special conditions of German agriculture; liquidation of uneconomic existing collective farms; agricultural policy to favor the small and medium farmer.

Restoration of complete freedom of thought. Peace with the Church, to end the alienation of the religious-minded parts of the population. Autonomy for the universities.

Total restoration of the whole of law. Abolition of the State security police. Abolition of secret trials.

Restoration of the supreme power of Parliament. Maintenance of the block system under the leadership of the reformed Socialist Unity Party. Elections on the single-list system, but with more candidates and seats so as to give the elector a real choice.

In foreign policy, maintenance of the existing alliances with the countries of the socialist camp, under reservation of full independence and equality; joint policies to be freely arrived at by equal and independent consultation with all other People's Democracies.

All-German Unity

If we carry out these reforms and attain an improved living standard (even if this remains inferior to that of West Germany), we can claim the right to lay down conditions for reunification with West Germany, too. The principle of our German policy is that reunification must not mean capitalist restoration.

Before we can reunite with West Germany, a future Social Democratic majority in the Bundestag would have to carry out the following measures in the Federal Republic:

Reversal of remilitarization. Withdrawal from NATO. Removal of Fascists and militarists from administrative positions in the Federal Republic. Nationalization of key industries. Agricultural reform—parcelling out of large estates wherever this is economically and politically appropriate. Educational reform—higher education must not remain a privilege of the rich.

Given such a policy on the part of the Social Democrats, we would agree to free all-German elections. In these elections the restorative forces in the Federal Republic and the Stalinists in the Democratic Republic would undoubtedly be revealed as isolated minorities.

We are aware that in such conditions the Social Democratic Party would almost certainly gain a majority in the whole of Germany. A reformed Socialist Unity Party would have to accept unconditionally and respect such a decision of the German people.

Unity of the Workers

Precondition of a future unity of the German working-class movement is a Socialist Unity Party freed from Stalinism and completely independent from foreign parties in its ideology and policy. After our intended reform, the Socialist Unity Party would simply be a left-wing Marxist party, which would have nothing in common with the Communist Party of the old type as it has come about by the Stalinist degeneration. This would remove the chief obstacles to a unified workers' movement.

Since in West Germany the unity of the German working class

has been realized inside the Social Democratic Party, a future united workers' movement would inevitably, through the greater weight of the Social Democratic Party, bear more likeness to the latter than to the reformed Socialist Unity Party. But it would doubtless have a stronger left wing than the present Social Democratic Party. However, before we can approach the Social Democrats and make demands on them, we have to look at the beam in our own eye.

We are at present separated from the Social Democrats by much which we criticize in them (bourgeois democratic illusions, tendencies to opportunism, and so on), but the chief thing that separates us from them is our own Stalinism. Hence the Socialist Unity Party must first make its own separation from Stalinism before cooperation with the Social Democratic Party can become honestly possible.

Only when we have purged ourselves from our own faults can we criticize the faults of the Social Democrats; even then the defamation of the Social Democrats as agents of capitalism should be ruled out once and for all.

However, as a first step to future cooperation, one thing should be possible at present—that is, covert cooperation of oppositional comrades from the Socialist Unity Party with Social Democrats in combatting Stalinism in the German Democratic Republic. Once the anti-Stalinist opposition has gained control of the Socialist Unity Party from within, official contacts between the Social Democratic Party and the reformed Socialist Unity Party should follow. From them, the germs of future unity might develop, though neither party must swallow up the other. No Stalinists who have to the last participated in the crimes of the Ulbricht group must be admitted to the new workers' party, but only people who have actively fought against the Stalinist degeneration of the Socialist Unity Party.

Our Present Tactics

Against us stand the Stalinist party and the State apparatus. This reactionary apparatus we have to fight with every means at our disposal.

The bases of our opposition activities are the Party's statute of the Socialist Unity Party, the Twentieth Party Congress of the Soviet Communist Party, and the resolution of the twenty-eighth plenary session of the Central Committee of the Socialist Unity Party. On this basis, we intend to conduct an open and legal opposition. But we are ready also to use the methods of party caucuses and conspiracy if forced to it.

We are taking up contact with oppositional forces in the People's Democracies and comparing notes.

The oppositional comrades must seek close contact with the people, criticize the policy of Party leadership among them, deepen the gulf between the population and the present leadership, but at the same time prevent a popular uprising.

The danger of a popular rising in the German Democratic Republic exists if the Stalinist Ulbricht group continues in power and the forces of the opposition fail to remove the Stalinists from the leadership. But if we succeed in reforming the Party from inside on the basis of the present platform, there will be no second popular rising in the German Democratic Republic.

Hence it is our duty to do everything in our power in order to cleanse the Party of Stalinists and to regain the confidence of the working class and the entire people through a changed policy.

Berlin, 1957.

Here, finally, is a third and relatively hostile view of national Communism by a man who broke with Marshal Tito in 1954. For Djilas, national Communism is "Communism in decline." The essay is reprinted from *The New Class*.

··

NATIONAL COMMUNISM

1.

In essence, Communism is only one thing, but it is realized in different degrees and manners in every country. Therefore, it is possible to speak of various Communist systems—that is, of various forms of the same manifestation.

The differences which exist between Communist states—differences that Stalin attempted futilely to remove by force—are the result, above all, of diverse historical backgrounds. Even the most cursory observation reveals how, for example, contemporary Soviet bureaucracy is not without a connecting link with the Czarist system in which the officials were, as Engels noted, "a distinct class." Somewhat the same thing can also be said of the manner of government in Yugoslavia. When ascending to power, the Communists face in the various countries different cultural and technical levels and varying social relationships, and are faced with different national intellectual characters. These differences develop even further, in a special way. Because the general causes which brought them to power are identical, and because they have to wage a struggle against common internal and foreign opponents, the Communists in separate countries are immediately compelled to fight jointly and on the basis of a similar ideology. International Communism, which was at one time the task of revolutionaries, eventually transformed itself, as did everything else in Communism, and became the common ground of Communist bureaucracies, fighting one another on nationalistic considerations. Of the former international proletariat, only words and empty dogmas remained. Behind them stood the naked national and international interests, aspirations, and plans of the various Communist oligarchies, comfortably entrenched.

The nature of authority and property, a similar international out-
look, and an identical ideology inevitably identify Communist states
with one another. Nevertheless, it is wrong to ignore and underestimate the significance of the inevitable differences in degree and
manner among Communist states. The degree, manner, and form in
which Communism will be realized, or its purpose, are just as much
of a given condition for each of them as is the essence of Communism itself. No single form of Communism, no matter how similar
it is to other forms, exists in any way other than as national Communism. In order to maintain itself, it must become national.

The form of government and property, as well as of ideas, differs
little or not at all in Communist states. It cannot differ markedly,
since it has an identical nature—total authority. However, if they
wish to win and continue to exist, the Communists must adapt the
degree and manner of their authority to national conditions.

The differences among Communist countries will, as a rule, be as
great as the extent to which the Communists were independent in
coming to power. Concretely speaking, only the Communists of
three countries—the Soviet Union, China, and Yugoslavia—independently carried out revolutions or, in their own way and at their
own speed, attained power and began "the building of socialism."
These three countries remained independent as Communist states
even in the period when Yugoslavia was—as China is today—under
the most extreme influence of the Soviet Union; that is, in
"brotherly love" and in "eternal friendship" with it. In a report at
a closed session of the Twentieth Congress, Khrushchev revealed
that a clash between Stalin and the Chinese government had barely
been averted. The case of the clash with Yugoslavia was not an
isolated case, but only the most drastic and the first to occur. In the
other Communist countries the Soviet government enforced Communism by "armed missionaries"—its army. The diversity of manner and degree of the development in these countries has still not
attained the stage reached in Yugoslavia and China. However, to
the extent that ruling bureaucracies gather strength as independent
bodies in these countries, and to the extent that they recognize that
obedience to and copying of the Soviet Union weaken themselves,
they endeavor to "pattern" themselves on Yugoslavia—that is, to
develop independently. The Communist East European countries
did not become satellites of the U.S.S.R. because they benefited from

it, but because they were too weak to prevent it. As soon as they become stronger, or as soon as favorable conditions are created, a yearning for independence and for protection of "their own people" from Soviet hegemony will rise among them.

With the victory of a Communist revolution in a country, a new class comes into power and into control. It is unwilling to surrender its own hard-gained *privileges,* even though it subordinates its *interests* to a similar class in another country, solely in the cause of ideological solidarity.

Where a Communist revolution has won victory independently, a separate, distinct path of development is inevitable. Friction with other Communist countries, especially with the Soviet Union as the most important and most imperialistic state, follows. The ruling national bureaucracy in the country where the victorious revolution took place has already become independent in the course of the armed struggle and has tasted the blessings of authority and of "nationalization" of property.

Philosophically speaking, it has also grasped and become conscious of its own essence, "its own state," its authority, on the basis of which it claims equality.

This does not mean that this involves only a clash—when it comes to that—between two bureaucracies. A clash also involves the revolutionary elements of a subordinated country, because they do not usually tolerate domination and they consider that relationships among Communist states must be as ideally perfect as predicted in dogma. The masses of the nation, who spontaneously thirst for independence, cannot remain unperturbed in such a clash. In every case the nation benefits from this: it does not have to pay tribute to a foreign government; and the pressure on the domestic government, which no longer desires and is not permitted to copy foreign methods, is also diminished. Such a clash also brings in external forces, other states and movements. However, the nature of the clash and the basic forces in it remain. Neither Soviet nor Yugoslav Communists stopped being what they are—not before, nor during, nor after their mutual bickerings. Indeed, the diverse types of degree and manner with which they insured their monopoly led them mutually to deny the existence of socialism in the opposite camp. After they settled their differences, they again acknowledged the existence of socialism elsewhere, becoming conscious that they must respect mutual differences if they wanted to preserve that which was identical in essence and most important to them.

The subordinate Communist governments in East Europe can, in fact must, declare their independence from the Soviet government. No one can say how far this aspiration for independence will go and what disagreements will result. The result depends on numerous unforeseen internal and external circumstances. However, there is no doubt that a national Communist bureaucracy aspires to more complete authority for itself. This is demonstrated by the anti-Tito processes in Stalin's time in the East European countries; it is shown also by the current unconcealed emphasis on "one's own path to socialism," which has recently come to light sharply in Poland and Hungary. The central Soviet government has found itself in difficulty because of the nationalism existing even in those governments which it installed in the Soviet republics (Ukraine, Caucasia), and still more so with regard to those governments installed in the East European countries. Playing an important role in all of this is the fact that the Soviet Union was unable, and will not be able in the future, to assimilate the economies of the East European countries.

The aspirations toward national independence must, of course, have greater impetus. These aspirations can be retarded and even made dormant by external pressure or by fear on the part of the Communists of "imperialism" and the "bourgeoisie," but they cannot be removed. On the contrary, their strength will grow.

It is impossible to foresee all the forms that relations among Communist states will assume. Even if cooperation among Communist states of different countries should in a short time result in mergers and federations, so can clashes between Communist states result in war. An open, armed clash between the U.S.S.R. and Yugoslavia was averted not because of the "socialism" in one or the other country but because it was not in Stalin's interest to risk a clash of unforeseeable proportions. Whatever will happen among Communist states will depend on all those factors which ordinarily affect political events. The interests of the respective Communist bureaucracies, expressed variously as "national" or as "united," along with the unchecked tendency toward ever-increasing independence on a national basis, will, for the time being, play an important role in the relationships among the Communist countries.

2.

The concept of national Communism had no meaning until the end of World War II, when Soviet imperialism was manifested with regard to not only the capitalist but the Communist states as well. This concept developed above all from the Yugoslav-U.S.S.R. clash. The renunciation of Stalin's methods by the "collective leadership" of Khrushchev-Bulganin may perhaps modify relations between the U.S.S.R. and other Communist countries, but it cannot resolve them. In the U.S.S.R., operations are not concerned solely with Communism but are simultaneously concerned with the imperialism of the Great Russian-Soviet State. This imperialism can change in form and method, but it can no more disappear than can the aspirations of Communists of other countries for independence.

A similar development awaits the other Communist states. According to strength and conditions, they, too, will attempt to become imperialistic in one way or another.

In the development of the foreign policy of the U.S.S.R. there have been two imperialistic phases. Earlier policy was almost exclusively a matter of expansion by revolutionary propaganda in other countries. At that time there were powerful imperialistic tendencies (as regards the Caucasus) in the policies of its highest leaders. But, in my opinion, there is no satisfactory reason for the revolutionary phase to be categorically considered imperialistic, since at that time it was more defensive than aggressive.

If we do not consider the revolutionary phase as imperialistic, then imperialism began, roughly speaking, with the victory of Stalin, or with the industrialization and establishment of the authority of a new class in the 1930's. This change was clearly shown on the eve of the war when Stalin's government was able to go into action and leave behind pacifist and anti-imperialistic phases. It was even expressed in the change of foreign policy; in place of the jovial and, to a certain extent, principled Litvinov, the unscrupulous and reserved Molotov appeared.

The basic cause of an imperialistic policy is completely hidden in the exploitative and despotic nature of the new class. In order that that class might manifest itself as imperialistic, it was necessary for it to attain a prescribed strength and to appear in appropriate circumstances. It already had this strength when World War II began.

The war itself abounded in possibilities for imperialistic combinations. The small Baltic states were not necessary for the security of so large a state as the U.S.S.R., particularly in modern war. These states were non-aggressive and even allies; however, they were an attractive morsel for the insatiable appetite of the Great Russian Communist bureaucracy.

In World War II Communist internationalism, up to that time an integral part of Soviet foreign policy, came into conflict with the interests of the ruling Soviet bureaucracy. With that, the necessity for its organization ceased. The idea of dissolution of the Communist International (Comintern) was conceived, according to Georgi Dimitrov, after the subjugation of the Baltic countries and in the period of cooperation with Hitler, although it was not effected until the second phase of the war, during the period of alliance with the Western states.

The Cominform, consisting of the East European and the French and Italian Communist parties, was created on Stalin's initiative in order to guarantee Soviet domination in the satellite countries and to intensify its influence in Western Europe. The Cominform was worse than the former Communist International, which, even if it was absolutely dominated by Moscow, at least formally represented all of the parties. The Cominform evolved in the field of real and apparent Soviet influence. The clash with Yugoslavia revealed that it was assigned to subordinate to the Soviet government those Communist states and parties which had begun to weaken because of the internal growth of national Communism. After the death of Stalin, the Cominform was finally dissolved. Even the Soviet government, desiring to avoid major and dangerous quarrels, accepted the so-called "separate path to socialism," if not national Communism itself.

These organizational changes had profound economic and political causes. As long as the Communist parties in East Europe were weak and the Soviet Union was not sufficiently strong economically, the Soviet government would have had to resort to administrative methods to subjugate the East European countries, even if there had been no Stalinist arbitrariness and despotism. Soviet imperialism, by political, police, and military methods, had to compensate for its own economic and other weaknesses. Imperialism in the military form, which was only an advanced stage of the old Czarist military-feudal imperialism, also corresponded to the internal structure of the Soviet Union in which the police and administrative apparatus, centralized in one personality, played a major role. Stalinism was a mixture of a personal Communist dictatorship and militaristic imperialism.

These forms of imperialism developed: joint stock companies; absorption of the exports of the East European countries by means of political pressure at prices below the world market; artificial formation of a "socialist world market"; control of every political act of subordinate parties and states; transformation of the traditional love of Communists toward the "socialist fatherland" into deification of the Soviet state, Stalin, and Soviet practices.

But what happened?

A change within the ruling class was quietly completed in the Soviet Union itself. Similar changes, in another sense, also occurred in the East European countries; new national bureaucracies long for ever-increasing consolidation of power and property relations, but at the same time they fall into difficulties because of the hegemonic pressure of the Soviet government. If earlier they had had to renounce national characteristics in order to come to power, now such action had become a hindrance to their further ascendancy to power. In addition, it became impossible for the Soviet government to adhere to the exorbitant and hazardous Stalinist foreign policy of military pressure and isolation and, simultaneously, during the period of the general colonial movements, to hold the European countries in infamous bondage.

The Soviet leaders had to concede, after long vacillation and indecisive argumentation, that the Yugoslav leaders were falsely indicted as Hitlerite and American spies just because they defended the right to consolidate and build a Communist system in their own way. Tito became the most significant personality in contemporary Communism. The principle of national Communism was formally acknowledged. But with that, Yugoslavia also ceased to be the exclusive creator of innovations in Communism. The Yugoslav revolution subsided into its groove, and a peaceful and matter-of-fact rule began. With that, the love between yesterday's enemies did not become greater, nor were the disagreements terminated. This was merely the beginning of a new phase.

Now the Soviet Union entered into the predominantly economic and political phase of its imperialistic policy. Or so it appears, judging from current facts.

Today national Communism is a general phenomenon in Communism. To varying degrees, all Communist movements—except that of the U.S.S.R., against which it is directed—are gripped by national Communism. In its time, in the period of Stalin's ascendancy, Soviet Communism also was national Communism. At that time Russian Communism abandoned internationalism, except as an instrument of its foreign policy. Today Soviet Communism is compelled, even if indefinitely, to acknowledge a new reality in Communism.

Changing internally, Soviet imperialism was also compelled to alter its views toward the external world. From predominantly administrative controls, it advanced toward gradual economic integration with the East European countries. This is being accomplished by means of mutual planning in important branches of economy, in which the local Communist governments today mainly voluntarily concur, still sensing themselves weaker externally and internally.

Such a situation cannot remain for long, because it conceals a fundamental contradiction. On the one hand, national forms of Communism become stronger, but on the other, Soviet imperialism does not diminish. Both the Soviet government and the governments of the East European countries, including Yugoslavia, by means of accords and cooperation, are seeking solutions to mutual problems which influence their very nature—preservation of a given form of authority and of property ownership. However, even if it is possible to effect cooperation with respect to property ownership, it is not possible with respect to authority. Although conditions for further integration with the Soviet Union are being realized, those conditions which lead to the *independence* of the East European Communist governments are being realized even more rapidly. The Soviet Union has not renounced authority in these countries, nor have the governments of these countries renounced their craving to attain something similar to Yugoslav independence. The degree of independence that will be attained will depend on the state of international and internal forces.

Recognition of national forms of Communism, which the Soviet government did with clenched teeth, has immense significance and conceals within itself very considerable dangers for Soviet imperialism.

It involves freedom of discussion to a certain extent; this means ideological independence, too. Now the fate of certain heresies in Communism will depend not only on the tolerance of Moscow, but on their national potentialities. Deviation from Moscow that strives to maintain its influence in the Communist world on a "voluntary" and "ideologic" basis cannot possibly be checked.

Moscow itself is no longer that which it was. It single-handedly lost the monopoly of the new ideas and the moral right to prescribe the only permissible "line." Renouncing Stalin, it ceased to be the ideological center. In Moscow itself the epoch of great Communist monarchs and of great ideas came to an end, and the reign of mediocre Communist bureaucrats began.

"Collective leadership" did not anticipate that any difficulties and failures were awaiting it in Communism itself—either externally or internally. But what could it do? Stalin's imperialism was exorbitant and overly dangerous and, what was even worse, ineffective. Under him, not only the people generally, but even the Communists, grumbled, and they did so at the time of a very strained international situation.

The world center of Communist ideology no longer exists; it is in the process of complete disintegration. The unity of the world Communist movement is incurably injured. There are no visible possibilities whatsoever that it can be restored. However, just as the shift from Stalin to "collective leadership" did not alter the nature of the system itself in the U.S.S.R., so, too, national Communism has been unable, despite ever-increasing possibilities for liberation from Moscow, to alter its internal nature, which consists of total control and monopoly of ideas, and ownership by the Party bureaucracy. Indeed, it significantly alleviated the pressure and slowed down the rate of establishment of its monopoly over property, particularly in the rural areas. But national Communism neither desires nor is able to transform itself into something other than Communism, and something always spontaneously draws it toward its source—toward the Soviet Union. It will be unable to separate its fate from that which links it with the remaining Communist countries and movements.

National modifications in Communism jeopardize Soviet imperialism, particularly the imperialism of the Stalin epoch, but not Communism either as a whole or in essence. On the contrary, where Communism is in control, these changes are able to influence its direction and even to strengthen it and make it acceptable externally. National Communism is in harmony with non-dogmaticism —that is, with the anti-Stalinist phase in the development of Communism. In fact, it is a basic form of this phase.

3.

National Communism is unable to alter the nature of current international relationships among states or within workers' movements. But its role in these relationships may be of great significance.

Thus, for example, Yugoslav Communism, as a form of national Communism, played an extremely important role in the weakening of Soviet imperialism and in the downgrading of Stalinism inside the Communist movement. The motives for changes which are occurring in the Soviet Union and in the East European countries are to be found, above all, in the countries themselves. They appeared first in Yugoslavia—in the Yugoslav way. And there, too, they were first completed. Thus Yugoslav Communism as national Communism, in the clash with Stalin, actually originated a new postStalin phase in the development of Communism. Yugoslav Communism significantly influenced changes in Communism itself, but did not fundamentally influence either international relationships or non-Communist workers' movements.

The expectation that Yugoslav Communism would be able to evolve toward democratic socialism or that it would be able to serve as a bridge between Social Democracy and Communism has proved baseless. The Yugoslav leaders themselves were in conflict over this question. During the time of Soviet pressure on Yugoslavia, they demonstrated a fervent desire for a rapprochement with the Social Democrats. However, in 1956, during the period of peace with Moscow, Tito announced that both the Cominform and the Socialist International were unnecessary, despite the fact that the Socialist International unselfishly defended Yugoslavia while the Cominform laboriously attacked Yugoslavia. Preoccupied with a policy of so-called "active coexistence," which for the most part corresponds to their interests of the moment, the Yugoslav leaders declared that both organizations—the Cominform and the Socialist

International—were "immoderate" solely because they were allegedly the product of two blocs.

The Yugoslav leaders confused their desires with reality and confused their momentary interests with profoundly historic and socialistic differences.

At any rate, the Cominform was the product of Stalinist efforts for the creation of an Eastern military bloc. It is impossible to deny the fact that the Socialist International is linked with the Western bloc or with the Altantic Pact, since it operates within the framework of the West European countries. But it would exist even without that bloc. It is, above all, an organization of Socialists of the developed European countries in which political democracy and similar relationships exist.

Military alliances and blocs are temporary manifestations, but the Western socialism and Eastern Communism reflect much more enduring and basic tendencies.

Contrasts between Communism and a social democracy are not the result of different principles only—these least of all—but of the opposing directions of economic and intellectual forces. The clash between Martov and Lenin at the Second Congress of Russian Social Democrats in London in 1903, concerning the question of Party membership, and concerning the question of lesser or greater centralism and discipline in the Party—which Deutscher correctly calls the beginning of the greatest schism in history—was of far greater significance then even its initiators were able to anticipate. With that began the formation not only of two movements but of two social systems.

The schism between Communists and Social Democrats is impossible to bridge until the very natures of these movements, or the conditions themselves which resulted in differences between them, are changed. In the course of a half century, despite periodic and separate rapprochements, the differences have on the whole increased, and their natures have become still more individualized. Today, Social Democracy and Communism are not only two movements but two worlds.

National Communism, separating itself from Moscow, has been unable to bridge this chasm, although it can circumvent it. This was demonstrated by the cooperation of the Yugoslav Communists with the Social Democrats, which was more seeming than actual and more courteous than sincere, and which was without tangible important results for either side.

For completely different reasons, unity has not been realized between Western and Asian Social Democrats. The differences between them were not as great in essence, or in principles, as they were in practice. For national reasons of their own, Asian Socialists had to remain separated from West European Socialists. Even when they are opponents of colonialism, Western Socialists—though they play no leading role—are representatives of countries which, solely because they are more developed, exploit the underdeveloped countries. The contrast between Asian and Western Social Democrats is a manifestation of contrasts between underdeveloped and developed countries, carried over into the ranks of the Socialist movement. Despite the fact that concrete forms of this contrast have to be sharply defined, proximity in essence—as far as can be deduced today—is obvious and inevitable.

4.

National Communism, similar to that in Yugoslavia, could be of immense international significance in Communist parties of non-Communist states. It could be of even greater significance there than in Communist parties which are actually in power. This is relevant above all to the Communist parties in France and Italy, which encompass a significant majority of the working class and which are, along with several parties in Asia, the only ones of major significance in the non-Communist world.

Until now, the manifestations of national Communism in these parties have been without major significance and impetus. However, they have been inevitable. They could, in the final analysis, lead to profound and essential changes in these parties.

These parties have to contend with the Social Democrats—who are able to channel the dissatisfied masses toward themselves by means of their own socialist slogans and activity. This is not the only reason for the eventual deviation of these parties from Moscow. Lesser reasons may be seen in the periodic and unanticipated reversals of Moscow and of the other ruling Communist parties. Such reversals lead these and other non-ruling Communist parties into a "crisis of conscience"—to spit on what, until yesterday, they extolled, then suddenly to change their line. Neither oppositionist propaganda nor administrative pressure will play a fundamental role in the transformation of these parties.

The basic causes for deviation of these parties from Moscow may be found in the nature of the social system of the countries in which they operate. If it becomes evident—and it appears likely—that the working class of these countries is able through parliamentary forms to arrive at some improvement in its position, and also to change the social system itself, the working class will abandon the Communists, regardless of its revolutionary and other traditions. Only small groups of Communist dogmatists can look dispassionately at the disassociation of the workers; serious political leaders in a given nation will endeavor to avoid it even at the cost of weakening ties with Moscow.

Parliamentary elections which give a huge number of votes to Communists in these countries do not accurately express the actual strength of Communist parties. To a significant degree, they are an expression of dissatisfaction and delusion. Stubbornly following the Communist leaders, the masses will just as easily abandon them the moment it becomes obvious to them that the leaders are sacrificing national institutions, or the concrete prospects of the working class, to their bureaucratic nature or to the "dictatorship of the proletariat" and ties with Moscow.

Of course, all of this is hypothesis. But even today these parties are finding themselves in a difficult situation. If they really wish to be adherents of parliamentarianism, their leaders will have to renounce their anti-parliamentary nature or change over to their own national Communism, which would, since they are not in control, lead to disintegration of their parties.

The leaders of Communist parties in these countries are driven to experiment with the idea of national Communism and national forms by all of these factors: by the strengthening of the possibility that the transformation of society and the improvement of position of the workers will be attained by democratic means; by Moscow's reversals, which by the downgrading of the cult of Stalin, ultimately resulted in destruction of the ideologic center; by concurrence of the Social Democrats; by tendencies toward unification of the West on a profound and enduring social basis as well as a military one; by military strengthening of the Western bloc, which offers increasingly fewer prospects for "brotherly aid" for the Soviet army; and by the impossibility of new Communist revolutions without a world war. At the same time, fear of the inevitable result of a transition to parliamentarianism, and of a breaking off with Moscow, prevents these leaders from doing anything of real significance. Increasingly deeper social differences between the East and the West work with relentless force. The clever Togliatti is confused, and the robust Thorez is wavering. External and internal party life is beginning to bypass them.

Emphasizing that today a parliament can serve as a "form of transition to socialism," Khrushchev intended at the Twentieth Congress to facilitate manipulation of the Communist parties in "capitalist countries," and to stimulate the cooperation of Communists and Social Democrats and the formation of "people's fronts." Something like this appeared realistic to him, according to his words, because of the changes which had resulted in the strengthening of Communism and because of peace in the world. With that, he tacitly acknowledged to everyone the obvious impossibility of Communist revolutions in the developed countries, as well as the impossibility of further expansion of Communism under current conditions without the danger of a new world war. The policy of the Soviet state has been reduced to a status quo, while Communism has descended to gradual acquisition of new positions in a new way.

A crisis has actually begun in the Communist parties of the non-Communist states. If they change over to national Communism, they risk forsaking their very nature; and if they do not change over, they face a loss of followers. Their leaders will be forced into the most cunning manipulations and unscrupulous measures if they are to extricate themselves from this contradiction. It is improbable that they will be able to check disorientation and disintegration. They have reached a state of conflict with the real tendencies of development in the world and in their countries that obviously leads toward new relationships.

National Communism outside of the Communist states inevitably leads toward renunciation of Communism itself, or toward the disintegration of the Communist parties. Its possibilities are greater today in the non-Communist states, but obviously only along the lines of separation from Communism itself. Therefore, national Communism in these parties will emerge victorious only with difficulty and slowly, in successive outbursts.

In the Communist parties that are not in power, it is evident that national Communism—despite its intent to stimulate Communism and strengthen its nature—is simultaneously the heresy that nibbles at Communism as such. National Communism *per se* is contradictory. Its nature is the same as that of Soviet Communism, but it aspires to detach itself into something of its own, nationally. In reality, national Communism is Communism in decline.

Belgrade, 1956